The New Naturalist

A Survey of British Natural History

The New Forest

Editors

Kenneth Mellanby, C.B.E., Sc.D.

S. M. Walters, M.A., Ph.D.
Professor Richard West, F.R.S., F.G.S.

Photographic Editor
Eric Hosking, O.B.E., F.R.P.S.

The aim of this series is to interest the general reader
in the wildlife of Britain by recapturing the enquiring
spirit of the old naturalists. The Editors believe that
the natural pride of the British public in the native
fauna and flora, to which must be added concern for
their conservation, is best fostered by maintaining a
high standard of accuracy combined with clarity of
exposition in presenting the results of modern scientific
research.

The New Naturalist

THE NEW FOREST

Colin R. Tubbs

With 20 colour photographs and over
100 photographs and diagrams in black and white

COLLINS
Grafton Street, London

William Collins Sons & Co. Ltd

London · Glasgow · Sydney · Auckland

Toronto · Johannesburg

First published 1986
© Colin R. Tubbs 1986

ISBN 0 00 219107 5 (hardback edition)
ISBN 0 00 219370 1 (limpback edition)

Filmset by Ace Filmsetting Ltd, Frome, Somerset
Colour and black-and-white reproduction by Alpha Reprographics, Harefield,
Middlesex
Printed and bound in Great Britain by Mackays of Chatham Ltd, Kent

Contents

6 CONTENTS

Editors' Preface

There is nowhere in the world quite like the New Forest. Established as a 'royal forest', primarily for hunting, by William the Conqueror more than 900 years ago, this large tract of 37,907 ha of woodland, heath, grassland and marsh has survived when so many other parts of Britain have been completely altered by man's activities.

The New Forest is important in the lives of many of the people of Britain today. Those who live within its boundaries have a strong sense of local patriotism, and are generally opposed to any developments which would alter the character of the landscape. The commoners, with rights to graze livestock, defend these rights even when they are not fully exercised, and resent any developments which they fear might reduce the number of cattle and ponies the land can support. The Forestry Commission, who now exercise management rights formerly held by the crown, have the difficult task of trying to satisfy all conflicting interests.

This is an area particularly valued by naturalists. In the Nature Conservancy Council's *Nature Conservation Review*, which identified the key sites to nature conservation in Britain, the New Forest was accorded a Grade 1* rating, which means that it is of the highest international importance. It is also a Site of Special Scientific Interest. The Forest is popular with tourists and holiday-makers, and control of their numbers and activities, to prevent destruction of what they come to enjoy is perhaps the most serious problem.

The Editors of the *New Naturalist* Series realize how fortunate they have been in securing Colin Tubbs to write this book. As a scientist, an ecologist and a dedicated conservationist, he has a unique knowledge and experience of the scientific value of the area. He has himself made important scientific studies of the flora and fauna, particularly the birds, and has helped many other scholars less familiar with the background, in their studies. He is not only deeply – and effectively – concerned with the problems of conservation, he also obviously loves the forest and has devoted his life to its preservation. Thus at Public Inquiries concerned with proposed developments of which he disapproves, his knowledge and understanding has always impressed even those whose interests he opposes.

In this book, Colin Tubbs deals authoritatively with the physical and biological features of the New Forest, as well as with its history and how it has been affected by changes in legal status and the management objectives of the crown, the government, landowners, commoners and the public.

Perhaps the most remarkable thing about the New Forest is that it has survived at all. The most important problem facing us today is to safeguard its continuing survival, without the sort of ecological deterioration so commonly seen elsewhere as a result of increased pressure from agriculture, industry and tourism. Although many areas which look like genuine 'wilderness' persist, the landscape is, like that elsewhere in Britain, almost entirely man-made.

What is unusual, is the effects of the large mammals, the ponies, cattle and deer. These control what happens in the unenclosed 'pasture woodlands'. Colin Tubbs rightly records that 'the vegetation in the unenclosed Forest can be perceived as nature's response to human activity'. But nature can only accommodate so much of this human activity – in this case mediated by the animals which man has introduced or encouraged. Thus there are many instances where overgrazing has damaged the habitat and decreased the numbers and even the species of several butterflies. A Forestry Commission policy, fortunately now abandoned, to replace the old broadleaved trees with conifers, had equally harmful effects. Air pollution from refineries and industrial plants has already damaged the lichen flora, and more widespread damage is a possibility.

The future of the New Forest depends on all of us, and on how we influence national policy to such important areas. In the past, it has sometimes been difficult to formulate effective policies because of our ignorance of past and present conditions. Now, for the New Forest at least, planners as well as naturalists have been supplied by Colin Tubbs with a unique and very readable account of the area, which should make rational protection policies possible, as these can now be based on real information and not, as so often in the past, on superficial impressions and emotion.

Author's Preface

In 1979 the New Forest celebrated the 900th anniversary of William I's act of afforestation. In a neat allusion, the event was commemorated for the New Forest Association in a 25-foot long embroidery depicting the Forest's history, designed and executed by Belinda Montagu with the help of fifty-five other local people. It hangs for the moment in the Council Chamber of New Forest District Council and a copy hangs in the Verderer's hall for which it was designed. On 12 April 1979 Her Majesty the Queen drove through the Forest in a landau, planted the inevitable oak tree and met many people and as many horses. The New Forest Association produced a profitable commemorative mug, and a fund for a New Forest Museum was founded.

The anniversary may have been spurious in the sense that we know only that the area was pronounced a royal forest sometime between the Conquest and the preparation of Domesday in 1086, but to say so at the time was tacitly agreed to be churlish and in any event there *was* something to celebrate in the survival for some 900 years, give or take a few, of a recognizable piece of medieval England, still with its unenclosed heaths and woods, still with its commoners and their stock; and still administered by the crown (albeit in the shape of the Forestry Commission) and by a Verderer's Court descended from the ancient forestal courts but with 20th century purposes and functions.

In the 18th and 19th centuries, most of the surviving royal forests were disafforested, and allotted between the crown and those with rights over them. The survival of the New Forest is a complex story, the main elements of which are touched on in this book; but the area's aesthetic appeal, its ancient institutions and well-founded economy, and in recent times its unique assemblage of natural habitats, have all attracted influential and powerful adherents and defenders. It has attracted its celebrants since the late 18th century when the Rev. William Gilpin, vicar of the Forest parish of Boldre, published his *Remarks on Forest Scenery*, the second volume of which is a contemporary description and appreciation of the New Forest. Gilpin was plagiarized and embellished by successive writers but there were also a number of original contributions in the early 19th century, and 1860 saw the publication of John Wise's *The New Forest: its History and Scenery*. Wise, like Gilpin, wrote from personal observation. He also excavated (some would say butchered) barrows and pottery kilns, dug for fossils and collected the natural history observations of his contemporaries. Somewhat later in the century, G. E. Briscoe Eyre, a local land-owner and active protagonist of the Forest in its most troubled times, wrote a classic treatise on the economy of its commoners, besides a delightful and evocative piece in the *Fortnightly Review* which is an outstanding description of the Forest in the 1860s. It is a pity he did not publish more, for his involvement in Forest affairs and his love of the place were great.

From the 1880s there began a steady output of books and journal articles. Most were superficial, anecdotal or romantic, or guide books (some of them very good), but the literature includes the remarkable writings of Heywood Sumner, a pioneer of field archaeology, who lived in the Forest; the Hon. Gerald Lascelles' account of his career as Deputy Surveyor of the Forest (the chief crown officer) from 1880 to 1915; F. E. Kenchington's account of *The Commoners' New Forest* in 1944; and much other valuable material, including a wealth of articles in entomological and historical journals.

In 1968 I sought to break new ground in a book called *The New Forest: An Ecological History*, which for the first time tried to see the Forest as an ecological system which had evolved through the interaction of soils, vegetation and its peculiar land use history. It has long been out of print. Since 1968 there have been great advances in understanding the Forest's physical structure, ecology and history. In particular, pollen analysis and soil research, especially into mire stratigraphy, have yielded a clearer picture of the Forest's geomorphological and vegetation history and particularly of the origins and structure of the Forest's fine series of valley and seepage step mires. We now know much more about the relationships between the large herbivores – ponies, cattle and deer – and the habitats which they inhabit and exploit. Much has been elucidated about the relationships between grazing by stock and deer, the numbers of small mammals, and the populations of their vertebrate predators. We have a much clearer perception than in the 1960s of the structure of the vegetation and its relationship to physical factors, grazing, burning and other activities, past and present. New advances have been made in our understanding of the development and ecology of the unenclosed woodlands, the grasslands and the mires of the Forest. David Stagg's scholarly research into the documented history of the Forest, and notably the publication in 1979 and 1983 of the two volumes of his *Calendar of New Forest Documents*, has cast new light on the administrative and land use history of the Forest before the present century. Anthony Pasmore's *Verderers of the New Forest*, published in 1977 to commemorate the 100th anniversary of the Verderers as they are now constituted, is a definitive account of the Verderers' part in the modern history of the Forest and tells a compelling story of Forest affairs.

Since 1968 the significance of the Forest to nature conservation and biological science has also come sharply into focus. We know now that it is a unique place. Though legally protected against gross physical change, it is not without problems. In 1968 the main problem was seen as impending aesthetic and biological disaster before an approaching tide of uncontrolled recreational demands. This problem was subsequently resolved by determined management, at least for a time. There remain today more fundamental and subtle problems concerned with the socio-economic and administrative structure of the Forest, and with the survival of the commoners whose animals are a vital part of the ecological system. Nor is the Forest immune from periodic development threats, nor from the longer term and partly intangible effects of the growth of nearby towns.

My intention in this book is to portray the Forest's ecology. The vegetation and the animals, both domestic and wild, are part of the picture, but people, their attitudes and the ways in which they use, exploit, administer and manage the Forest, are also key elements. The book is inevitably in part an elaboration (though not simply a revision) of the earlier text, but I hope it leans more heavily towards the Forest of today and is more relevant to the Forest of the future.

No book of this sort can be written without incurring a debt to many like-minded seekers after truth. They have succumbed happily to long discussions about many topics; carried out much of the recent research on which the book depends; willingly permitted me to use their unpublished material; and helped over the years to shape my perception of the New Forest. I owe some or all of these debts to David Stagg and Anthony Pasmore (whose critical faculties and historical research have contributed enormously to my understanding of the Forest); Nicholas Flower (who greatly advanced our knowledge of woodland history and ecology); Geoffery Fisher (who did much to elucidate the origins and nature of the terrace soils); Mike Clarke (who helped my understanding of the Forest's vegetation history and allowed me to use data from his Ph.D. thesis on the origins, development and ecology of New Forest mires); Jon Pollock, Rory Putman, Peter Edwards, Ruth Ekins and Bob Pratt (who carried out much of the recent work on the large herbivores and their effects on the vegetation); Chris Packham (who researched the badger population); Stephen Hill (whom I indirectly landed with researching a nearly non-existent small mammal population); Graham Hirons (who like me, works on avian predators); Karen Eide and John Catt (who permitted me to use unpublished soil and soil pollen data); Francis Rose (some of whose ecological wisdom I hope has rubbed off over the years); Alan Stubbs (who has helped my understanding of invertebrate ecology); Geoffery Dimbleby (who carried out most of the earlier soil pollen analyses of Forest sites); Keith Barber (who has inspired recent analyses of the pollen preserved in New Forest peat bogs); Jim Grant (who has still failed to satiate his curiosity about New Forest cicada after twenty years); and numerous friends and colleagues, whether scientists, historians, commoners, Verderers, foresters, keepers or Deputy Surveyors. However, my greatest single debt is to my wife, who has shared my involvement in the Forest so that this book is as much hers as mine; she has tolerated my perpetual abstraction in its writing and has read and corrected the manuscript.

Phillip Allison, Eric Ashby, Robert Coles, Edward Jewell, Anthony Pasmore and Kenneth Self generously helped in searching for photographs and have permitted the reproduction of some in their respective collections, each of which is individually acknowledged.

I wish to record my thanks to the Forestry Commission for making available a variety of information including pest control records, deer census and badger numbers, and permitting me to use information from the New Forest Forestry Commission Management Plan 1982–1991 for Fig. 27. I am particularly grateful to successive Deputy Surveyors and their staffs for their ultimate tolerance of one who has not always seen eye to eye with the Forestry Commission; and to the Forest Keepers, present and retired, who have helped in a multitude of ways and whose interest in and concern for the Forest is equal to my own. I thank the Verderers of the New Forest for permitting me access to documents at various times and for providing information about stock numbers; and, as important, for the shared interest and friendship of Verderers past and present: we have sometimes been adversaries but never with ill will. I thank also the Nature Conservancy Council (abbreviated to NCC hereafter), which I have served for a time which occasionally seems uncomfortably long, for permitting me to use data from the contract report on the food and feeding behaviour of ponies and cattle in the New Forest; and from the England Field Unit's survey of selected valley mires in the New Forest, which remains formally unpublished. I owe a greater debt to the NCC for the opportunity of playing a part in the recent affairs of the Forest; and I owe much to the many colleagues to whom I have been able to turn for advice and with whom I share common interests. Finally, I am grateful to the British Trust for Ornithology and to individual observers who provided data from the Common Bird Census Scheme; and to Mrs Oliver Hook who helped locate some of the records of her late husband, who was one of the many people who enriched my appreciation of the New Forest.

In the text, area and distance measurements are given in metric units except where sources (e.g., historical documents, legislation) render this inappropriate. Metric units are then given in parenthesis but should in most contexts be regarded only as approximations. Historical references are made wherever possible to the most accessible printed source rather than to original documents. However, I have not been able invariably to follow this rule. Where archival documents are referred to, PRO=Public Record Office; and HRO=Hampshire Record Office. I have drawn on the reports and minutes of evidence of successive 19th-century Select Committees on the New Forest, and on the 19th-century annual reports of the Commissioners of Woods, and have drawn general conclusions without necessarily identifying every contributary reference. Further, I have used some records of the Office of Woods (the Forestry Commission's predecessor) which survived in the Queen's House, Lyndhurst (beneath whose roof are the offices of the Forestry Commission, the Verderers' Hall wherein the bi-monthly courts are held, and the office of the Verderers' Clerk) in the 1960s, but which were evidently lost or destroyed around 1970, when much other material was transferred to the Public Record Office. In particular, and sadly, some of a series of notebooks and diaries of 19th-century Keepers seem to have vanished at that time. Similarly most of the Verderers' records seem to have been stolen, lost or destroyed at various times, though what survives is now safely lodged in the Hampshire Record Office.

C.R.T.

A Perspective

I recall the New Forest in childhood and explored it in the 1950s. It has been my home and I have been involved in its affairs since 1960 when almost by accident I found myself working in the Nature Conservancy (since 1974 the NCC). The Forest has not been my only professional concern or research interest since then, but it has been of constant and absorbing interest. The absorption grows with time – partly because over long time spans, it becomes possible to measure and witness changes which illuminate the relationships between soils, vegetation, animals and management in ways which no short-term study can achieve; and partly because time increases rather than diminishes the degree of spiritual renewal and intellectual wonder to be derived from the familiar woods and heaths.

Seen obliquely from the air, the Forest is a series of eroded flat terraces, highest in the north, lowest in the south. The middle terraces are scoured into wide hollows drained by two south-flowing stream systems which empty into the solent. The terrace surfaces are mostly mantled in heathland and the hollows and valleys between them are a mosaic of woodland, heath, grassland and mire. Superimposed are the mainly regular blocks of Silvicultural Inclosures dating from the early 18th century onwards, and the more rounded enclaves of farmland and settlements.

The New Forest is an ecological system which is constantly developing under the influence of large, free-ranging herbivores – mainly deer, domestic cattle, and ponies. The exercise of common rights (by which stock are depastured on the unenclosed forest) is as intimate a part of the ecosystem as the vegetation. The botanical composition of the Forest and the morphology of many individual species are much modified by grazing and browsing. At the same time, the inherently low productivity of the poor, acid Forest soils, combined with the effects of intensive grazing, influences both the productivity (in terms of live weight gains and young produced) and behaviour of the animals.

The unenclosed Forest is the largest area of wild, or 'unsown' vegetation in lowland Britain and includes large tracts of three formerly common habitats that are now fragmented and rare in lowland western Europe – heathland, valley mire and ancient pasture woodland. Nowhere else do these habitats now occur on so large a scale and nowhere else do they occur in such an intimate mosaic. There are nearly 20,000 ha of unenclosed Forest. Nearly

3700 ha of this is mainly oak, beech and holly woodland – much of it on sites which can probably claim an unbroken history of woodland cover for 5000 years or more. There are nearly 12,500 ha of heathland and acid grassland; and 2900 ha of valley, seepage step mire, and wet heath. There are also 837 ha of plantations, of which about 40% are broadleaved, including large tracts of fine 18th- and 19th-century oakwoods. The woods, heaths and mires are drained by many small streams which, though locally modified by canalisation, remain of great interest for their little-disturbed communities of aquatic plants and animals.

The scale of the Forest heaths, mires and pasture woods is such that they offer the best chance of survival to the widest possible spectrum of their characteristic flora and fauna. Many of the species found would seem unable to persist on smaller fragments of habitat. The three main habitat formations of the unenclosed Forest are intrinsically rich in species, relatively undisturbed, and managed and used in such a way as to ensure their survival. A key element is the persistence of a pastoral economy based on the exercise of common rights of grazing and mast (the right to turn out pigs in the autumn). This inhibits a succession to uniform woodland and gives rise to great local variation in plant communities. The pastoral use of the Forest depends on the continued existence of a close-knit human community of mainly part-time farmers and smallholders. Most comparable communities and the attendant grazing of commons, have disappeared from the lowlands of western Europe. The Forest survives as an ecological system of interacting natural and social elements which now has no parallel, at least in scale.

The perambulation of the Forest encloses 37,907 ha. In medieval times the perambulation was the limit of the area within which the forest law had jurisdiction. Today its main significance is that it delimits the area within which the New Forest Verderers apply their by-laws for the control and health of the stock depastured on the commons, and within which the animals are contained by road grids and, where necessary, fencing. Nearly a quarter of the area within the perambulation consists of farmland and settlements, among which the animals forage only on lane sides and greens. A further 1399 ha are composed of the unenclosed wastes of various manors that border the crown lands, and are indistinguishable on the ground from the unenclosed Forest proper. Most of these are owned by the National Trust, but a large and important group on the western edge of the Forest is within the Somerley Estate and there are a number of other, smaller areas in private ownership. The National Trust's Bramshaw Commons, detached from the main area of the Forest by the enclosed lands of Bramshaw and the Warren's Estate, have always tended to maintain a separate identity and life of their own, and have an active management

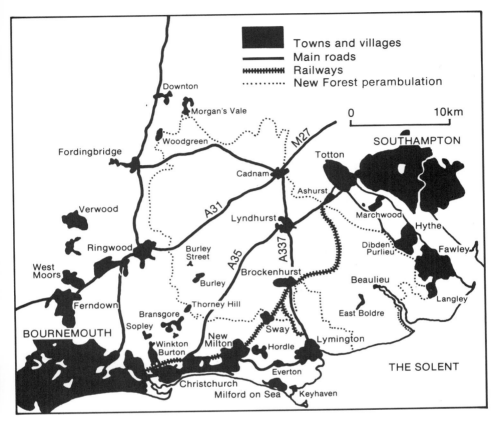

Fig. 1.
The New Forest and
Major Settlements

committee on which interests besides those of the commoners are represented.

The crown lands, which form nearly three-quarters of the Forest, comprise most of the unenclosed land, the Silvicultural Inclosures, and numerous farm holdings. The crown's tenure of the Inclosures is not straightforward. Most (7104 ha) were enclosed under specific Acts of Parliament and are known as Statutory Inclosures. They are free of common rights only so long as they remain fenced, and at least 12% has to remain unenclosed at any one time. The crown can use them for no purpose other than silviculture. A further 814 ha comprise the so-called Verderers' Inclosures, enclosed under peculiar conditions in the late 1950s and with only a limited life span. In addition there are 494 ha of crown freehold woodland, most of which seems to derive from the demesne of the manor of Lyndhurst, which was a crown manor; and 198 ha leased from adjoining estates.

Fig. 1 shows the Forest in its local context of major settlements

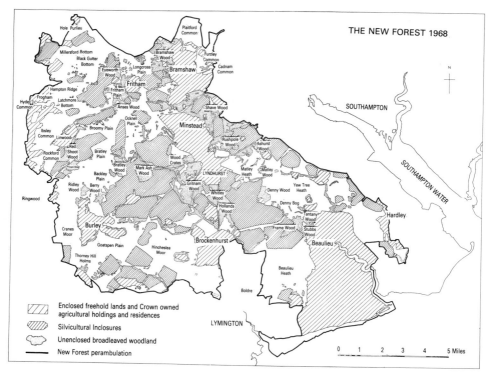

THE NEW FOREST 1968

SOUTHAMPTON

SOUTHAMPTON WATER

Hole Purlieu
Plaitford Common
Millersford Bottom
Black Gutter Bottom
Bramshaw Wood
Furzley Common
Eyeworth Wood
Longcross Plain
Cadnam Common
Bramshaw
Fritham
Hampton Ridge
Fritham Plain
Frogham
Latchmore Bottom
Hyde Common
Anses Wood
Shave Wood
Ocknell Plain
Broomy Plain
Minstead
Ibsley Common
Linwood
Rushpole Wood
Ashurst Wood
Red Shoot Wood
Bratley Plain
Wood Crates
Rockford Common
Bratley Wood
Mark Ash Wood
Matley Heath
Matley Wood
Backley Plain
LYNDHURST
Ridley Wood
Berry Wood
Gritnam Wood
Yew Tree Heath
Ringwood
Whitley Wood
Denny Wood
Cranes Moor
Hollands Wood
Denny Bog
Hardley
Burley
Tantany Wood
Goatspen Plain
Hinchelsea Moor
Frame Wood
Stubbs Wood
Thorney Hill Holms
Beaulieu
Brockenhurst
Beaulieu Heath
Boldre

LYMINGTON

⫽⫽ Enclosed freehold lands and Crown owned
agricultural holdings and residences

⫽⫽ Silvicultural Inclosures

◯ Unenclosed broadleaved woodland

— New Forest perambulation

0   1   2   3   4   5 Miles

Fig. 2.
Land Uses in the New Forest

in south-west Hampshire. Fig. 2 depicts the distribution of the main land uses within the perambulation. Fig. 3 summarizes information about land uses and Fig. 4 summarizes information about the vegetation of the unenclosed Forest and Inclosures.

I write as a biologist involved in nature conservation, and inevitably my view of the Forest is coloured by this. Thus, paramount in my mind is the extent and rate at which habitats similar to those found in the Forest have been destroyed elsewhere in Britain and Europe. Agricultural reclamation, conifer afforestation, and urban and industrial development have left few large areas of natural vegetation in the lowlands of western Europe away from the Mediterranean. The ancient woodlands, heaths and mires of the Forest are now internationally rare habitats. Let us consider them in the perspective of history.

The Woodlands

By Tudor times, comparatively little of the natural woodland cover of Britain had survived clearance, and the fragments which remained were mostly modified by long histories of management,

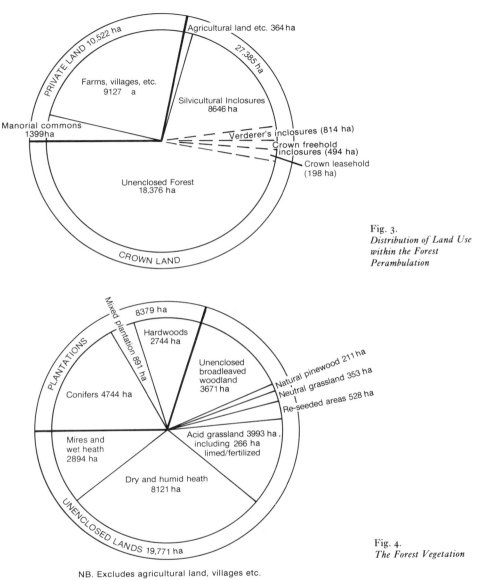

Fig. 3.
Distribution of Land Use within the Forest Perambulation

Fig. 4.
The Forest Vegetation

NB. Excludes agricultural land, villages etc.

exploitation or grazing. In the New Forest, large-scale clearance began in the late Bronze Age and something close to the present disposition of woodland and open habitats (excluding the Inclosures) was probably reached by the 13th century.

In medieval England, most woodland survived as coppices at least periodically enclosed against grazing, or as relatively unexploited woodland in forests, chases, parks and on common lands, where the woods were grazed by deer and domestic animals. The distinction was blurred because coppices were commonly grazed once they had regrown after cutting, and there were many woods which changed roles from pasture wood to coppice and back again. In coppices, the underwood was cut on rotation for fuel, charcoal, wattle, hurdles, fencing and other produce, and low densities of standard trees were grown to relative maturity for structural materials. The pasture woods were exploited periodically and such practices as shrouding and pollarding (chapter 9) were common. However, many trees were permitted to grow to their natural span, and the age structure and species composition of the woods were influenced less by human choice than by the intensity and periodicity of grazing.

Where they survive, these medieval woods retain strong elements of the flora and fauna of the woodland environment which confronted our Neolithic or Bronze Age predecessors. Their little-disturbed soils can yield valuable evidence about the natural long-term development of woodland ecosystems. Their plant and animal communities are richer than those of the woods planted since the 17th century and they include a high proportion of rare, locally occurring and more vulnerable species which require long-term habitat stability to survive. Such species usually have poor powers of dispersal and thus seldom colonize woods of recent origin. Moreover, the diversity of micro-habitats is greater in ancient than in modern woods, for in the latter such habitats as winding streams, glades, flushes, and irregular clearings and edges will have been lost to the uniformity and regularity of plantations.

It has been estimated that in the 13th century, about 160,000 ha of pasture woodland remained in the royal forests of England alone, and there was much more in chases, deer parks and on commons. Possibly 90% has since been destroyed (G. F. Peterken). Much was lost on disafforestation of the forests and the enclosure of commons in the 18th and 19th centuries, but losses have continued since, and in recent times much has been converted to farmland or conifers. In 1975, the NCC commissioned the Institute of Terrestrial Ecology to prepare an inventory of surviving examples south of the Highlands. Stretching the definition to its limits, they found 407 fragments. Most were less than 30 ha and most were in upland Britain, where there are different and more impoverished conditions than in the lowlands of southern England. The New Forest woods were far and away the largest remnant. Only here has the wood pasture not dwindled in area since medieval times and it is here, at present, that there is the best prospect of ecological and management stability. Moreover, the flora and fauna of the Forest woods is in many respects richer than in other remnants, and the woods remain set in their context of secondary habitats derived from similar soil parent materials.

Much more medieval coppice survived into the present century than pasture woodland, but there have been massive losses since the 1930s as coppice markets declined, forestry policies favoured coniferization, and it became profitable to convert woodland to farmland. Taking all ancient woods, the NCC has estimated that between a third and a half of those surviving to 1946 were destroyed by 1980.

Casting around Europe, the Forest woodlands now appear to have no lowland counterpart. Some lowland broadleaved forests, particularly in northern France, appear to have contained pasture woodland until at least the 17th century, but were intensively managed and cropped thereafter. Neither the upland pasture woods of temperate Europe (including Britain) nor the lowland pasture woods of the Mediterranean, are ecologically comparable, though some oakwoods I have seen in Spain come close to it.

The pasture woods of the Forest today are discontinuously spread across the clays and sands and transported infill of the hollows and valleys, here and there reaching up onto the gravelly soils of the terraces. Much of the drainage pattern is marked by linear woodland in which ash is common, or by carrs, mainly of alder. The woods are wet and humid for the English lowlands, where most woodlands are too small to sustain a distinctive micro-climate or have been artificially drained. In the Forest woods there remains an abundance of wet clearings, flushes, springs, runnels and meandering streams. There are frequent clearings and the woodland margins are irregular, often grading raggedly into the neighbouring vegetation. In such characteristics the woods must begin to resemble the vast Atlantic forests of 5000 years ago, of which they are a unique, if modified, survivor. Like all ancient woodlands they are not merely an irreplaceable natural resource, but because they are the living survivors of a formerly widespread land use, they are as validly a part of our cultural heritage as the medieval cathedrals raised when the woods were already old. They are both a link with the forest environment of our predecessors and a living record of centuries of land use.

The Heathlands

Clearance of the early woodland on base-deficient parent materials resulted in the destruction of the relatively stable woodland soils, the leaching of nutrients down the soil profile and the formation of acid-tolerant dwarf shrub heathland. Most heaths occur in the humid conditions of continental fringes, notably in western Europe, South Africa, and south-east Australia, and on some oceanic islands and mountain ranges. In Europe they occur from Portugal to

Norway and Estonia, but are best developed in Spain, western France, Ireland and Great Britain. Noirfalise and Vanesse (1976) recognized twenty-one varieties of heathland in Europe, of which nine occur in Britain. Most of the English lowland heaths belong to the Anglo-Norman type, which is characterized by the presence of bell heather (*Eric cinerea*) and dwarf gorse (*Ulex minor*) in the matrix of heather (*Calluna vulgaris*). They are climatically distinct from the heaths, or moors, of the uplands, where rainfall and humidity is much higher and peat formation occurs more readily.

The lowland heaths formerly occupied extensive tracts of the Hampshire Basin (Dorset and Hampshire), Thames Basin (Hampshire, Berkshire and Surrey), Weald (Hampshire, Surrey and Sussex), the south-west peninsula, and the East Anglian coast. Some heath may be natural in origin in the sense that it may have arisen independent of man's activities, but the evidence suggests that most lowland heaths derive from prehistoric woodland clearance and have since been maintained by grazing, burning and the removal of invading trees. They must have expanded progressively at the expense of the woods until they were at their maximum extent in about the 16th century, since when they have declined. They have existed long enough to develop a distinctive fauna and flora which includes species confined to heathland in Britain, and to sustain socio-economic systems based on free-ranging stock.

In practice, the lowland heaths have been regarded as a mixture of acid grassland, mires and transitional habitats set amongst heaths and heathers; all past estimates of the area of heathland appear to have included these other plant communities. On such a basis, I estimate from maps that there must have been at least 190,000 ha of heathland in lowland England around 1800. In 1983 there was at most 48,134 ha – which is a 75% loss. In fact, the total area is probably considerably less, because much of the Surrey heathland was in an advanced stage of succession to woodland – a phenomenon associated with the withdrawal of grazing. The rate at which the heaths have been destroyed has accelerated since the 1930s, mainly through conifer afforestation, conversion to farmland, and urban development. In east Dorset, what were once Canford, Poole and Bourne Heaths, linking the New Forest to the heaths that still survive in Purbeck and beyond, have now been destroyed by the urban encroachment of Bournemouth (Tubbs, 1985).

Heathland losses in England have been exceeded by those in continental Europe, where the heaths have universally and drastically declined since the mid-19th century. The scale of loss has been huge – for example, almost all of the vast 200,000 ha tract of heathland in coastal Aquitaine has been afforested or converted to farmland since 1850 – and a formerly common and distinctive ecosystem has been reduced to rarity in less than a century. Except in France, most of what remains is protected in reserves (Noirfalise & Vanesse, 1976).

Despite the losses sustained in lowland England, the most extensive and intact heaths survive here. The largest continuous areas are those of the New Forest and the Isle of Purbeck. Only in the Forest has the loss rate this century been negligible, and there remains probably the best chance of a complete heathland fauna surviving. It is the only place where the formerly universal pastoral use persists. Like the pasture woods, the heaths of the Forest stand a good chance of long term survival, for not only are they still grazed, but they are actively managed on a large scale to prevent tree invasion.

In the Forest it is important to isolate two particular elements of the lowland heaths – the acid and neutral grasslands, and the mires. The heavily-grazed grasslands are distinctive in species composition and in the morphological adaptions of the plants which permit them to survive grazing. In general composition, they seem to have counterparts only in a scatter of meadows in the Hampshire and Thames Basins, which have escaped fertilizer, lime or herbicide applications. Some comparable grasslands occur in moorland valleys in parts of south-west Britain. Thus, though seldom recognized, these Forest grasslands are rare habitats in a national perspective and may be so in a European context: data are lacking.

The mires are of established international importance. They occur both in valley bottoms and below hill-slope seepages, and exhibit complex gradations of hydrological and chemical conditions which result in an equal complexity of plant communities. The Forest mires are of enormous ecological importance because they are relatively undamaged and provide some of the best examples of this habitat known in Europe. Few valley mires have survived elsewhere in lowland Europe and most of those which remain have been subjected to some artificial drainage, eutrophication from agricultural fertilizer runoff and other sources, and piecemeal reclamation.

Nearly all mires are fragmentary and many now support vegetation which has been either greatly modified or totally replaced by secondary plant communities. The Forest mires are exceptional in that most have not suffered appreciable damage of this kind and are in a relatively natural condition. Importantly, they form virtually intact ecosystems in continuity with catchments comprised of the Forest's heathlands and woodlands. In this respect they contrast strongly with most other valley mires in lowland Europe, which are now isolated within an agricultural environment.

There are some ninety separate valley mires distributed in about twenty separate catchments in the New Forest; there are probably no more than twenty valley mires in the rest of the English lowlands, and only a handful (it is difficult to obtain a reliable figure) around the European littoral from Denmark to Spain. This is a measure of the Forest's importance.

Diversity and Importance of Forest Habitats

However, the Forest is more than a collection of internationally rare and important habitats. Its overall biological wealth is greater than the sum of its parts. Woodland, heath, gorse thicket and invading birch and pine, acid grassland, neutral lawn, valley and seepage step mires and the abundant flushes, ponds, pools and streams, form a single coherent system. Changes in vegetation are related to changes in soil texture, topography and associated

Diversity of habitat is a key feature of the Forest (note browse line on the holly)

chemical and hydrological gradients, upon which are superimposed the effects of grazing, fire, drainage and the vagaries of chance. Diversity of habitat at a local level occurs side by side with large continuous tracts of wood, heath and mire. Irregular woodland margins straggle into birch groves and open, heathy parkland; ragged riverine oakwoods mingle with thorn thickets; brakes of gorse and bog myrtle flank stream-side lawns; and groves of holly and whitebeam spread across dry knolls above hillside seepage mires and wet heaths. Such local diversity is the essence of the Forest, and provides a combination of space, warmth, shelter, and variety of food plants which attracts a greater range and biomass of invertebrates than occur in uniform habitats. It is a general maxim that ecotones are richer in species than the uniform habitats between which they are gradients. The biological wealth of the Forest is enormously enhanced by the abundance of such situations.

Scale is an important factor in species–richness. Norman Moore pointed out in his early study of the Dorset heaths and their conservation, that when a habitat is reduced in size, edge effects become increasingly important and key species become increasingly liable to extinction through inbreeding or such accidents as fire (Moore, 1962). In recent studies of the Dartford warbler, it was found that population density increased with the size of heathland area (Bibby & Tubbs, 1975). Thus, if fragmentation accompanies habitat loss, this increases the vulnerability of many characteristic species. The process of fragmentation has been well documented for heathland (Moore, 1962; Webb & Haskins, 1980; Tubbs, 1985). The large, continuous tracts of the early 19th century have been reduced to many small fragments. The process has advanced least in the New Forest and it is thus here that the most complete heathland flora and fauna is most likely to survive. Much the same could be said of the Forest's other component habitats.

The Inclosures

Although the Forest Inclosures replaced the natural vegetation (save for some pasture woods which were trapped within their fences and survive there today) they greatly enlarge the total area of broadleaved (mainly oak) woodland. Together with the unenclosed woods, they form one of the largest tracts of native, broadleaved woodland in southern England. Scale is again important – for example in supporting populations of predators with large home ranges, and in helping to perpetuate a distinctively humid local microclimate. This is associated with a rich flora of lichens, mosses and ferns, concentrated mainly in the pasture woods but now beginning to spill over into the old plantations. Of equal ecological importance, the Inclosures have, in general, been less heavily grazed than the unenclosed Forest, though this is not so at the moment. The absence of heavy grazing in the past has had far-reaching ecological consequences for the Forest which I explore in later chapters.

Richness of the Flora and Fauna

Hampshire, on the warm, mild, central south coast, is probably the richest place in Britain if this is measured by the number of plant and animal species which have been recorded. Species with essentially easterly, westerly and southerly ranges all overlap here. In the New Forest, scale and diversity of natural habitat capitalizes on this potential. Thus, for example, Colonel Dougie Sterling (unpublished) has calculated that of 2251 species of Lepidoptera (butterflies and moths) known in Britain, 1234 species (55%) have been recorded in the New Forest; and of 3242 British species of Coleoptera (beetles), 1539 (47.5%) are known to occur in the Forest. Of 38 species of Odonata (dragonflies) now breeding in Britain, 27 (73%) breed in the New Forest (Welstead & Welstead, 1984); and (from my own experience) of 33 native species of Orthoptera (crickets, grasshoppers and cockroaches), at least 22 (67%) occur in the Forest. Similarly high percentages of such Orders as Diptera (flies) and Aculeate Hymenoptera (bees, wasps and ants) are believed to occur. At a conservative estimate, roughly 50% of all British insects occur in the New Forest. The invertebrate fauna includes a large number of species now endangered or vulnerable through habitat loss elsewhere, and others which are naturally confined to a small geographical range of which the Forest is part. Some invertebrates have only been recorded in Britain from the New Forest. For many it is now the most important British locality.

Similarly, the Forest supports all but one of the native reptiles and amphibians. It is exceptionally rich in woodland hole- and crevice-nesting insectivorous birds; and it supports large proportions of the national populations of at least five heathland bird species. At least 46 plant species which are nationally or internationally rare because of habitat destruction, occur in the New Forest, and for many it is their most important remaining locality in Britain. Eight are listed in the British *Red Data Book*.

The New Forest is recognized internationally as an important natural resource. Its size, intactness and diversity, the existence of habitats largely lost elsewhere, and a socio-economic system which is inextricably part of its ecology and which, too, has been mostly lost to north-west Europe, combine to make it unique. There are opportunities for research and learning not available elsewhere in Europe. Dutch scientists, for example, have studied the Forest in order to provide basic information needed for such diverse projects as the reintroduction of the tarpan, the European wild horse (*Equus caballus*), into Dutch woodland, and the restablishment of heath on abandoned agricultural land. Dutch, French and German biologists have all turned to the New Forest to derive models of the ecology of the natural woodland cover of northern Europe. Here is a teaching arena for numerous academic institutions, the destination of innumerable amateur naturalists, and of others who simply draw from the Forest a deep and particular aesthetic satisfaction. The New Forest is a natural resource of national and international importance and concern.

The Shaping of the Land

The rocks beneath the New Forest are soft, sedimentary clays and sands of Tertiary age. In the Pleistocene era they appear to have received a capping of superficial gravel or brickearth, which subsequent erosion has largely removed to re-expose the successive strata beneath. Late Pleistocene surface movements of material resulted in partial infilling of valleys and hollows between terraces still capped with gravel, and the distribution of a veneer of transported material over much of the solid strata. The texture and chemical composition of soils therefore varies enormously, and is reflected in the great local variation in vegetation so characteristic of the New Forest. Some surface processes remain active today

and continue to modify the topography, soils and vegetation. This chapter sketches the geology and denudation history of the Forest landscape as a broad background to its ecological development.

The Forest landscape – Digden Bottom, between the gravel terraces of Rockford and Ibsley Commons

Geology

The New Forest is in the centre of a chalk syncline known as the Hampshire Basin. The rocks are of Eocene and Oligocene age and are sands and clays evidently laid down in a series of sedimentation episodes during the Tertiary Era. The Eocene strata rest directly on the Chalk, which, by the time of deposition, had been extensively eroded and subjected to slight earth movements, so that there is non-sequence between the Chalk and the younger rocks. Subsequent risings and sinkings of the land surface can be deduced, during which marine, estuarine, deltaic and fluviatile deposits were left as the sea first invaded the land, and then retreated to leave erosion and redistribution of the sediments to river systems. The present Hampshire Basin, during this long period of geological flux, represented the western extremity of an extensive area of deposition known as the Anglo-Franco-Belgian Basin. Folding of the earth's surface and widespread subsequent denudation have left only relicts of the consolidation Tertiary formations, mainly in synclines such as the Hampshire and Thames Basins.

In the New Forest, the rocks tilt gently southwards at an angle of $1°-2°$, with the oldest exposed in the north and the youngest in the south. The earliest formations are the Eocene Reading Beds and London Clays, which outcrop at the margin of the Chalk immediately north of the Forest. Southward there are sequential exposures of Bagshot Sands, Bracklesham Beds, Barton Sands and Barton Clays. Though the strata are described in general terms as sands and clays, they are lithologically variable. The Bagshot Sands are exposed in the extreme north of the Forest, as poor sands of fluviatile origin. The Brackleshams are mainly marine, often rich in the green mineral glauconite, and with abundant fossils, interbedded with sandier material, and similar variation occurs in the Bartons, which are also of marine origin, and exposed across a broad central belt of the Forest. Further south, the Oligocene Headon Beds overlay the Eocene strata. The Headon Beds are evidently derived from a variety of contemporary conditions – lakes, brackish lagoons, estuaries and shallow seas – and occur mainly as loams, clays and clay marl. They extend in a belt flanking the Solent, though the solid strata are extensively obscured by sheets of Pleistocene gravel or brickearth which are less eroded here than further north.

Ecologically, the most important features of these deposits are their texture and chemistry, which in turn depend on the circumstances in which they were deposited. In sheltered estuaries, particles in suspension and available for deposition are small and include much organic matter. In turbulent conditions they are coarse, with little organic matter. Deposits therefore vary from the biologically richer mudflats and saltmarshes of inner estuaries, to the sand flats of estuary mouths and offshore bars – much as on today's coastline. Similarly, river deposits tend to be more impoverished than those of marine origin.

Texture is important in determining soil fertility in the sense that the coarser and more porous the material, the more susceptible it is to the leaching of nutrients from the surface downwards. Marine clays and loams yield the better soils, but the whole New Forest series, except for the Headon clays and clay marls and some of the glauconitic Bracklesham clays, tend to produce base-poor, or at best, near-neutral soils.

Owing to the generally later deposition of the more enriched material, and the steeper dip of the strata compared with the gradient of the land surface, the Forest soils become progressively less impoverished from north to south. This pattern is reflected in the greater diversity of flora in the south of the Forest. The settlement pattern also reflects the distribution of the better soils, and it is significant that most traces of abandoned field systems to be found on the Forest occur also on the Headon Beds and on some of the less impoverished clays elsewhere.

The Miocene and Pliocene periods, which succeeded the Oligocene, left no record in the Hampshire Basin. The Tertiary strata, however, were mantled by superficial sheets of gravel and brickearth, the oldest of which were probably deposited at the end of the Pliocene and early in the succeeding Pleistocene period. These removed much of the superficial deposits and left a landscape of broad valleys and hollows in which gravel, alluvium and other transported material have accumulated; between them, remnants of the gravel and brickearth sheets survive as flat terraces or plateaux.

The plateau gravels have a maximum recorded depth of 6.5 m, but most sheets, particularly on the higher ridges, are 1–3 m deep. Fisher (1971, 1975) examined the gravel soils in over sixty pits throughout the Forest, and Keen (1980) sampled twenty-four sites

The eroded landscape of Vales Moor: east-west ridges and intervening valley filled with peat

on the lower terraces flanking the Solent. They agree in describing the gravel as coarse, angular local flint derived from the chalk, with small amounts of Greensand chert and sandstone, rounded quartz pebbles, sarsan fragments and blocks, and minor quantities of other material secondarily derived from the Tertiary deposits. Mud clasts and silt blocks occur and the gravels have a high clay content, giving rise to impeded soils and a distinctive 'humid' heath vegetation today. On the terraces below 80 m there are extensive deposits of brickearth up to 3 m deep resting on top of the gravel or infilling ancient channels. From grain size analysis, Keen (1980) described the brickearth as 50% fine sand, 30% silt and 20% clay; small flakes of flint also occur. Over large areas it has been mixed with the underlying gravel by solifluxion to produce tracts of loamy gravel, often with poor subsoil drainage; most brickearth soils however, are a relatively free-draining and fertile sandy loam.

Geomorphological History

The Forest landscape is dominated by the gravel terraces (Fig. 5). For 13 km along the north-west boundary, there is a north-easterly facing, gravel-capped escarpment at 120–128 m, which includes the Forest's highest point at Black Bush Plain (SU248162). From

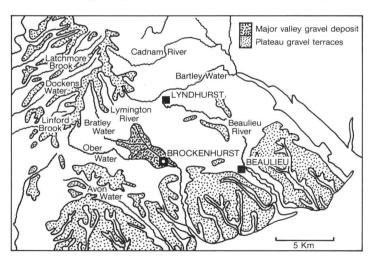

Fig. 5.
Gravel Terraces and the Drainage Network

here the land descends south and east to the Solent, and south and west to the Avon, in a series of terraces separated by wide, eroded valleys and hollows. Everard (1944a; 1954b) described eleven terraces between 128 m and 5 m, besides others now below sea level, but there is little agreement between authors about terrace elevations or numbers. On the lower terraces flanking the Solent

Keen (1980) felt able to identify only three, well-marked height ranges, 40–25 m, 22–14 m, and below 10 m.

The eroded landscape of Cranesmoor – undulating heathland on Bagshot Sand, with valley mires filling broad hollows in the drainage pattern

The main Forest watershed runs approximately north–south and separates six westerly-flowing streams with few tributaries, which descend to the Avon, from five larger drainage networks and some smaller streams, which drain south and east. Of this latter group, the Blackwater and Cadnam Rivers drain to the River Test, Bartley Water to the Test estuary, and the Beaulieu and Lymington Rivers to the Solent. They are separated by two well marked watersheds, probably of late Pleistocene origin, on which the sites of several river captures can be detected. A number of streams rise on the southern terraces and drain direct to the Solent in short, immature valleys (Fig. 5).

West of the watershed, the streams are deeply incised between long, narrow, gravel-capped ridges. The valleys are wide, and in the north of the Forest, nearly U-shaped in section. Their short, steep profiles have evolved in response to recurrent downcutting by the Avon, the position of which has remained relatively constant. In contrast, the drainage networks east of the watershed appear to have evolved in response to a retreating river or shoreline. There, the trend is north-west to south-east, following the gentle tilt of the rocks, but the Lymington and Beaulieu Rivers show a distinctive southward trend upstream of their estuaries, and there is an easterly trend in the upper Blackwater River, Cadnam River, Bartley Water, Beaulieu River and Avon Water. Four of the five largest streams rise close to the watershed in the north of the Forest near Fritham, at about 90 m. The Beaulieu River, however, rises near the centre of the Forest, at Lyndhurst, at 46 m, and clearly lost most of its upper catchment through Pleistocene river captures.

The remaining substantial stream, the Avon Water, rises at 50 m near the watershed in the south-east of the Forest and flows east and then south to the Solent.

A succession of authors have attempted to deduce the geomorphological history of the Hampshire Basin, and in particular the origins of the superficial gravels. Everard (1954a, 1957) concluded that the terraces were deposited during pauses in the emergence of the area from the sea which covered much of south-east England in the late Pliocene. The difficulties with this hypothesis are numerous. The flint is angular, not wave-worn.

The deposits include fragile mud clasts and silt blocks which would not have survived marine action. They show a clear west-east directional bedding and channel lineation, characteristic of a riverine environment. They include brickearth, which Fisher (1971; 1975) showed to be consistent in grain structure with fluvial material. Finally, there is a definite west–east slope to the terraces, reflected in the trending of the modern Forest streams, which is inconsistent with a retreating shore. David Keen (1980) concluded from this and other evidence, that the gravels were deposited by the Pleistocene River Solent as it migrated south and east to its present position in response to progressively falling sea levels and long after the retreat of the Pliocene sea. A fluvio–glacial origin for the gravels – that is, that they were the outwash of major ice-sheets – is difficult to sustain, if only because they incorporate none of the far-travelled material to be expected in such a scenario. On the contrary, they comprise strictly local material.

Keen argued convincingly that the gravel and brickearth were deposited under a periglacial regime at the transition between interglacial and glacial episodes, when there was vigorous solifluxion and seasonally abundant melt-water. He envisaged an environment with braided streams depositing coarse gravel in the spring and finer loamy material (the brickearth) in late summer. The brickearths are often loessic in character (Fisher, 1971; 1975; Swanson, 1970; Catt, 1977), which is also consistent with a periglacial environment. In modern periglacial conditions, dust clouds commonly arise from unvegetated surfaces on flood plains in late summer (French, 1976). Similar gravel and loamy deposits can be seen forming today in high arctic areas characterized by extreme spring discharges capable of transporting and depositing huge quantities of coarse material. The fragile mud clasts and silt blocks found in the Forest deposits also suggest rapid erosion and deposition in circumstances in which they would have remained frozen in transit. Finally, the width of the terraces is also characteristic of the high seasonal discharges of the modern arctic. Coupled with frequent channel movement this produces wide, channelled terraces exactly like those of the Hampshire Basin (Tricart, 1970; French, 1976; Castleden, 1977).

Only for the lowest terraces flanking the modern Solent can a date be suggested. At Stone Point (SZ458984), on the present shore, the gravel rests on peat and silt containing brackish-water molluscs and dated by pollen analysis to the time of maximum warmth in the last interglacial period (Brown *et al.*, 1975). Hypothetically, the gravel was deposited as sea level fell at the end of the interglacial, but before the Solent cut down to the low base levels of the last glaciation.

The landforms and drainage pattern of the Forest appear to have evolved concurrently with terrace formation, in phases of erosion related to the progressive fall in sea level during the million or so years of the Pleistocene period. Each fall in base level initiated stream rejuvenation and a new cycle of erosion, which in periglacial conditions of seasonally abundant water, partially destroyed the higher terraces and redeposited the material at lower levels.

Tremlett (1965) studied the evolution of the Beaulieu River catchment and deduced that for a long period in the presumably later Pleistocene, the easterly trend in the upper sections of the Beaulieu and Lymington Rivers found a logical outfall to Southampton Water rather than to the Solent as at present. This requires that the Lymington River formerly flowed eastward to join the Beaulieu River, the combined system entering Southampton Water somewhere near the present town of Hythe. The gradient of the valleys was low, and the rivers deposited spreads of gravel in their lower reaches, some of which have survived subsequent denudation as low ridges in a wide, eroded landscape of low relief. This now occupies a central zone of the Forest between the southern terraces flanking the Solent, and the higher, northern terraces associated with the main watershed. The easterly-flowing river system was eventually captured by two streams which arose on the southern terraces and flowed to the Solent. These streams – now the estuaries and lower reaches of the Beaulieu and Lymington Rivers – eroded headward, with successive falls in base level, until they broke through into the more northerly drainage system and made a succession of river captures. The remaining streams which arose on the lower terraces, are still eroding headward but none have yet succeeded in breaking through the terraces.

Numerous other river captures appear to date from the late Pleistocene period, when the present drainage pattern probably became established. At the same time, alluvium, gravel and brick-earth were deposited in the lower sections of the present valleys, forming successive layers in places. Extensive surface movement of material took place elsewhere within the catchments, leaving soil profiles today in which a veneer of sand and loam, often with small flints, overlays the bedrock, which is often of clay. None of the transported materials can have been derived beyond the relict terraces which marked the limits of the catchments. Subsequently, the low sea levels of the last glaciation resulted in further down-cutting of the valleys and with the post-glacial rise in sea level, deposits of alluvium and peat accumulated in the over-deepened valleys.

Postglacial Surface Processes

For most of the post-glacial period, the amount of water in the terrestrial environment has been small. The present climate is relatively dry and temperate, and despite periodical oscillations of rainfall and temperature, has probably not changed in essentials for two millennia or more. Recent records (1971–81) for the New Forest give an average annual precipitation of 86.5 mm. Precipitation was lowest during April–August (46–62 mm) and highest during December–January (94–105 mm). Almost all falls as rain. Prolonged snowfalls have occurred only intermittently this century and snow seldom persists long. Since 1950 there has been only one really severe winter – 1962–3 when the Forest was snow- and ice-bound for nearly eight weeks – and another four or five when snow stayed on the ground for more than a week. In most winters it has been confined to brief, light falls, and in many there has been no snow at all. Frosts, however, are common, and though night temperatures seldom fall below $-9°C$ they have a discernible fracturing effect on exposed surfaces. Today's climate is certainly very different from the periods when denudation produced the present landforms.

The present streams are of low volume. However, the generally low porosity of the rocks and superficial deposits, which mostly have a high clay content, produce sudden increases in stream volume and local flooding. On the other hand, the numerous peat bogs (or mires) delay the discharge of water to streams and are important in maintaining minimal flows during May–September. Watercourses whose catchments are poorly endowed with mires are frequently dry in summer. This was particularly evident in the 1970s and 1980s, in contrast to the wetter summers of the previous decade.

Despite the limited erosion potential of the climate, it is still possible to detect the nearly spent force of the most recent cycle of denudation. Surprisingly large quantities of material are still being removed by quite small streams. Tuckfield (1973a; 1979) found from a survey of all the Forest streams, that the highest erosion rate occurred in the headwaters of the Cadnam River (SU2414). He found the limit of the latest erosion cycle nearly at the heads of the tributaries, where it was represented by series of headward-migrating steps, some more than a metre high, below which there were eroding sections of channel deeply incised into a small flood plain left from an earlier erosion cycle. Deposition in the stream bed

Migrant erosion step and plunge pool

began 400 m downstream of the nick point, and the flood plain of the present cycle could be recognized another 200 m downstream, contained within that of the earlier one. The flood plain widened steadily and another 150 m downstream supported oaks and beeches probably over 200 years old. Measurements during 1969–72 showed that the erosion steps were migrating upstream at 1–2 m/ year. A longer term observation confirmed this. In the 1948–9 winter, a bridge was destroyed by the arrival of the migrant erosion step. In 1972 the step was 50 m further upstream, giving a migration rate of about 2 m/year. These tiny streams have a surprising erosion capability. Between June 1969 and May 1972, a little over 100 cu m of material were removed from 45 m of channel below the erosion step, equivalent to about 0.75 m^3/metre/year. The next highest rate found in a Forest stream by Cyril Tuckfield was 0.64 m^3/metre/year, removed by the Blackensford Brook (SU231069).

The flood plain of the present together with an earlier erosion cycle can be traced down the Cadnam River to Cadnam (SU293136), where Everard (1957) placed the late Pleistocene capture of the upper part of the river (previously flowing to the Bartley Water) by a tributary of the Blackwater. The present erosion cycle must post-date the capture, but it was probably not initiated by it, though the earlier traceable cycle may have been. At 1–2 m/year, and even allowing for an extended lifetime in the low downstream gradients, the erosion step began its upstream migrations only 3–6000 years ago, in the postglacial Atlantic period or later. Nonetheless, there is something almost eerie in the likelihood that in the migrant erosion steps in streams of today, we are witnessing the final stages of a process than began three or six millennia ago.

Although there is evidence of present-day headward erosion in the headwaters of most catchments, there is no evidence of a more recent erosion pulse downstream, save where it has been locally initiated by artificial drainage. The bedload of gravel carried by Forest streams in their lower reaches is insufficient, and the streams of too low a volume, to generate other than local flood plain growth today. Only the thinnest veneer of silt remains after the recession of floodwater from alluvial plains. However, some of the superficial flood plain silts and alluviums are derived from postglacial erosion pulses (witness the Cadnam River), and there is also evidence to suggest that the valleys were also infilled with material mobilized by early forest clearance and primitive farming in Bronze Age and later times.

Artificial drainage has contributed to denudation. Since the 1840s there has been periodic canalization or regrading of some stream channels. Tuckfield (1976, 1980) investigated seventy channels cut or re-cut by the Forestry Commission since 1960, and found that when the bed gradient of the stream exceeded $1.5°$, erosion had invariably occurred, and on slopes of $2.5°$ or more channels were liable to rapid downcutting and bank collapse. Erosion steps and plunge pools could migrate headward at more

Migrant erosion step cutting into valley mire, Silver Stream, Rhinefield

than 1 m/year, and in quite small drains, 0.1–0.3 m³ of material is commonly eroded per metre of channel per year as a result of human interference. In extreme cases, more than 0.5 m³/metre/year was eroded. Deposition occurred where gradients fell to about 1°, or where the disturbed tributary discharged to a parent channel. Stream blockage, diversions and secondary erosion could result. Some of the results of interference in stream morphology have been destructively spectacular. Some migrant erosion steps threaten the stability of valley mires into which they are now beginning to penetrate.

Large amounts of material are eroded from gulleys that occur when steep slopes are exposed to constant wear from the passage of stock, people or, particularly, the shod hooves of ridden horses; deep trenches commonly develop very rapidly. Tuckfield (1964) found that over a ten-year period, 1084 m³ of gravel was removed from a gulley – a rate of 98.5 m³/year. In a second measured example, a 64-m long gulley developed in two and a half years and an estimated 280.5 m³ of material was removed from it during this time. Both active and relict gulleys are common in the Forest and must have contributed in no small way to the process of denudation.

Characteristic erosion features of the Forest are the seepage steps which commonly occur on steep terrace slopes and arise through the seepage of ground water above the junction between impermeable and permeable strata (Tuckfield, 1973b). In profile, a convex slope descends from the terrace surface to a near-vertical step, below which there is a convex dome, or debris slope of eroded material, and, below that, the concave lower slope of the valley. The debris slope immediately below the step usually has an uneven surface which becomes more regular as the jumble of slipped

Over-deepening of drain, leading to bank collapse, Silver Stream, Rhinefield

material is absorbed into a heterogenous dome of clays, sands and gravels derived from above. The rate of erosion and down-slope movement is slow, and peat accumulates in hollows in the debris slope to form the seepage step mires which are a distinctive element in the Forest vegetation. Though many faces are temporarily in-active and have achieved an angle of repose which has permitted colonization by heath vegetation, others are actively eroding and recent slipping can be detected in successive curved slices from the face and above deposited in the top of the debris slope. The highest known face is 6 m in Shobley Bottom (SU185060). The average of 54 valley sides measured by Cyril Tuckfield was 2.16 m.

Seepage stems form arcuate lines along the contour of most of the valleys that cut into the higher terraces in the north and west of the Forest, and also very locally on the sides of the lower terraces. They occur most commonly at the junction of the Barton Clay with the overlying Barton Sand in the valley sides between Picket Post

Downstream gravel deposition following drainage, Silver Stream, Rhinefield (gravel actually blocking the stream has been removed)

(SU190061) and Stoney Cross (SU260118). Comparable litho-logical changes, sometimes in what is nominally the same bedrock, determines their location elsewhere. The position of the foot of the step appears to be determined directly by the level of the water table above the impermeable strata, rather than by the junction itself – which sometimes lies several metres below the toe of the step.

Tuckfield (1973b) suggests that the seepage steps may have been

initiated early in valley development – i.e., at various times in the late Pleistocene period – when a stream flowing in permeable strata cut down to near a junction with impermeable rock. At this point, lateral seepage to the stream would give rise to seepage steps immediately above the water table, in the permeable rock. Subsequently, as the stream eroded downwards, so the steps would migrate up-slope away from the stream and tend to become closer to the junction in the strata. At the heads of valleys, seepage steps are continuous and located close to the stream, but progressively distance themselves down-valley. At the same time, the debris slope and its bog extend continuously from seepage step to stream in the upper valley but migrate laterally downstream, leaving a dry heath zone between steepage step, bog and stream. This general picture is sometimes confused by the occurrence of successive seepage steps on valley sides, or by shallow, peat-filled hollows linking the seepage step mires with the stream or valley mire.

Foulford Bottom – valley mire with seepage steps visible as linear features on the upper valley slopes

Finally, terrace slopes with slight gradients and the necessary juxtaposition of strata commonly give rise to seepages and seepage mires which have yet to trigger the fracture which produces the step. They are presumably unlikely to do so because of the low gradient of the slopes, and the relatively low rainfall.

Some of the steepest terrace sides in the north of the Forest have relict landslips which are superficially similar to seepage steps, but which in fact are due to slope failure following massive waterloading of Barton and Bracklesham Clays. In plan, the rear scarps of the slips form a scalloped pattern along the upper hill slope. Below each scarp lies a trough and then successive down-slope undulations of decreasing amplitude and wave-length, formed from the slipped material. Relict landslips are almost continuous along the north-east-facing escarpment of the Forest, and in seven other locations at the edges of the highest terraces. Tuckfield (1968), who first described them, thought that the climate under which such mass movement occurred must have been very different from today's – probably periglacial or perhaps an extremely wet post-glacial episode. I recall however, Gilbert White's account of the landslip near Selbourne on 8 March 1774, when 'a considerable part of the woody hanger at Hawkley was torn from its place' – an event precipitated by the water-loading of the Gault Clay by seepage through the Upper Greensand escarpment against which it rested. In the Forest, small slips still occur at the rear scarps, but there is neither written nor folk record of major movement. Almost all the slips bear a mantle of natural beech and oak woodland believed to be of ancient origin (as, indeed, at Hawkley Hanger) and so contrast vividly with the seepage steps which have remained active and are devoid of trees.

Settlement Through the Ages chapter 3

The morphology and soils of the Forest were largely determined by natural processes which took place in the Pleistocene period, but in Quarternary times, man has assumed an important role in further shaping the environment (Fig. 6). In the early post-glacial period, woodland spread northwards over Europe in the wake of the retreating ice-sheets and tundra. As early as late Boreal times, Mesolithic hunter-gatherer cultures may have influenced this woodland by the use of fire. Simmons (1969) pictured a sequence in which clearings were fire-created near hunting camps and subsequent concentrations of herbivores prevented regeneration. Large-scale forest clearance began in Neolithic times (*c*.3200–2000 BC in Britain) with the advent of settled agriculture, and continued during succeeding cultural periods. On base-poor soils, woodland clearance and arable cropping by primitive techniques led to the depletion of the nutrient capital and abandonment to rough grazing. Around the European coasts, a combination of woodland clearance, cultivation, grazing, burning, and the resultant leaching of nutrients down the soil profile, led to the development of extensive acid-tolerant heathland and acid grassland.

Woodland clearance began in different places at different times, but in the New Forest, the first significant clearance probably began in the middle or late Bronze Age (*c*.1200–500 BC). The progressive expansion of heathland at the expense of woodland continued to the 17th century, though it was retarded after the 11th century by controls over land use arising from its appropriation as royal forest. The later ecological history of the Forest is inextricably associated with this legal status, which gave some protection to the surviving woodlands, regulated pastoral and other uses and limited enclosure and cultivation. Since the 18th century, it has been technically possible to reclaim even the most impoverished forest soils, and this would have undoubtedly happened but for its peculiar status. That the New Forest has survived into the late 20th century in a condition which has unbroken links with prehistory, seems nothing short of a miracle.

The triumph of the wilderness over human aspirations has left an archaeological legacy which from present knowledge includes large numbers of barrows, boiling mounds and pottery kilns; the wasted banks and ditches of 35–40 enclosure systems, 46 isolated pounds or enclosures, over 100 small fields thought to be Forest-edge encroachments (chapter 5), 30 known or presumed medieval coppices (chapter 10); two medieval emparkments (chapter 8); and numerous bank fragments of obscure origin and purpose. However, few habitation sites have been detected and few of the earthworks have been unequivocally dated. More are found annually. Collectively, they remain an archaeological challenge and possess great potential for increasing our understanding of the ecological and land use history of the Forest. This chapter reviews the archaeological and documentary evidence for the settlement chronology of the Forest. In itself, however, this is too slight to confirm or refute the notion of early woodland clearance by man. For this, we must turn, in chapter 4, to pollen analysis.

The Pre-Domesday Record

The chronology of settlement in the Forest conforms with that of most other areas of base-poor soils in south and east England. Mesolithic occupation, evidenced by surface or sub-surface aggregations of worked flints, was widespread and may be under-represented, since Metholithic man left no structures. There is a contrasting absence of Neolithic evidence, save for a few chance finds of arrowheads, perhaps left by hunting parties from the densely-populated chalkland to the north. In contrast again, there is abundant Bronze Age evidence in the form of round barrows. These burial mounds are the most conspicuous artefacts of pre-history on the Tertiary deposits of the Hampshire Basin. More than 200 remain in the Forest today, though two-thirds or more were mutilated before this century, by treasure-seekers, antiquarians, or early archaeologists. Most New Forest barrows excavated this century have been dated to the middle or late Bronze Age.[*]

Analysis of pollen preserved in the upper horizons of soils buried beneath Bronze Age barrows on modern heathland has yielded a general picture of local cultivation in a landscape partially cleared of woodland, and the pollen sequence down the profile provides evidence of the recent opening up of the former woods. The pollen from a buried profile beneath a Late Bronze-Age barrow on heathland near Berry Wood conformed closely to such a picture (McGregor, 1962; Dimbleby, 1962).

How much the barrows reflect the density of occupation is conjectural. We do not know the time span during which they were built, nor how commonplace they were as memorials to the dead. Over 700 or more years, 200 barrows could equally suggest a small and scattered population at any given time, or more concentrated construction over short periods of denser occupation. The barrows do indicate how early human communities were distributed, since the pollen analyses suggest that they were usually

*Sumner, 1921–2; Preston & Hawkes, 1933; Grinsell, 1938–40, 1958; Piggot, 1943; McGregor, 1962.

constructed on or close to farmland. In the New Forest, most are on the terraces – now mainly impoverished heathland – which show how much things have changed ecologically over the past 3000 years.

Few traces of Bronze Age settlements have so far been identified. The ditch of a wasted enclosure bank in Fawley Inclosure yielded fragments of late Bronze Age or early Iron Age pottery when the feature was destroyed by subsoiling in 1963. The pollen from the soil beneath the wasted bank of a small enclosure on Beaulieu Heath suggested a Bronze Age date (Tubbs & Dimbleby, 1965); and pollen analyses and a rough radiocarbon date for two enclosure banks at Dark Hat suggested occupation around 550 BC at the notional Bronze Age/Iron Age transition (Eide, 1982). All are on the terraces. A more revealing light on the times may perhaps be thrown by the 100 or more boiling mounds now identified in the Forest.

Boiling mounds are low, crescent- or kidney-shaped piles of calcined flints, up to 15 m across and with the opening directly facing a water supply and slightly downslope of it. The mound often carried heather in contrast to the boggy vegetation around the flush or spring which provides the water. Excavation of a mound in 1967 confirmed that within its arms there had been a trough and beside it a fireplace. Boiling mounds were places where flints were heated and cast into a trough to heat water. That it works has been demonstrated by experiment. The mound grew from the cold flints removed from the trough and thrown on three sides, leaving the other open to permit the channelling of water to the trough. The excavated New Forest boiling mound yielded pottery of the Late Bronze Age (Pasmore & Pallister, 1967). A mound in the Avon valley yielded pottery of similar age (S. J. Shennen).

Most New Forest boiling mounds are wasted and spread, few achieving the full crescent or kidney shape. Many were damaged or destroyed by forestry work in the 1960s and 1970s. More come to light annually. Before heat-resistant vessels were available, they must have been commonplace. Yet their wet locations in the Forest do not generally commend themselves to habitation, nor do the mounds seem large enough to reflect long-established settlement. Perhaps they did serve settlements on the terraces up-slope, but they also suggest a more transient pastoral or hunting people, per-haps migrating on established seasonal circuits. It is possible that they also indicate the extent of heathland in the late Bronze Age. Their functions require the heating of flints, yet remarkably little charcoal has been found. Can it be that heath turves were used for fuel, as they were until recently in the Forest? Were heathland the fuel source, it must have been relatively extensive; and if the mounds are any guide, the late Bronze Age heathland covered much the same area as that of today.

The tribes which brought the Iron Age to Britain constructed hill forts that commanded the estuaries of the Beaulieu and Lymington Rivers, with four more on the main Forest watersheds, and two on the terrace edge overlooking the Avon. All, except Buckland Rings on the Lymington estuary, are small and do not suggest extensive settlement.

Other evidence of Iron Age settlement is scant. Of the 35–40 more extensive field systems, three have a superficial resemblance to the 'Celtic' fields of the chalkland, and for two, the pollen in the soil buried by the banks suggested an Iron Age date (Tubbs & Dimbleby, 1965). One of these is not far from a barrow which yielded an Iron Age cart burial (Piggot, 1943). Early this century, Heywood Sumner excavated what he described as a pastoral enclosure on Gorley Hill and dated it from pottery to the late Iron Age (Sumner, 1917): it has since been destroyed by gravel workings.

More recently, two settlement sites have been found and excavated and both proved to have been first inhabited late in the Iron Age. One was a wasted mound within an extensive field system on Beaulieu Heath – the 'Crockford Complex', excavated by the Hampshire Field Club in 1965–6 and named after an adjoining valley. No clearly-defined occupation layers could be distinguished, but the pottery suggested that the site was in use from the early 1st century BC until the Roman conquest or later (Pasmore, 1978). The fields were probably not contemporary: their layout and the state of their banks suggests a much more recent date. At a point only 200 m from the excavated habitation, they are superimposed on the small enclosure tentatively dated to the Bronze Age by pollen analysis. This, in turn, is one of a number of small enclosures and bank fragments in the area similar in their degree of wastage. The present-day heathland in the area may have seen at least three phases of occupation spanning 3000 years.

Excavations at the second site, Church Green, Fritham, also by the Hampshire Field Club, began in 1976 and are continuing. ('Church' place names become attached to unexplained earthworks in the Forest and elsewhere.) The surface irregularities and low mound here attracted at least two 19th-century hole-diggers who left no more than a casual reference to having found Roman pottery. The current excavations have revealed a probably extensive settlement occupied from not later than the early 1st century BC until the 4th century AD, thus spanning the late Iron Age and most of the Romano-British period. For most of this time, there were pottery kilns in the area, and indeed, one was excavated. Carbonized cereal grains were recovered from a range of dated contexts between the 1st and 4th centuries. Their low contamination with arable weed seeds suggested that the crops had been winnowed elsewhere, so there is no way of deducing if cereals were grown locally (Pasmore & Fortescue, 1977–83; Green, 1983).

Church Green is in a valley which drains west to the Avon from the dissected northern terraces. In Romano-British times, this and neighbouring valleys supported a pottery industry producing distinctive 'New Forest ware'. The known kilns are concentrated in four main groups, with an outlying cluster near Burley, in the south-west of the Forest. Many kilns were excavated, or rather mutilated, before the present century. Some were excavated by Heywood Sumner early this century (Sumner, 1919, 1921, 1927); two were excavated in 1955 (Cunliffe, 1965); two in 1966 (Pasmore, 1967); and three in 1970 (Fulford, 1973). Sadly, the excavations in 1966 and 1970 were necessary because of the impending destruction of the kilns by Forestry Commission gravel road construction and tree planting. Collectively, excavation results date the industry mainly to the 3rd and 4th centuries. The earlier history of Church Green, however, hints that we are only scratching the surface of Iron Age and Romano-British occupation. The archaeological evidence provides no indication of the scale of the industry at any one time and we cannot estimate its environmental impact. It is reasonable to suppose that there must have been abundant coppice available to fire the kilns and that woodland was deliberately managed for the purpose. I remain puzzled by the absence of significant clay workings, although the potteries were clearly located where suitable outcrops of clay occurred in the valleys. Has time erased the traces of the workings? Was the industry too small to make significant inroads on its raw material? Whatever its scale, there must be settlement sites yet unfound, and there must have been livestock kept and crops grown, a supposition supported by the numerous, but undated, enclosure bank fragments around the main areas of the industry.

Site of a Romano-British pottery industry

In 1982, what appears to have been a substantial Romano-British settlement was found in a 'new' locality remote from the known kilns. Surface evidence comprised a pattern of earthworks, quantities of burnt matter and pottery of the 4th century and probably earlier (Pasmore & Fortescue, 1977–83). At another site far removed from the kilns, on the upper valley side of Long Slade Bottom, the bank of a field group has been tentatively placed in the 2nd century AD by pollen analysis and radiocarbon dating of the buried soil (Eide, 1982). Such discoveries tend to reinforce the suspicion that our knowledge of the times remains fragmentary.

Our perception of the Forest in the centuries which followed the withdrawal of the Roman legions in AD 410 is even poorer. The potteries fade into obscurity. Radiocarbon determination of the soil surface buried beneath an abandoned enclosure at Burley Moor gave an approximate late 8th-century date (Eide, 1982) and perhaps some other, undated, field systems and other enclosures are Saxon in origin. However, it seems clear that the centuries after invasion saw consolidation of permanent settlement on the more productive soils. This formed the basis of the settlement pattern which was first comprehensively recorded in Domesday, and which is essentially extant today.

Domesday and the Royal Forest

The Domesday records registered the product of five centuries of Saxon occupation. By then, south-west Hampshire was divided into the seven administrative districts, or Hundreds, of Bovre, Rodbridge, Rodedic, Sirlei, Egheiete, Rincvede and Fordingebrige. It was from these Hundreds, and mainly from Bovre and Rodbridge, that the New Forest was formed by William I sometime between the conquest and 1086, the date of Domesday. Domesday recorded 137 holdings (manors) in the seven Hundreds, comprising forty-seven in the 'Forest' itself and unassessed for taxation (though their pre-conquest values were given); forty-nine which were reduced in value evidently because their outlying woods and wastes were afforested; and forty-one which were unaffected by afforestation. Varying degrees of doubt remain about the location of thirty or more, mostly afforested, holdings, though localities for most have been suggested.

All but two of the partially afforested holdings were peripheral to the perambulation of 1217–18, which is the earliest surviving legal boundary to the Forest (Stagg, 1974a). Most were on the coastal belt and the fertile terraces of the Avon valley. In contrast, all the completely afforested holdings were within the 13th-century boundary. Of the unaffected holdings, only Brockenhurst was in the hinterland of the Forest and most were in parts of the

Hundreds furthest removed from the perambulation. The 1217–18 perambulation evidently approximated to the effective boundary of the Forest when it was made. It remained more-or-less unchanged until 1964.

Domesday shows that the modern settlement pattern of southwest Hampshire was well established 900 years ago, though there was then much woodland and heath where now there is enclosed farmland. Within the Forest, the present settlements of Lyndhurst, Burley, Minstead, Boldre and Brockenhurst were represented by small manors. There was a scatter of holdings immediately inland of the Solent on what are now the Sowley, Beaulieu, Exbury and Cadland estates. In addition, Stagg (1974b) deduced that nineteen 'lost' holdings were also here, on either side of the Beaulieu estuary and within the later Cistercian estate of Beaulieu. He makes the interesting suggestion that the holdings were not 'lost' on afforestation, but follow King John's gift of twenty-five hides at Beaulieu to the Cistercian foundation in 1204 (it is said in expiation of his misdeeds). The area was certainly settled before the Order's arrival, though it reclaimed more waste* – several positively identified Domesday villages were there and, later, John held property there.

Of the larger enclaves of enclosed land in the modern Forest, only Fritham and Linwood cannot be certainly identified in Domesday. Juare, said to be Eyeworth Lodge and Slacham (possibly Sloden Inclosure), may have been the precursors of nearby Fritham. On the other hand, Fritham has the characteristic rounded boundary of a later medieval vaccary (or cattle farm) and, with Linwood, may post-date Domesday. If they have been accurately placed, Juare and Slachem were near the Romano-British potteries, though there is nothing to suggest that they were the direct descendents of the older settlements.

It is not possible to tell from Domesday how much land within the Forest was enclosed and farmed by the 11th century, but most holdings were low in value and presumably small. The unit of measurement was the hide, but though originally a unit of area, usually said to be 120 acres (49 ha), it evolved as a fiscal measurement, influenced by land quality as well as area, and by the presence of such profitable enterprises as salterns and mills. In Bovre and Rodbridge Hundreds, which bore the brunt of afforestation, only six of sixty-nine holdings were assessed at more than 2 hides. Only one of these, Minstead, ($3\frac{1}{2}$ hides) was in the Forest hinterland. Finn (1962) suggested a population somewhat in excess of 2000 for the forty-seven completely afforested holdings. The Forest was a place of small hamlets among the woods and heaths, on which the inhabitants depended for grazing and other resources.

*Waste = unenclosed land, though exploited for grazing, fuel, etc.

What were the implications of afforestation for the wholly or partly afforested holdings? The forty-seven wholly afforested manors were reduced to nothing in taxable value except that in twenty-one holdings, 40 ha of small meadows remained unaffected. The partly afforested manors were reduced in value. Most were at the Forest margins, but three – Lyndhurst, Minstead and Canterton – were in its hinterland. Within the Forest, only Brockenhurst remained unaffected in value.

Until the late 19th century the recurrent theme of chroniclers and historians in interpreting Domesday, was of depopulation and the destruction of churches and villages by William I in order to 'make' the New Forest. Subsequent views have ameliorated the extent of depopulation, but so far as I know, only Stagg (1974b) has taken the final step of rejecting it and hence its implications of peasant suffering. I concur with David Stagg in concluding that the reduced taxable values in Domesday meant no more than that the inhabitants were relieved of taxation in compensation for being in the Forest. Afforestation meant that lands and inhabitants became subject to a legal code – the forest law, designed to protect the beasts of the forest. Of paramount importance, the afforested land, at least in theory, could no longer be enclosed against the deer, making cultivation difficult or impossible.

On the other hand, there was compensation not only in tax relief, but in rights to depasture stock over the unenclosed lands of the

Queen's Meadow, isolated in the Forest and similar to those surviving disafforestation

whole Forest – rights that were ultimately enshrined in legal form. Doubtless, the forest law imposed hardship, but it probably conferred sufficient advantages to permit the survival of a smallholding and cottage husbandry which persisted until the 20th century. The many small meadows which remained free of afforestation, and which could thus be shut up for hay, may have played a useful role in maintaining the peasant economy. Many isolated meadows survive in the Forest today, though none can be identified with particular Domesday entries, and many others have probably been absorbed by the later expansion of the boundaries of the enclosed lands. Other lost meadows may, perhaps, be sought among the numerous remains of former enclosures on the Forest today.

Although some of the lost holdings may have been abandoned through economic decline following afforestation (and perhaps one day may be recovered from among the Forest's abundant earthworks), the Domesday evidence suggests long-term stability in a settlement pattern established in Anglo-Saxon times. Whatever the immediate effect of afforestation, all the main settlements of the Forest, including Linwood and Fritham, are named in the earliest surviving court roll of 1257 (Stagg, 1979), when they were evidently well-peopled townships. I wonder if a single hedge was grubbed out, a single fence thrown down or a single gate laid open to the deer as a result of afforestation?

Successive perambulations of the Forest also provide evidence of long-term stability. A formal perambulation of the bounds may not have been necessary in the 11th century, but the aspirations of successive monarchs to extend the royal forests, and the land hunger of a growing population, made an established legal boundary essential by the 13th century. Perambulations which describe the boundary of the New Forest survive for the turn of the 13th century, 1217–18, 1278–9, 1297–8, 1300–1, 1670, 1801, 1839 and 1964. All except the last are essentially similar, and separate the wholly afforested holdings from the peripheral zone of partly afforested ones, of which only the outlying woods and wastes fell within the Forest. A discordant note is struck by a brief description recorded at the forest eyre of 1280, which claimed all the land in Hampshire between the Avon and Southampton Water as forest (Stagg, 1979). However, the episode is best interpreted as part of a more general, and ultimately unsuccessful, attempt to further the territorial ambitions of the crown in the 12th and 13th centuries.

The perambulation is important because it was the limit within which there were definite constraints on land use and settlement (chapter 5). The forest law, though abused, circumvented and reinterpreted over the centuries, restrained, if it did not wholly prevent, the expansion of farmland and settlement at the expense of the wilderness. There were also physical restraints on farming.

The poor soils demanded great labour in marling and manuring and it was not until the 18th century that improved techniques made it possible on a large scale. Then, much heathland adjoining the Forest was allotted under Enclosure Awards and subsequently converted to farmland. Willis (1808) described the reclamation of 2835 ha of heathland which had hitherto extended southward in a great tract from the Forest nearly to the sea just east of Christchurch. A few, sad, relics survive, a reminder that the Forest was once part of a greater expanse of wilderness.

The Archaeology of the Royal Forest

Many of the abandoned enclosures whose wasted banks and filled ditches are visible in the Forest today were probably constructed after afforestation. If there are common characteristics among the field systems, it is that they are large, regular in shape and layout, and have banks and ditches which are well preserved and 'look' recent. Of nine field systems investigated by pollen analysis of the soils buried beneath the banks, a medieval date was suggested for two (Tubbs & Dimbleby, 1965; Eide, 1983). One of these – the 'Crockford complex' – is also the most extensive, and covers more than 80 ha of Beaulieu Heath. The layout suggests large-scale estate management rather than peasant enclosure, and the proximity of the site to Beaulieu at first suggested monastical enclosure. Cistercian sheep husbandry is further suggested by the name 'Shipton ('Sheeptown') Holms', attached to a small holly wood within the site. However, no supporting documentary evidence can be found, and the only clue is in the records of the forest eyre of 1280, when Peter le Crock of Crockford was among a number of venison offenders (Stagg, 1979).

The second field system, at Setley, has few internal divisions, and I conjecture from its disposition, that it may represent an attempt to consolidate the claim of an adjoining manor to part of the Forest waste. The soil buried beneath the bank, like the surrounding heath today, was too degraded to be a likely candidate for farming before the 19th century.

For a third site there is documentary evidence of a medieval date. This is an enclosure of about 10 ha on the eastern boundary of the Forest which can be identified in the perambulation of 1300–1 as 'the land . . . of John of Fandon', and in that of 1670 as 'a place called John of Farringdon's Close . . . where there are yet to be seen (banks) where the ancient enclosure was'. Perhaps many of the undated enclosures, including such places as the Crockford complex and John of Farringdon's Close, were enclosed in the land-hungry 13th and 14th centuries and abandoned during the Black Death or the succeeding period when livestock husbandry – in the Forest, based on the common grazing – was more profitable

Eyeworth Lodge, an isolated holding, perhaps an early settlement, perhaps a medieval lodge

than arable farming. I cannot, however, clearly distinguish such trends in David Stagg's calendars of New Forest documents for 1244–1334 and 1487–94 (Stagg, 1979, 1983a).

Some of the field groups were very probably medieval Keepers' lodges, not dissimilar in scale and layout to the groups of small fields which surround surviving lodges, now mostly rented or sold by the Forestry Commission.

There is documentary evidence to suggest that some of the smaller enclosures in the Forest were the sites of medieval lodges. Four such enclosures are similar in size and position and hence probably contemporaneous. They are embanked and ditched, about 23 m square and placed in commanding positions remote from settlement. None have, or apparently ever had, attendant fields. In 1968, Anthony Pasmore discovered that two were littered with a fine debris of slate fragments probably of West Country origin. Strong links, including a place name, were subsequently established between the earthworks and an order of Edward III in 1358 for the construction of four lodges in the New Forest, each to be of timber frame and plaster construction, roofed with Purbeck and Cornish slate, with accommodation, kitchen and fireplace, and surrounded by a ditch. In 1969 a fifth lodge was discovered, in a very different position, beside the Highland Water at Queen Bower, this time working from a reference of 1428 to the repair of various Forest lodges including 'Queneboure'. There are doubtless others as yet undiscovered.

I suspect that most of the former pounds and paddocks so numerous in the Forest are of comparatively recent origin. For some, there are place name clues to their uses, though perhaps these ought not to be taken too literally. A square enclosure of about 0.2 ha is situated in Milking Pound Bottom, its banks and ditches little less wasted than some which remain functional today. Another, this time near-circular and with much-wasted banks, lies on Goatspen Plain, and probably dates from sometime before 1635 when 'Gotespendhill' is mentioned in a court roll. Some were clearly pounds for collecting stock during drifts, or round-ups: one, a pound about 27 m square near King's Passage, Matley Heath, has guidebanks clearly designed to funnel animals to its entrance. Others may have been used for the night-folding of livestock, and if so perhaps date from a period when wolves were present, which I suspect effectively takes us back to Saxon times. However, some claims to Forest rights registered at the forest eyre of 1670 included the making of 'hedges, ditches and huts . . . for their hogs and pigs . . . there to be inclosed, to be fed' (Abstract of Claims, 1776). A small 'pig pound' excavated in 1961 yielded medieval pottery. Another, excavated in 1968, yielded late medieval or early modern pottery (Pasmore, 1964). A third, however, excavated in 1969–71, was dated to the late Romano-British period, though its function may have been similar (Devenish, 1964). Yet more small enclosures were described by Heywood Sumner as 'bee-gardens', in which the straw skeps were kept for protection against stock, a custom which he said was remembered as hearsay by old men still living (Sumner, 1923). Two such enclosures, both small and circular, are to be found at Hive Garn Bottom and King's Garden respectively, and there are 'garden' and 'garn' place names elsewhere in the Forest.

While the numerous small enclosures testify to an ancient pastoral economy, the larger field systems, whatever their origins, are witness to some of the ecological consequences of man's economic activity. Today, most are on very impoverished soils and it is difficult to believe they could have been enclosed for agriculture in their present state until the technical innovations of the 18th century. They are thus an indication of the degree to which the Forest soils have been depleted of their nutrient capital in the three millennia since the first major assault on the woods in the Bronze Age.

The Landscape's Mantle

Much of our knowledge of vegetation history derives from the convenient fact that the walls of pollen grains decay very slowly under anaerobic or acid conditions. The pollen rain which falls on the surfaces of peat bogs (or mires) and is preserved by the water-logged conditions, provides a stratified record of the vegetation from which the pollen derives. The record can extend back in time for as long as the peat has taken to accumulate. The plant remains of which the peat is composed at the same time provide information about the vegetation history of the mire itself.

The pollen which occurs in acid soils is another source of evidence about past vegetation. Pollen grains falling on the soil surface are gradually washed down the profile so that their vertical distribution indicates their relative age and the changes in vegetation which have taken place. Fortunately, earthworms and other soil-mixing animals are rare in acid soils. Interpretation is complicated by differing rates of pollen production and decomposition between species, and by variations in the rates of passage down the profile. However, soil pollen analysis can provide a general picture of past changes. Much depends on interpreting the representation of light-demanding species unlikely to flourish under a tree canopy, and the proportion of pollen to non-tree pollen. Most soil pollen analyses probably record changes in the near neighbourhood; most peat pollen analyses probably record changes over a wider area. They are therefore complimentary (Dimbleby, 1967).

Because pollen stratification in soils is not absolute, and because the record usually covers only a comparatively short time, soil pollen analyses are best interpreted against the background of pollen profiles from local peat deposits. However, soil pollen analysis has one special value. Pollen in soils 'fossilized' beneath earthworks can provide a picture of the local environment at the time of construction and before, which is especially valuable if the earthwork has been dated archaeologically or from documents. Conversely, comparison of the pollen in buried surfaces, with the regional picture of vegetation change provided by other pollen analyses, can suggest a rough date for otherwise undated earthworks (Dimbleby, 1955). Of equal importance to the pollen record, the soils buried beneath earthworks can be compared with the active soils of adjoining land surfaces and from this we can construe some measure of the ecological changes which have taken place since construction.

Pollen analyses of twenty-seven soil profiles from twenty-three localities in the New Forest have been carried out since the early

1950s.* The only detailed pollen diagram published for a New Forest mire remains that of Seagrief (1960) for Cranesmoor Bog, though more recently Barber (1973) has described a preliminary analysis of Church Moor Bog, and under Keith Barber's supervision the pollen profiles of at least eleven valley mires have been examined in undergraduate and postgraduate studies at Southampton University. Caution is required in their interpretation but collectively they permit some interesting conclusions. Radiocarbon dates have been obtained for stages in the profiles of several mires. Considerable advances in understanding the origins and development of the mires themselves have been made in recent studies of their morphology and stratigraphy by Michael Clarke. This chapter can do no more than summarize the vegetation history of the Forest derived from these sources, set against a more general picture of postglacial environmental change in northern Europe as a whole (Fig. 6).

Fig. 6.
*Post-glacial Changes in
the New Forest
Environment*

*Dimbleby & Gill, 1955; Dimbleby, 1962; Tubbs & Dimbleby, 1965; Eide, 1983.

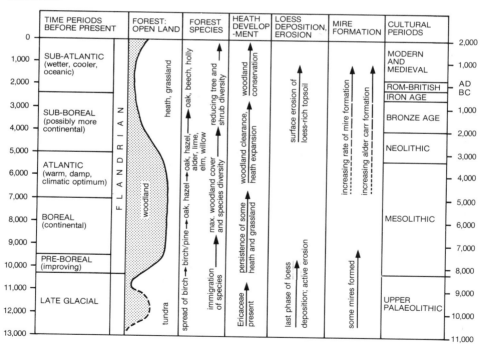

With improving climate, woodland spread to achieve its maximum extent 7-8000 years ago. Human activity subsequently led to its retreat. In the New Forest, heathland spread, mires were formed, and there was much surface erosion. The composition of the surviving woodland changed extensively with time. The figure summarizes the chronology of these changes.

The Background

Peat pollen analyses from northern Europe reveal a consistent pattern of change in the composition of the tree and shrub flora during the postglacial period. Radiocarbon determination has played a major role in dating these changes. A general relationship has been distinguished between them and the climatic changes which have occurred since the last ice age (Pennington, 1969; Godwin, 1975). Early in the postglacial first birch (*Betula*), then pine (*Pinus*) spread northward. Later, as the climate became warmer and drier in the Boreal period, such species as hazel (*Corylus avellana*), elm (*Ulmus*), oak (*Quercus*) and ash (*Fraxinus excelsior*) invaded the woodland. What is generally considered the climatic optimum was achieved in the Atlantic period, 5000–7000 years ago, when the climate was warmer and wetter than today, the tree and shrub flora achieved its maximum diversity and the forest its maximum cover. The late Boreal and Atlantic woodland was dominated by oak, with such species as elm, lime and ash on richer soils and pine and birch on the northern mountains. With the onset of wetter conditions at the Boreal–Atlantic transition, alder (*Alnus glutinosa*) spread widely in the forest environment. At about the same time the severing of the land bridge between Britain and Europe limited further additions to the British flora mainly to those species introduced deliberately or accidentally by man.

Post-Atlantic vegetation history is a record of impoverishment and the spread of open habitats at the expense of woodland. Man's clearance of the woods for farming and settlement, and the deterioration of soils on acid rocks through leaching, are central elements of the tale. It is often difficult to allocate causal effects between them.

Elm declined suddenly and rapidly across Europe within a few centuries either side of 3000 BC. Woodland clearance on the rich soils preferred by elm, the feeding of elm to livestock, soil deterioration and adverse climatic change have all been invoked but there is no completely satisfactory explanation for the elm decline. Having witnessed the modern decimation of elms by the fungus *Ceratocystis ulmi*, carried by elm bark beetles of the *Scolytus* genus, it is tempting to speculate that the elm decline of the early Neolithic was caused by a similar epidemic, perhaps triggered by the drier Sub-Boreal climate or the opening of the Forest by Neolithic farmers.

Calcicoles such as lime and ash also declined in relative abundance during and after the Sub-Boreal period. In southern England pine apparently died out in the Iron Age (early Sub-Atlantic) and was absent until re-introduced in the 18th century. Hazel steadily declined in abundance, especially on acid rocks. On the other hand beech (*Fagus sylvaticus*), now common in the New Forest and elsewhere in southern England, was poorly represented there before the Iron Age and may have been favoured by the cooler and wetter climate which has prevailed for most of the Sub-Atlantic. In the New Forest it has achieved its present co-dominance with oak only within recent centuries. Holly (*Ilex aquifolium*), also seems to have become common only since the late Bronze Age. Like beech, it probably did not achieve its present dominance in the Forest, until recently (Fig. 25).

These changes in the dominant woodland trees and shrubs have been paralleled by the steady retreat of the Atlantic forests, and consequent soil deterioration. In undisturbed forest, the removal of nutrients by root systems and their return to the soil surface as leaf litter counteracts any tendency for soluble bases, clay particles and humus to leach down the soil profile. On acid rocks such a balance is precarious but with the removal of the trees any equilibrium reached will most likely be lost and acute leaching result. In the oceanic climate of the European continental fringe, acid rocks are prone to colonization by secondary, acid-tolerant dwarf-shrub vegetation dominated by heather (*Calluna vulgaris*) and heaths (*Erica* spp.), which form a raw, acid litter which further exacerbates soil acidity. This vegetation is also fire-prone, with the consequent risks of physical damage to the soil and exposure to weathering. Leaching may often have been initiated by cultivation without adequate replacement of the lost nutrients with fertilizer or lime. On the heathlands which succeeded woods and short-lived arable, the rearing and removal of livestock, the cutting of bracken for bedding and turf for fuel and the periodic use of fire to encourage a flush of new grass or heather for stock, must all have contributed to the continued depletion of soil fertility.

Leaching is readily visible in heathland soils. In coarse, permeable material, homo-ferric podsols are common. Beneath a layer of acid humus and humus-stained mineral soil there is a pale, bleached horizon from which soluble bases and the finer clay particles and humus have been removed. These accumulate beneath in successive layers of dark brown humus and a precipitate of red- or orange-brown iron compounds which can form a hard conglomerate, the iron-pan. Clay illuviation is evident in all New Forest soils except porous sands, the clay content increasing with depth so that the lower horizons are mottled by seasonal changes in water content. The upper horizons are often extremely bleached (gley podsols). Between the podsols and the brown forest soils which precede them are a range of acid brown earths which are more-or-less leached. These occur beneath grassland, grass-heath and many ancient woods – for on acid soils few have completely escaped soil degradation.

Pollen Analyses from New Forest Mires

Unfortunately, few New Forest mires have completely escaped peat cutting. Aerial photographs show characteristic parallel marks lateral to the drainage axes, and on the ground these sometimes appear to be causeways left between the cuttings. If so, they may yet preserve the undisturbed profiles from which complete pollen sequences can be retrieved. This apart, there is an element of luck in finding the right place to insert a peat borer to take samples. The pollen record obtained by Seagrief (1960) for Cranesmoor Bog ceased about 4000 BC and had clearly been truncated by recent peat digging, although this was not realized at the time. However, it does provide an indication of earlier postglacial conditions. Boreal pine forest with smaller amounts of birch, dominant in the early part of the record, are replaced by oak-hazel in the late Boreal or early Atlantic, with elm, then lime and alder invading during the Atlantic, and rising values for birch towards the end of the truncated record. Two more recent analyses by Andrew Tilley (unpublished) confirm this general picture but appear to show a well-marked decline in elm and lime, presumably in the early Sub-Boreal. Two radiocarbon dates suggest that the earliest pollen, which occurs in creamy basal mud probably derived from erosive inwash, began to accumulate around the Late-Glacial/Pre-Boreal transition, 10-11,000 years ago.

Two of the mires investigated recently – Church Moor (SU 248068) and Warwick Slade (SU276067) – are of comparable age to Cranesmoor. Radiocarbon dates near the base of the profiles suggest that peat began to accumulate in Church Moor around 13,000 years ago and in Warwick Slade about 9000 years ago. Both mires are in the centre of the Lymington River catchment, an area sparse in evidence of early settlement. The pollen record yielded no evidence for heathland development and Barber (1981) suggested that in this central core of the Forest, woodland may have persisted relatively undisturbed for most of the postglacial period. Certainly, it was still well wooded in medieval and later times, although the woodland was interspersed with glades and extensive heathy clearings, a pattern shown clearly on Isaac Taylor's map of Hampshire in 1759. That the heathy element is not well reflected in the pollen suggests that these sheltered mires, deep in woodland, received only very local pollen rain.

Barber (1973) gives a preliminary analysis of the Church Moor profile. The earliest part of the profile recorded Boreal woodland of oak, pine, birch and hazel, with some elm and willow (*Salix*). There is a striking increase in alder, marking the Boreal-Atlantic transition, and lime (*Tilia*) appears about the same time. Pine, elm and lime subsequently disappear, perhaps at the Atlantic-Sub Boreal transistion, and oak–alder–hazel woodland persists prob-

Warwick Slade mire:
peat began to accumulate
here about 9000 years
ago

ably until comparatively recently. The upper part of the diagram
records the invasion of the woodland by beech and holly, the
former rapidly achieving 40% of total tree pollen, and the decline
of hazel, changes thought to have occurred mainly in recent
centuries (chapter 9). Pine also reappears at the top of the profile,
presumably reflecting its re-introduction in the 18th century.
Today, Church Moor is a narrow mire with a central alder carr
in the head of a second order tributary of the Lymington River
among oak–beech–holly woodland with pine-colonized clearings
and nearby plantations.

Barrow Moor (SU250076) is only 600 m from Church Moor and
is superficially similar but much younger. Wood remains from
1.4–1.6 m down the profile gave a radiocarbon date of AD 449±70.
Extrapolation of peat accumulation rates suggest that the bog
began growth early in the Sub-Atlantic, say in the late Iron Age,
possibly in response to increased runoff associated with woodland
clearance somewhere in the catchment and increased rainfall
(Barber, 1981). The pollen record, as at Church Moor and Warwick
Slade, carries no suggestion of heathland. It is dominated by the
continuous presence of oak and beech, the latter achieving 60%
of the tree pollen at the top of the profile. Neither elm nor lime
occur but hazel and ash were present until comparatively recently.

Of the remaining mires, the oldest is probably in Dibden Bottom
(SU395062), which is thought to date from the Boreal-Atlantic
transition, about 7000 years ago. Four others are evidently Atlantic

or Sub-Boreal in origin, and three, like Barrow Moor, originated late in the Sub-Boreal or around the Sub-Boreal/Sub-Atlantic transition. Of the latter group, Stephill Bottom (SU355056) has been dated by radiocarbon determination to 2660–3290 BP (before present); Hive Garn Bottom (SU196147) to 2560–2840 BP; and a seepage step mire on the upper hillside of Hive Garn Bottom, to 2250–2490 BP (M. J. Clarke). All but one of these eight mires are in open heathland catchments and may have been initiated by Bronze or Iron Age woodland clearance with consequent increased runoff. Collectively, they record the spread of heathland at the expense of the woodland in the Sub-Boreal and since, and a general sequence of adjustment in the representation of tree species as occurs in the Church Moor profile.

Dibden Bottom provides the longest pollen record, beginning from the increase in alder characteristic of the Boreal-Atlantic transition. The Atlantic woodland included elm and lime in an oak–alder–hazel matrix, the lime persisting until after the 18th century reappearance of pine. The upper part of the profile is dominated by the spread of heathland, with cereals and weeds of cultivation represented. The bog stratigraphy is of special interest. In the core taken for pollen analysis there were two charcoal layers, each associated with heather and weeds of cultivation, at 0.7 m and 0.8 m depth; and at 0.42 m there was a wedge of bleached sand which could only have derived from surface erosion of the neighbouring heath. Above this, heather pollen had a continuous and increasing representation (Barber, 1981). The tentative conclusion is that early farmers were clearing the surroundings of the mire for cultivation or pasture. It is not not difficult to imagine the scouring by storm water of a soil surface denuded of woodland. Although it is not possible to date these events from the pollen evidence, they were probably prehistoric and certainly post-Atlantic. Basal deposits and bands of fine loamy or sandy material occur widely in New Forest valleys and particle-size analysis of one such deposit in Stephill Bottom reveals it to be loessic. It seems likely that woodland clearance and primitive farming during and after the Bronze Age triggered erosion which removed much fertile topsoil into the valleys. Such a scenario would help to explain both the spread of heathland and the prehistoric cultivation which preceded it.

Soil Pollen Analyses from the New Forest

Of the twenty-seven soil pollen analyses for New Forest sites, fifteen are for buried soils at eleven sites; two are for modern heathland soils; and ten are for woodland soils.

Of the many traces of fields and field systems in the Forest, the buried soils, and in many cases the banks and adjoining soils, of

Locality	Earthwork	Age	Source
Burley Moor SU212052	round barrow	late Bronze Age (A)	Dimbleby (1962)
Beaulieu Heath SZ355994	small embanked enclosure	Bronze Age (P)	Tubbs and Dimbleby (1965)
Homey Ridge SU232160	complex of enclosures	c. 550 BC (R) – Bronze Age/Iron Age	Eide (1983)
Holmsley SZ208998	much wasted enclosure bank	Iron Age (P)	Tubbs and Dimbleby (1965)
Pilley SZ344984	group of small embanked fields	Iron Age (P)	Tubbs and Dimbleby (1965)
Long Slade Bottom SU266099	group of embanked enclosures	c. 130 AD (R) – Romano-British*	Tubbs and Dimbleby (1965) Eide (1983)
Burley Moor SU213042	embanked enclosures at present settlement margin	c. 750–800 AD (R) – Anglo-Saxon	Eide (1983)
Setley Plain SZ303994	extensive embanked enclosures	Medieval (P)	Tubbs and Dimbleby (1965)
Beaulieu Heath SZ355994 SZ358993 (Crockford complex)	extensive system of embanked fields	Medieval (P)	Tubbs and Dimbleby (1965) Eide (1983)
Lyndhurst Old Park SU314077	medieval park bank	first documentary reference 1291 AD	Dimbleby (1962)
Hatchet Gate SU367018	abandoned field at margin of crown land	probably 18th–19th century (pollen analysis and historical evidence)	Eide (1983)

* originally given a tentative medieval date by Tubbs and Dimbleby (1965)
(A)=date derived from archaeological evidence
(P)=date derived from pollen analysis
(R)=date derived from radiocrabon determination

Fig. 7.
*Pollen Analyses of
Buried Soils*

eleven have now been studied, besides those of a Bronze Age barrow and the massive medieval bank of Lyndhurst Old Park (Fig. 7). These earthworks date from various times between the late Bronze Age and the 19th century. Most of the enclosures were probably pastoral but there is evidence of cereal cultivation in the homogenized soils and the pollen samples at field systems on Homey Ridge (late Bronze Age) and Beaulieu Heath (medieval). At the former site, Eide (1983) found chemical evidence for the treatment of the land with phosphorus-rich manure, whilst a thin iron-pan had developed at 15–16 cm at the upper surface of a layer compacted by smearing during ploughing. At a third site, Longslade Bottom, cultivation had probably preceded enclosure.

The earliest vegetation suggested by the pollen in most buried soils is a mosaic of grassland or grassy heathland, bracken, hazel scrub, birch groves and areas of woodland in which oak, alder and hazel were dominant, with some pine, lime and sometimes hornbeam (*Carpinus betulus*), holly, elm and beech. There are indications of arable fields among such a matrix of natural vegetation. Such a picture probably dates from the middle or late Bronze Age. Most profiles suggest that heathland was spreading at the expense of woodland during the period before the building of the earthwork. In some places the late Bronze Age vegetation was hazel and birch, which Eide (1983) thought was probably secondary regrowth after earlier forest clearance. Generally, the later the earthwork, the more open the surroundings in which it was built. The Bronze Age enclosure at Beaulieu Heath, the Romano-British enclosures at Long Slade Bottom, and the Anglo-Saxon enclosures near Burley, all seem to have been embanked in relatively wooded surroundings, although the Bronze Age barrow on Burley Moor was built after heather and bracken had replaced hazel–oak–alder woodland interspersed with heathy clearings. By the time the later earthworks were built, woodland and scrub had largely retreated from their vicinity to leave grass-heath, or perhaps a mosaic of grassland and heathland. The pollen buried beneath Lyndhurst Old Park bank, which crosses the open heath of White Moor, east of Lyndhurst, showed that Ericaceae had completely replaced hazel scrub by the time of construction. The 13th-century vegetation of White Moor was little different to that of today.

Although the environs of the enclosures might be open, woodland persisted at a distance. In the Sub-Atlantic period it was mainly oak–hazel, with alder – presumably linear carr beside watercourses – and small quantities of other species. Lime and elm became rare on acid rocks in England after the Sub-Boreal, perhaps as a result of decalcification associated with woodland clearance, but lime persists in small amounts as late as Anglo-Saxon and medieval times in a number of New Forest pollen profiles. Beech and holly are also characteristic of Forest Sub-Atlantic pollen assemblages, although none of the soil pollen analyses from archaeological sites reflect the increasing abundance of these species in the woods in recent centuries, probably because their pollen does not disperse far.

At nine of the eleven archaeological sites, the buried soils were already to some degree podsolized when the earthwork was built. In some cases (e.g. Lyndhurst Old Park bank) there was little difference between the buried soil and that of the adjoining heath. At most sites, however, comparison of the buried soil with those of nearby land surfaces indicated continuing soil degradation after construction of the earthwork. At Dark Hat, one of the buried soils examined was an argillic (clayey) brown earth, but the neighbouring unburied soils were podsols. Only at the Crockford Complex on Beaulieu Heath were both buried and unburied soils relatively little leached, though the latter was very acid. Most earthwork structures show some degree of podsolization since construction and their soils are invariably more acid than those buried beneath the mound. However, most earthworks comprise the material dug to form their ditches and their upper horizons therefore have a subsoil likely to be relatively resistant to leaching.

A trend towards increasing acidity is suggested by comparison of the pollen in the buried soils with that illuviated into the lower part of the bank (and thus representative of the post-enclosure vegetation) and that of the present land surface. The trend is towards the spread of acid-tolerant heather and the withdrawal of grassland and woody species. However, grassland has often persisted within enclosures in contrast to Ericaceae outside. This is conspicuous, for example, at Crockford, Pilley and Hatchet Gate, where the enclosure soils are only incipiently podsolized but those outside are more degraded (chapter 13).

Of the two analyses of active heathland soils, one was from Burley Moor (SU211051), near the Burley barrow, and the other from White Moor (SU314077) close to the point where the Lyndhurst Old Park bank was sampled. Both soils are podsolized Barton Sand. The lowest part of the Burley Moor profile records a woodland in which oak, alder, hazel and lime were dominants. Above this, the stratification is disrupted, possibly through solifluxion, but the upper part of the profile shows a change from hazel dominance to the present vegetation of heather and purple moor grass (*Molinia caerulea*). Oak, hazel, alder, birch, lime and elm persisted in the area, perhaps in woods at a distance from the site. The occurrence of lime and elm suggest a prehistoric date for heathland development. This was perhaps contemporary with the events recorded in the buried soil beneath the nearby barrow, but a more recent, Sub-Atlantic date is possible in view of the late persistence of lime in the Forest. In this, as in other heathland profiles, the recent record of heathland vegetation has been truncated by recurrent destruction of the humus layer by fire and the cutting of turf for fuel.

The White Moor soil was poor in pollen, although it was very acid. Ericaceae were dominant at all levels, but oak, hazel, alder, and lime were consistently present, together with grasses and plantains. The pollen record is clearly Sub-Atlantic and probably relatively recent; perhaps the tree and meadow pollen are derived from the fields and woods around Lyndhurst, which begin only 200 m away.

The soil pollen analyses, combined with the distribution of barrows and boiling mounds, suggest that the modern disposition of woodland and heathland was emerging in the New Forest in the Bronze Age. The nature of the soil parent material has evidently influenced the pattern, for it cannot be coincidence that most heathland is on gravels, loessic brickearths and sands, and most woodland is on clays. Presumably the former were easier to clear and settle and, before the conjectural removal of fertile topsoil into the valleys, were more productive to cultivate than the clays.

In summary, a recurrent pattern of change can be distinguished in pollen analyses from Forest heathland:

oak–hazel–alder woodland with lime, elm and other species	hazel scrub, grassland,	Ericoid dwarf shrub heath

Such a pattern is consistent with the evidence from soil pollen analyses elsewhere on English lowland heaths (Dimbleby, 1962). The changes did not occur everywhere simultaneously, but the second stage in the sequence was evidently common in the late Bronze Age, when most barrows were built and farming took place on what is now heathland. Rapid soil deterioration was probably contemporary. To judge from the buried soils and their pollen, podsolization commenced under heathy grassland and hazel scrub, although the later establishment of heather must have accelerated the process. Acid grassland, often with thickets of gorse (*Ulex europaeus*) and extensive bracken (*Pteridium aquilinum*) is widespread in the Forest today, often on soils which are visibly leached and in some cases can be termed incipient podsols.

Most acid grassland is on less obviously degraded soils, often in flushed localities, but how long the habitat has persisted in a particular place, and whether it will inevitably complete the transition to heath, is conjectural. On many sites a scatter of oak, holly and hawthorn, and sometimes the burnt remains of trees, marks recent woodland retreat, but change is not all one way and elsewhere woodland has recolonized grassland and heath.

An unpublished pollen diagram for Must Thorns Bottom (SU194149) prepared by George Peterken gives an interesting picture of the ebb and flow of woodland over the heath. I dug the soil pit about 10 m from a small clump of holly and oak, which with a few scattered trees, was all that remained of a much larger area of woodland depicted on the Old Series Ordnance Survey (1811). Numerous dead holly stumps testified to the recency of woodland destruction. The site was on the foot-slope of the Bottom and the soil was developed in a clayey head deposit derived from further up. It had a bleached horizon beneath raw humus and was strongly mottled in the lower horizons. The earliest pollen comprised the familiar assemblage of oak, hazel and alder with some lime and elm, and may have been Sub-Boreal. The record then shows the ascendence, first of Ericaceae, then of holly with some oak, heather, grasses and bracken. The fires which destroyed the holly thickets and oaks have also removed the more recent pollen record. Must Thorns Bottom has therefore seen the successive retreat, reappearance and withdrawal of woodland.

There are soil pollen analyses from nine other Forest woods. At two of six small woods investigated by Dimbleby & Gill (1955), oakwood had become established on heathland in the wake of colonizing holly, probably in recent times, the mull humus of the holly having a regenerative effect on the raw heathland podsols. The analyses also showed clearly the recent invasion of some oakwoods by beech. At Berry Wood (SU213053) the pollen record revealed a long period when the site was a mosaic of wood and grass-heath, before the present oakwood became established.

At Matley Wood (SU332076) woodland became established on former cultivated farmland, probably a long-established settlement. In both of these latter cases the record is probably wholly Sub-Atlantic. Both soils remained little-leached brown earths. The remaining site, Pondhead Inclosure (SU312075) is an oak–sweet chestnut (*Castanea sativa*) plantation established on former farmland in 1811. The farmland had been preceeded by heath, which in turn had succeeded oak–hazel–alder–birch woodland. The heathland soil had been a humo-ferric podsol, but this, like the soils beneath the colonizing oakwoods, was overlaid by a deep mull humus and was evidently regenerating (Dimbleby, 1962).

Open Habitats and the Primeval Forest

Most pollen analysts (e.g. Godwin, 1975; Pennington, 1969) picture the Boreal and Atlantic vegetation of northern Europe as a continuous forest, which subsequently retreated before the assault of man. On base-deficient parent materials, acid-tolerant heathland vegetation arose in the wake of the Forest, a process possibly assisted by the progressive natural acidification of these soils since the Atlantic. However, pollen analysts have failed to account satisfactorily for the survival during the forest phase of the large proportion of European plants and animals which are adapted to open habitats – on heathland, for example, the silver studded blue butterfly (*Plebejus argus*), smooth snake (*Coronella austriaca*), and Dartford warbler (*Sylvia undata*). Such doubts are usually met by suggesting such refuges as transient glades, sea cliffs, mountain tops and above the altitudinal limits of trees in mountains. It seems unlikely, however, that large numbers of open ground species persisted for millennia with the fragmented distributions and in the unsuitable habitats which this explanation requires. On the other hand it seems unrealistic to contemplate their mass migration northward (from where?) as the forest was opened up.

Scaife & MacPhail (1983), in a review of heathland development, suggest that on particularly poor parent materials heathland which developed in the Late Glacial period persisted subsequently in small pockets where podsols developed direct from the raw soil without any intermediary brown earth formed beneath the Boreal and Atlantic woodland. Several pollen analyses show that heathland occurred locally near Mesolithic habitation sites and although these have generally been interpreted as manmade clearings, their nuclei at least may have been natural.* Gimingham (1972) commented that heathland communities were similar to the shrub layer and glade vegetation of northern Boreal forests today. It is a short step to argue that Late Glacial dwarf shrub communities persisted in the forest matrix as tracts of heath, beneath which brown forest soils were never able to develop.

In the New Forest, Michael Clarke's research into the stratigraphy of valley mires, including those known to date from the earliest times, casts a new light on the former extent of open habitats. Wood occurred in less than 20% of 172 samples of basal peat and mud from twenty mires, and mostly comprised fragments of alder, suggesting that the mires originated on open sites. For most of their history, the species growing on mire surfaces, and forming the peat, have changed little. Of the older mires, the basal macrofossils at Church Moor suggest that the mire began to form in a park-like tundra of sedges and mosses with scattered birch. Dwarf birch (*Betula nana*), an arctic species, occurred at the base of the profile. At Cranesmoor, another early mire, growth commenced in open vegetation in which heather, *Sphagnum* mosses and sharp-flowered rush (*Juncus acutiflorus*) were common. In the younger mires, purple moor grass dominated the basal peat. The alder carrs which today follow the axes of many of the more enriched mires, post-date mire formation.

It may be argued that the earliest mires began growth before the spread of forest, and that the later mires post-date woodland clearance. However, it can equally be claimed that mires are located in the places that were least likely to be cleared by early man, a contention supported by the distribution of his earthworks.

An observer of the modern New Forest will acknowledge the potential importance of large herbivores in maintaining open habitats. Clearings and glades are created and maintained by herbivores and they also control the degree to which the woodland can recolonize heathland. Such phenomena must have been commonplace in earlier times. Glades and clearings are often conceded to the animals but their influence may have been of greater magnitude than this.

*Rankine *et al.*, 1960; Keef *et al.*, 1965; Palmer & Dimbleby, 1976.

I am aware that the argument for the persistence of heathland through the postglacial can be met by invoking the modern propensity of birch and Scots pine at least, to invade heathland. However, Scots pine became extinct in southern England soon after the Sub-Boreal/Sub-Atlantic transition and was presumably much less vigorous then than now. Similarly, birch representation in pollen diagrams in prehistoric times is low considering its modern prolific pollen production. Thus, the behaviour of these species in prehistory seems at variance with that of more recent times, and the same may be true of other trees and shrubs. There are also many tracts of heath on the older gravel terraces of the Forest which do not seem capable now of supporting vigorous, or in some places, any, tree growth today. Perhaps it is these areas which are most likely never to have supported woodland in Boreal and Atlantic times.

The Conqueror's Forest CHAPTER 5

The establishment of the royal forest between 1066 and 1086 was crucial in the New Forest's ecological history. The legal status conferred on it severely restrained the expansion of settlement, and resulted in pastoral land uses which persist in modified form today. The Forest became governed by complex judicial and legal structures which have left a 20th-century legacy of dual administration by the Forestry Commission, as managers of the crown interest, and the Verderers, as managers of matters relating to the commoners and common rights, and as the guardians of the Forest.

This chapter sketches the development of the Forest's management and administration. The crown's interest at first lay in deer conservation and the raising of revenue in licences and fines for forest offences; and, from the late 15th century, increasingly in income from timber sales. The latter interest culminated in a succession of enactments from 1698 onwards, providing for the enclosure of Forest land for the growth of timber (the Statutory Inclosures). Side by side with the crown interests have run those of the commoners in grazing their animals on the Forest and in exploiting its other natural resources. In the 19th century, the Forest survived threats of disafforestation, enclosure and partition (the fate of most royal forests), mainly because of the persistence of a vigorous pastoral economy based on the common rights and the emergence of an articulate and influential lobby committed both to the commoners and the protection of the Forest.

The Deer Forest and the Local Economy

According to the 16th-century lawyer John Manwood, a medieval forest was a

'territory of woody grounds and fruitful pastures, privileged for wild beasts and fowls of forest, chase and warren, to rest and abide there in the safe protection of the King, for his delight and pleasure' (Manwood, 1598).

Legally it was a place subject to the Forest Law, which was designed to conserve the deer (the venison) and other beasts, for the chase and for meat and hides; and to protect the woodland and other natural vegetation (the vert) on which the deer depended. It is now difficult to perceive the motive for deer conservation on the scale indulged by the Norman kings, and it can only have arisen from the necessity of provisioning troops and court in an era of low farm productivity. It also proved a convenient means of extending the landed estate of the crown.

Our knowledge of medieval forest law and administration depends heavily on a limited number of statutes, notably the Charter of the Forest (1217): a succession of forest assizes which list the rules of forest administration; and the court rolls and other documents for individual forests. Most of the New Forest documents from the 13th to 17th centuries have been calendared, with important commentaries, by Stagg (1979, 1983a). Of particular importance in illuminating the 16th-century management of the Forest is a document called the *Orders and Rules of the New Forest*, dated 1537 and claimed to represent ancient usage (Stagg, 1974c).

Much of the New Forest was held by the crown before the conquest, but most forests mainly comprised manors held by others than the crown. For Forest law precluded the assarting – that is, the reduction of woodland and waste to pasture or cultivation – of all land in a forest. However, this was evidently difficult to sustain, for the Charter of the Forest (an expansion of the forestal clauses in *Magna Carta*) regularized existing assarts and instituted what amounted to a licensing system for future similar enterprises.

Forest Law regulated the hitherto customary and probably little-restrained exploitation of the natural resources of the unenclosed wastes, to ensure the conservation of vert and venison. It provided for the removal of domestic stock during the 'fence' month (supposed to be fourteen days either side of midsummer day, when the deer gave birth); and during the winter heyning, when there was least forage (Michaelmas to Hocktide in the Orders and Rules of 1537, and 22 November–4 May since the 17th century). The period during which pigs could be turned out was restricted to about two months in the autumn when the seed harvest fell when, hopefully, they would remove the green acorns which, though digestible to pigs, can be fatal to cattle, ponies and deer if eaten in excess without bulk fibre. The cutting of turf fuel and the collection of fuel wood were regulated and limited to conserve the vert. It is difficult to trace the development of regulations of this kind, but customary and regulated practices ultimately became the legally established rights of common which survive today. In late medieval times, the exercise of common rights was usually subject to small payments, evidently intended to finance the local bureaucracy rather than the Exchequer, but whether such payments were as ancient as the forests themselves or were later innovations remains obscure.

The medieval documents for the New Forest contain abundant references which testify to its customary exploitation for pasture and fuel. By the late 13th century, any early grip on land uses there may have been, was relaxing. By then, payments were made in lieu of removing stock from the Forest in the fence month. By 1537, this was a right purchased 'of old time', and in 1670 it was claimed before the grand jury of the justice in eyre that 'from time out of mind the commoners have had common of pasture for their cattle throughout the fence month' in return for a payment.

By 1537, manors within the Forest paid no dues except month money and evidently grazed their animals on the Forest free, throughout the year. Most manors which claimed rights but were outside the perambulation paid either for summer grazing from Hocktide (after Easter) to Michaelmas (29 September), or for winter grazing (Michaelmas to Hocktide) or both; all paid month money. Turfdel, a payment for each load of turf claimed, was paid by most but not all manors both within and outside the Forest. Many of the payments for grazing and turf were still being paid in 1670 and subsequently, though their individual significance had by then been lost and they were regarded collectively as forest rents. It may be that the relative freedom from payment enjoyed by individual manors depended on the degree to which they were originally afforested and thus required financial relief for survival.

Each forest had a hierarchy of officers. In the New Forest in 1537, the Warden charged with the care of the Forest (the Earl of Arundel) appointed a Lieutenant, Steward, Auditor, Receiver, two Rangers, eight Yeoman Foresters, a Bowbearer, Verminer and other officers. Many of the appointments appear to have been prestigious sinecures of the gentry, who employed others of lowlier status to perform most of the menial duties of office. After 1542, a second hierarchy of officers, responsible to the Exchequer for the management of the woods, was to be superimposed on the first.

The judicial system in forests was complex and there remain uncertainties about its structure. The earliest evidence is for the 13th century when according to Turner (1901) there were two courts. The lower court, usually called the Swainmote, was held by the Verderers, who were elected by the County on the king's writ. They sat with a jury and heard presentments of forest offences, decided the issue and except for minor cases in which they could exact a fine, obtained sureties and enrolled the offences for sentence by the higher court, the forest eyre, which originally was supposed to sit every three years in each forest. Interpretations of the documents vary but some such system seems to have prevailed and was devised to separate the forest officers from the judiciary and the local from the national judiciary. Such a system owed much to the demands for natural justice which recur through medieval history.

The functions of the eyre were investigative as well as judicial, and extended to enquiring into the administration of forests by officers with rich opportunities for misappropriation and oppression. In this the justices were assisted by the Regarders. Like the Verderers they were elected by the County. They were supposed to inspect the forest every three years and report its condition in answer to an interrogatory known as the Chapter of the Regard. In the New Forest their main function came to be the inspection of the woods and the marking of trees for felling.

The forest eyre was originally intended to be held in each forest every three years, but the historical record, fragmented though it is, suggests that they were only of infrequent occurrence. Since the 17th century, lawyers and historians have claimed that the Forest Law decayed and became forgotten or ignored by the 16th century because of the decline of the forest eyre. Stagg (1979, 1983a), adduced evidence that in the New Forest, the infrequent eyres were supplemented by the judicial activities of deputy justices, who dealt with offenders on a more regular basis but who left few documentary traces beyond endorsements of fines on the Swainmote rolls and the records of special adjudications called Inquisitions. The Order and Rules of 1537 lay down exact instructions for dealing with felons and vert and venison offenders which suggest anything but decay into anarchy. Felons were held in the king's prison at Bartley until committal proceedings in the next Steward's court, from which they were transferred to the King's Gaol at Lyndhurst to await trial. Forest offenders were tried by the two Verderers in the Swainmote and, if guilty, were committed to a prison called the Blindhouse in Lyndhurst, until sureties were given for their appearance at the next eyre (or before the deputy justice) for sentencing.

The Orders and Rules lay down an annual cycle of management in which dues were collected, animals marked, drifts (round-ups) made, and the beasts of strangers impounded for fine and collection. Such ordinary matters of common land management, and of identifying vert and venison offenders, were the province of the Steward and his Clerk, and the Riders. The Steward was to hold courts of the Forest (Attachment courts) every three weeks at Lyndhurst. There, the Forest officers were to present offences. Those of vert and venison were evidently enrolled for the Swainmote, but others appear to have been decided by the Steward, who also seems to have decided disputes between commoners, presumably over such matters as the ownership of animals. He held two special Forest courts annually, at which all holding land in the Forest were to attend, evidently to hear or agree decisions about the management of the commons. It is all strikingly consistent with the picture of the royal forests in the 16th century painted by Hammersley (1960):

'the laws were known and observed in principle at least; now they served through the lower courts, to regularise the exploitation of traditional forest privileges, to prevent excess, and to exclude strangers. A law designed to establish a royal privilege now safeguarded the commoners' interests.'

The Order and Rules set down the local system for executing royal warrants for deer and timber and for the enclosure of coppices. There are directions for checking abuses of the timber and deer by forest officers, for rooting out poachers, and fo limiting disturbance in the fence month – a matter of great and minute concern. The deer were to be censused annually – would that the data survived, if it ever existed! We do not know how closely the Orders and Rules were followed and over what period, but there is a general consistency between this and other medieval and early modern documents, which suggests not so much the decay of the forestal system, but an evolving continuity of management. Certainly it was preyed upon by forest officers, landowners and peasantry alike, but this does not mean it was wholly obsolete.

In the 17th century, Charles I revived the forest eyre as a source of income, and justice seats were held in the New Forest in 1622, 1634, 1635, 1670 and probably other years. The post-Restoration eyre of 1670 was the last in forestal history although the justice seat was not formally abolished until 1817. The Swainmote, however, continued to function. The *1698 Act for the Increase and Preservation of Timber in the New Forest* gave the Verderers powers to impose fines of up to £5 for breaking Inclosure fences, burning heather and fern, destroying covert (a catch-all) and stealing wood. Venison offences could by then be dealt with more efficiently and with the prospect of harsher punishment, at common law. More effective deterrents to timber offenders were instituted by the *Preservation of Timber Acts 1765–1766*. The Verderers received a variety of powers to deal with encroachments and other trespasses, abuses by forest officers, and the regulation of common of pasture, in a succession of enactments from 1800 to 1829. Eventually, the *New Forest Act, 1877*, breathed new life into the Verderers' Court. It ceased then to owe allegiance to the crown and thus to protect the crown's interests, and came formally to be responsible for safeguarding the interests of the commoners and for managing the exercise of common rights. One suspects that this is what the Steward's court was all about in 1537.

Assarts and Purprestures: The Expansion of Settlement

Though the formal purpose of the royal forests was the conservation of deer and their habitat, forests were part, albeit a peculiar part, of the landed estate of the crown, and they were called on to provide an income to the Exchequer. They did so in peculiar ways. Revenue arose from the enclosed demesne land of the crown, but it was also raised in the shape of fines for poaching, purloining timber, assarting (reducing waste to cultivation), making purprestures (usually smaller land encroachments), and for other less heinous offences against the forest law. Assarts and encroachments were in effect, licensed retrospectively with a fine and gave rise to subsequent annual rentals, whether they were on crown or private land. In later times, the sale of timber and other produce contributed to the forestal income.

Through assart, purpresture or land grants, the margins of the settled land crept inexorably over the waste. Probably most of the larger units of land were assarted during the land hunger of the 13th and early 14th centuries, when population grew rapidly but crop yields remained low, and indeed, on average fell, as cultivation spread on to less productive soils. In such circumstances it would be surprising if the crown had maintained an unrelaxed hold on so large an area as the New Forest in the English lowlands. Land demand declined with the onset of an economic depression and successive epidemics of plague characterized by pustules and pulmonary diseases, which peaked around the mid 14th century and continued into the next – a classic piece of biological control.

The crown made substantial grants of land in the Forest, although it is difficult to know if they were of enclosed demesne, or waste. The best-known is John's gift for the founding of the Cistercian abbey at Beaulieu, said to be of twenty-five hides (say 1215 ha, but from the bounds in the foundation charter, nearer 2000–2500 ha). Between 1236 and 1324 another 417 ha of 'waste' and 'heath' were granted to and assarted by the monks. Beaulieu's property lay mainly east of the River Otter, the Beaulieu River. The daughter house of Netley, founded in 1239 across Southampton Water, received an endowment of 3 caracutes (say 480 ha) east of the estuary in 1253, and further areas in 1248, 1252 and 1331, much of which was assarted from heathland. Some grants were retrospective: the monks assarted first and asked afterwards (Donkin, 1969; Hockey, 1976).

Besides making grants, the crown was probably assarting waste itself. A survey dating from about 1300 lists twelve vaccaries, or dairy farms, and there were probably more (Stagg, 1979). Identifiable places include several post-Domesday holdings, invariably with rounded boundaries which, like medieval coppices, follow the margin of the better land. Most were probably of 12th century or earlier origin and had the notional purpose of supplying the royal entourage on its visits (Moens, 1903).

The Forest documents contain abundant evidence of smaller-scale enclosure. Because areas and localities are seldom exactly retrievable, it is difficult to chart its progress, but its scale is apparent from a number of grants made between 1608 and 1631. By then, rents of assarts and purprestures were granted for a fixed sum. The 17th-century grants were for at least 2780 ha of land, 298 dwellings, numerous orchards, gardens and stables and three mills (Stagg, 1983a). Assart rents seem to have become uncollectable after the 17th century, but forms of acknowledgement persisted until the

Wild Creatures and Forest Laws Act 1971 abolished the relics of
the forest law. Until then, the keepers entered the ancient assarts
and fired a ritual shot to declare the crown's rights each year.
Creeping encroachment from the Forest edge continued in the
18th and 19th centuries and was only finally checked by providing
a legal means of prosecuting offenders for less than the value of
the land they had encroached (Tubbs & Jones, 1964).

The Ascendance of Silviculture

Medieval silviculture depended mainly on the natural regeneration
of trees and shrubs in enclosures, or coppices, from which deer
and stock were excluded. The underwood, mostly hazel, was cut
on a short rotation for fuel, faggots, wattle and other essentials,
and the standard trees, mainly oak, provided structural materials.
Coppices characteristically have rounded or irregular boundaries
dictated by the shape of the wood to be regenerated or the limits of
suitable soils. In the New Forest they contrast sharply with the
regular boundaries of the later silvicultural inclosures.

The earliest-known reference to silviculture in the New Forest
is the sale of 109 acres (44 ha) of timber and underwood in various
coppices in 1389 (PRO E101/142/21), but in this and other early
documents, there is an implicit acceptance that the periodic enclosure of woods to obtain natural regeneration after cutting was
of much greater antiquity. An Act of 1483 recited the enclosure of
forest coppices for three years after cutting as accepted practice,
and extended the period to seven years.

From the 15th century, the crown interest in the New Forest
turned increasingly to its timber and underwood resources. Timber
production for ship-building finally gained precedence over cash-
cropping for underwood in the 17th century and resulted in 1698
in the first Act for the enclosure of Forest land for growing navy
timber.

The changing emphasis in management was gradual. The 15th
century saw increasing exports, especially of woollen goods, and
the construction of the first purpose-built warships. The national
tonnage of shipping increased sharply in the 16th century. The
management of the crown woods was formalized in an Act of 1542
which created the Court of Surveyors and the post of Surveyor
General of the King's Woods, responsible for managing the
resource as a going concern. Two years later, the *Statute of Woods*
laid down what amounted to a management plan for coppices and
extended the period of enclosure in forests to nine years. Thus,
there arose a second hierarchy of officers with forestal functions,
headed in each forest or group of forests, by a Deputy Surveyor.
This position survives today in the form of Forestry Commission
officers in charge of the New Forest and Forest of Dean. The dual

hierarchies, one responsible for protecting the vert and venison, the other for profitably managing the woods, inevitably became locked in acrimony and conflicts of interest.

The usual practice was to lease coppices, reserving the timber trees and ensuring that sufficient saplings were spared when the coppice was cut. In the New Forest, in the 16th and 17th centuries, there were increasing difficulties in leasing coppices, and they were frequently neglected by their tenants, and abused by deer forest officers and commoners alike. They were used as convenient stock pounds, and the young hazel provided succulent deer browse (Tubbs, 1964, 1968; Flower, 1980a, 1980b). Such a situation was common to many forests, and reflected the loss of many industrial fuel markets to coal, increasing transport costs to towns, and the rising price of food in relation to other cash commodities (Hammersley, 1957). A few coppices were still let at the end of the 17th century but the 1698 Act ended the system, leaving only a few whose leases ran on into the 18th century.

As the coppice system declined, so the crown interest in growing timber increased. Reports of the Regarders from 1570 to 1610, and again in 1670, 1673 and 1677, testify repeatedly to the inadequacy of the system for conserving timber in the new Forest.* At the best of times there was no incentive for the tenant to conserve the timber, and the coppices were too impermanent for the necessary continuity of management. Meanwhile, resources of harvestable timber on crown land declined to a low point in the late 17th century. The earliest attempts to remedy the impermanence of the coppices was the enclosure of 100 acres (40 ha) at Holmhill (SU 260085) in or before 1670, and another 300 acres (121 ha) at Aldridgehill (SU275033) and Holidays Hill (SU265075) between then and 1673 'for a nursery and supply of timber'. These enclosures were of doubtful legality and it is not known if they were successful. However, in 1698, there followed *an Act for the Increase and Preservation of Timber in the New Forest.*

The 1698 Act provided for the immediate enclosure and planting with oak of 2000 acres (810 ha) and the subsequent enclosure of 200 acres (81 ha) annually for twenty years. Though it also gave statutory recognition to common rights, and stipulated that the enclosures were to be on land which 'could best be spared from the commons and highways', more than 1000 freeholders and commoners petitioned against it. In fact, only 3296 acres (1334 ha) were ever enclosed. The Act was a victim of the endemic conflict between Lord Warden and Surveyor General, and of local resistance manifest in broken fences and the admission of stock.

Seven Inclosures totalling 1000 acres (404 ha) were made in 1700–3, and two surviving coppices, North and South Bentley, were replanted with oak by the crown, though they were not

*Tubbs, 1964; Flower, 1980a, 1980b; Stagg, 1983.

formally recognized as Statutory Inclosures until the 19th century
(Flower & Tubbs, 1982). Today, their rounded shapes testify to
their origins. After 1703, forty-nine years elapsed before further
enclosure was attempted: then, in 1752, 252 acres (102 ha) were
enclosed, ploughed and broadcast with acorns, a technique which
reportedly failed (Glenbervie MS, HRO 11/M/74). Finally, 2000
acres (810 ha) were enclosed and planted between 1771 and 1778,
the difficulties between Lord Warden and Surveyor General
having been temporarily surmounted.

At the end of the 18th century, the landed estate of the crown
was scrutinized by Parliamentary Commissioners. After a century
of difficulties in the supply of shipbuilding timber, they sought
ways of securing future reserves on the crown lands, and as a con-
comitant, of maximizing crown estate revenues. *The Fifth Report
of Commissioners to Enquire into the Woods, Forests and Land
Revenues of the Crown*, 1789, reported on the New Forest. It
focused on the critical problem of the split administration. The
only produce of the Forest besides timber was said to be deer, of
which less than 200 were killed annually and most of these were
the perquisites of Forest officers or given to neighbouring landowners as compensation for damage to their estates. The Forest
was devoted to conserving uneconomic deer in such numbers as
widely preclude the survival of young trees. The Deputy Surveyor,
though responsible for growing and marketing timber, had no
control over the Lord Warden's establishment, many of whose
appointments, often sinecures, carried perquisites of timber,
grazing, deer and land. The keepers on whom the care of the
plantations rested, obtained most of their income from wood sales,
fees for deer killed, sales of rabbits, pig-keeping and grazing. Their
posts carried occupation of a smallholding from which to exploit
the Forest and their authority carried special opportunities for so
doing.

Most of the customs of the Forest were said to have lapsed by
1789. Neither fence month nor winter heyning were observed.
Rights of estovers (fuel wood) were exploited for re-sale. 'Fern,
heath and furze' were cut everywhere 'with the certain effect of
destroying whatever young shoots are coming through them'. The
enclosure fences were in a state 'as to keep out neither deer, horse,
cattle or swine'. Three enclosures were managed as rabbit warrens
by the keepers, and generated substantial profits. Of the twenty-
three enclosures made in the 18th century, only ten are shown with
a complete woodland cover on the map accompanying the 1789
report. In the conviction of their cause, the Commissioners were
probably selective in their presentation, but their portrayal echoes
from the past and it is probable that in 1789, the Forest was
burdened with an accumulated debt of maladministration. The
Report recommended negotiation with the freeholders to decide

what area might be enclosed for silviculture in exchange for removing the deer, withdrawal of forestal restrictions and the compounding of forest rents. A subsequent Bill of 1792, however, failed in the Lords, partly through the opposition of the freeholders who saw it as reducing the value of the common rights without adequate compensation. Significantly, the Bill held the notion of a 'rolling power' of enclosure, which permitted the crown to plant on whatever land would grow trees provided no more than 20,000 acres (8087 ha) were behind fences at a time.

The early 19th century saw the emergence of a new silvicultural professionalism. In 1810, the new Commissioners of Woods took over the Surveyor General's function and began to gain the upper hand over the deer forest officers. In 1808 *An Act for the Increase and Preservation of Timber in Dean and New Forests* was passed, confirming the Inclosures already made and providing for a further 6000 acres (2029 ha) which could be fenced at a time. Protest is unrecorded, probably because in effect the Act mainly re-enacted the 1789 Act, which had become of doubtful legal competence. Between 1808 and 1817, 5557 acres (2250 ha) were enclosed, and a further 1147 acres (464 ha) were enclosed during 1830–48.

In 1848 a Select Committee was appointed to investigate the finances and management of the crown estate. By then, most forests had been profitably disafforested and partitioned, and such a course was now advocated for the remainder – with the exception of the New Forest, where there were evidently too many commoners and their rights too valuable to make the exercise profitable to the crown. The alternative course lay in reducing the value of the rights by further silvicultural enclosure, which could be justified as compensation for surrendering the right to keep deer, in turn conveniently presented as a nuisance to the neighbourhood and as competitors with the commoners' animals for food. Thus the way would be paved to eventual disafforestation with the lion's share to the crown. What ultimately followed the 1848 Committee was the most significant single event in the Forest's history since afforestation – the *New Forest Deer Removal Act, 1851*.

1851 to 1923

The *Deer Removal Act* relinquished the interest of the crown in the deer, which were to be 'removed' within three years, and in compensation allotted a further 10,000 acres (4049 ha) for silviculture in addition to land enclosed under the 1698 and 1808 Acts. The crown continued to claim an unlimited rolling power, conceding only that no more than 16,000 acres (6478 ha) should be fenced at one time. The Act also provided for the compilation of a register of claims to common rights, presumably seen as a necessary precursor to eventual disafforestation and partition: certainly the

Office of Woods was vigorous in opposing claims during preparation of the register. Finally, the Act resulted in the abolition of the old deer forest hierarchy, leaving a clear field for the Office of Woods.

The Act was followed by a determined attack on the value of common rights. Though most of the deer were killed in the 1850s (resulting in profound ecological change) the Act had not extinguished the forest laws and the Office of Woods now attempted to enforce the fence month and winter heyning. This and other irritants, but above all the appalling change being wrought by blanket enclosure in the ancient mosaic of wood, heath, bog, and lawn, on which the earlier Inclosures had only a peripheral impact, provoked an eruption of opposition.

In a sense the crown over-played its hand by provoking the gentry. It was mainly the landowners who organized opposition. The financial advantages to them of partition were largely outweighed by the higher rents arising on holdings with common rights. Perhaps as important, there was distaste for the Office of Woods, who at one point threatened to impose the obsolete forest laws on the private estates, a blunder which was doubtless regretted. Finally, there was a definite liberal element among those involved. The fight to save the Forest has been too vividly described by Pasmore (1977) to bear detailed repetition, but the bones of the story are as follows.

In June 1866, the New Forest Association was formed to organize opposition and petititon Parliament. It succeeded first in precipitating a Select Committee of the Lords, which sat in 1868, but the Committee concluded that conflict between crown and commoners was inevitable and that disafforestation and partition was the only practical course, despite the ruin this would bring to the small commoner. A Bill for disafforestation was introduced in the Commons in 1871 but abandoned before second reading and a resolution passed:

'That in the opinion of this House, pending Legislation on the New Forest, no felling of ornamental timber, and no fresh inclosures should be permitted in the New Forest, and that no timber should be cut except for the purposes of thinning the young plantations, and satisfying the fuel rights of the commoners.'

In 1875, on the motion of Lord Henry Scott, the owner of the Beaulieu Estate, a Select Committee of the House of Commons was appointed to enquire into New Forest affairs. This time the local lobby was supported by a newly-awakened concern for the Forest as part of a diminishing natural heritage. The outcome was a report on which the innovative Act of 1877 was based.

The *New Forest Act, 1877* restricted enclosure to the 17,645 acres (7144 ha) enclosed under the Acts of 1698, 1808 and 1851.

No more than 16,000 acres (6478 ha) were to be behind fences at any one time. The remaining 45,000 acres (18,376 ha) of crown common land were to remain permanently unenclosed. A nominal quit-rent was to be paid by the Verderers on behalf of the commoners for the right to depasture animals in the fence month and winter heyning. The Verderer's Court was to be completely reconstituted.

The 1877 Act abolished the oath of the Verderers to the crown and increased their numbers from four to six, of which one (the Official Verderer) was to be appointed by the crown and the others elected by commoners and Parliamentary voters in New Forest parishes. They became a Body Corporate, with powers to sue and be sued; to hold land; to employ officers; to make bye-laws for the management and health of stock on the Forest; to maintain the Register of Claims to Common Rights made in the 1850s; to defray costs by levying dues (marking fees) on animals depastured on the Forest; and to dispose of money derived from the sale of land for the London–Dorchester railway (which traversed the Forest) for the benefit of the commoners. Each Verderer became a Justice of the Peace for Forest affairs. As Anthony Pasmore remarked, they were (and are) legislature, judiciary and executive all rolled into one (Pasmore 1977). They were to be the guardians of the commoners, common rights and – though this is less explicit – the Forest landscape.

The forty years or so following 1877 witnessed constant friction between the Office of Woods and the Verderers over the limits of their respective powers to control the unenclosed Forest. The former claimed an unimpeded right to permit such facilities as accesses, sawmills, military exercises and firing ranges on the unenclosed Forest and to agree to the alienation of land for allotments and public works, without recourse to the Verderers. For their part, the Verderers maintained that since 1877, the crown had rights over the unenclosed Forest only insofar as the area available for the exercise of common rights remained undiminished. Beyond that point, the Verderers' consent was necessary. Underlying this position lay a determination that the Forest landscape should be vandalized no further. The contest, however, was expensive and litigation finally drained the Verderers' funds, leaving no clear legal resolution of the issues.

The Forestry Commission and the Modern Forest

The management of the New Forest passed to the Forestry Commission under the *Forestry (Transfer of Woods) Act, 1923*. For most of its history, the Commission has been geared to expansion, based on fast-growing conifers. In the Forest, this found expression in successive attempts to intensify management by converting the broadleaved Inclosures to conifers, commercially exploiting the pasture woods, and enclosing more land. Crisis points were reached in the 1920s, 1950s and 1960s. Each time the aspirations of the Commission were checked by an explosion of public revulsion (chapters 6 and 10). Each episode left the Forest aesthetically and biologically more impoverished.

In 1949 the constitution of the Verderers and the administration of the Forest were adjusted once more. In 1946, the Minister of Agriculture, to whom the Forestry Commission was, and is, responsible, appointed a committee to investigate the Forest and make recommendations for adjusting it to modern requirements. The committee's report (the Baker Report) was laid before Parliament in September 1947 (Forestry Commission, 1947). Petitions against the subsequent Bill were heard by a Select Committee of the Lords in 1949. The most controversial of the Bill's proposals were for the enclosure of another 5000 acres (2024 ha) of the unenclosed Forest, for which highly specious arguments were advanced in the Baker Report; and a reconstitution of the Verderers' Court which weakened control by the commoners through their elected representatives. On these issues the local petitioners failed to convince the committee. The resulting Act, which became law in November 1949, together with the older Act of 1877, and two more recent Acts of 1964 and 1970, together largely govern the administration of the New Forest today.

CHAPTER 6 The Forest Today

The New Forest Act 1949

The *New Forest Act, 1949* increased the number of Verderers from six to ten, comprising an Official Verderer nominated by the crown; five Verderers elected by persons occupying not less than one acre of land to which common rights attached; and four Verderers appointed respectively by the Minister of Agriculture, Forestry Commission, local planning authority and a body 'specially concerned with the preservation of the amenity of the countryside', at first the Council for the Preservation of Rural England, latterly the Countryside Commission. The qualification for an elective Verderer became similar to that for an elector, instead of the occupation of 75 acres (30 ha) of land with common rights demanded by the 1877 Act. Electoral procedure was modernized. The constitution of the Verderers and the qualifications of electors and elective Verderers remain unchanged today.

The 1949 Act widened the powers of the Verderers to make bye-laws; gave them power to contain stock in temporary enclosures in the event of an outbreak of contagious or infectious disease; and resolved two problems which had surfaced persistently since 1877. First, it answered the prickly question of who was responsible for drainage, the maintenance of bridges and the control of encroaching pine and scrub on the open Forest, by assigning these duties to the Forestry Commission. Section 11 of the Act is important enough to quote in full because it is the basis on which the open Forest is managed today:

'It shall be the duty of the Forestry Commissioners from time to time to carry out such work as appears to them after consultation with the Verderers, and with due regard to the interests of amenity, reasonably necessary, or as the Minister may direct, for securing that the Forest will be properly drained, that culverts and bridges crossing drains or streams in the Forest (other than culverts or bridges which some other authority have power to maintain) will be properly maintained, and that the grazing will be kept sufficiently clear of coarse herbage, scrub and self-sown trees.'

Second, the Act charged the Forestry Commission with replacing the register of claims to common rights prepared in the 1850s by large scale plans showing what rights attached to each parcel of land registered. The old Register had defined both rights and land only by reference to tithe map numbers, which had made consultation increasingly difficult. The *Atlas of Claims to Common Rights*, made after 1949, occupies seven volumes of 1:2500 scale Ordnance Survey sheets. Another eight volumes joined them after the *New Forest Act, 1964*, when the perambulation was extended.

The 1949 Act also took the first step towards resolving the increasing problem of road accidents involving stock. The Baker Report had recognized the problem but understandably had not foreseen its future magnitude. The Report noted that many accidents occurred outside the Forest and recommended containing road grids. It also recommended that when the main east–west trunk road through the Forest (A31) was modernized, stock should be denied it by 'ha-ha' walls. Section 16 of the 1949 Act provided for fencing of the A31 but went no further towards a general solution of the problem.

The Act made three provisions permitting significant changes in the Forest landscape:

1   It gave the Verderers power to authorize the Forestry Commission to enclose up to a further 5000 acres (2024 ha) of open Forest for plantations. The trap was baited with a requirement that the Forestry Commission should pay compensation to the Verderers for any land enclosed. The bait was in due course made more palatable by offering reseeded grazing strips round the Inclosures; and by deploying the Inclosures so that (it was claimed) they were a barrier to urban expansion from the industrial areas bordering Southampton Water, and a means of keeping stock off roads. A glance at the disposition of the Inclosures which were finally made suggests that such claims were largely spurious. In 1955 a proposal for thirty-seven Inclosures totalling 4995 acres (2022 ha) was narrowly rejected by the Verderers. The Deputy Surveyor returned in 1958 and this time obtained approval for 2005 acres (812 ha), despite strong opposition from the New Forest Commoners' Defence Association, the New Forest Association, and local residents. The so-called Verderers' Inclosures were completed in the next few years. Unlike the earlier statutory Inclosures they are not enclosable in perpetuity but are held on a 150-year lease and have to be opened to stock for much of that time. The balance of 2995 acres (1213 ha) remains: times have not been propitious for a further application to the Verderers' Court.

2   The Verderers could authorize the Minister of Agriculture to enclose land from the open Forest for cultivation and improvement of grazing, the main qualification being that not more than 3000 acres (1215 ha) should be fenced off at any one time. In theory, this means that should either the Minister or the Verderers so desire, they could eventually re-seed all of the Forest's heaths and grasslands, though in practice to embark on such a course would be to invite an outcry of unprecedented dimensions. Between 1941 and

1952, 350 ha of open Forest had been enclosed, cropped and re-seeded by Hampshire War Agricultural Executive Committee with the agreement of the Verderers, though there had been no legal basis for the work. The new Act sought to remedy this in case further reclamation was contemplated, and, indeed in the late 1950s, the Verderers enclosed and reseeded three areas totalling 39 ha, supposedly located to draw stock away from main roads.

3   The Act gave the Forestry Commission powers, with the consent of the Verderers, to enclose parts of the unenclosed wood-lands in order to secure their regeneration, if necessary by felling and replanting. I shall argue in chapter 10 that the work which ensued was unnecessary and caused immense damage to a unique biological resource.

The New Forest Act 1964

In the 1950s and 1960s, two long-standing problems crystallized. First, the numbers of road accidents involving commoners' animals increased steadily. In 1955 it reached 170, or 5% of the depastured stock. In 1963 it was 349, or 8.2% of the total, in addition to which 62 deer were killed on the roads: 104 accidents (30%) with stock occurred outside the perambulation and, within it, the two main trunk roads – the A31 and A35 – claimed 133 accidents. Such a situation was intolerable.

The second issue arose from the exercise of common rights over the manorial wastes around the northern and western fringes of the Forest but outside the perambulation. Large numbers of animals were depastured on the so-called 'adjacent commons' and by the custom of vicinage they could legitimately exploit Forest as well as commons (and *vice versa*). Many commoners avoided pay-ment of marking fees by nominally turning out stock on the com-mons. The adjacent commons were not regulated in any way and a multiplicity of problems arose from the proximity of controlled and uncontrolled common land, particularly in relation to animal health.

By 1960 it was clear that the linked problems of road accidents and the adjacent commons could only be resolved by bringing the commons within the Forest and fencing the new boundary to prevent straying. Within the Forest the fencing of the A31 and A35 roads would reduce accidents still further. There was already provision in the 1949 Act for the fencing of the A31, but to extend the perambulation and bring the commons within the Verderers' control, required legislation, as probably did much of the work needed to seal the new boundary. Thus, in 1963, the Verderers promoted a Bill which was steered through Parliament and owed its survival to Sir Oliver Crosthwaite-Eyre, Member of Parliament for the Division and an elected Verderer.

It is easy now to forget the extent to which ponies and cattle formerly ranged beyond the Forest. They went as far as Christchurch to the south-west, nearly to Salisbury to the north, and penetrated the Southampton suburbs to the east. During 1956–63 between 20.7% and 37.5% (average 30.6%) of road accidents involving stock each year occurred outside the Forest. The 1950s and 1960s were times of pony-raided gardens, impoundment and pound-breaking in the towns around the Forest. For many years, the highway authority – Hampshire County Council – were reluctant to help finance road fences or grids, but by 1963 they bowed to the inevitable. Most of the new perambulation grids and the fencing of the A31 was completed during 1963 and 1964, before the New Forest Bill became law.

Before 1964 stock ranged along lanes and roadsides miles outside the Forest. Some lanes, like this, remain within the perambulation

The preparation and passage of the Bill involved protracted and difficult negotiations with those who would be affected. Despite all the ground work, it was petitioned against by some of those who depastured on the adjacent commons (who now had their protective grids and thus had second thoughts about paying marking fees), by a national gravel company (who saw in it an impediment to exploiting gravel resources), and by a number of insubstantial groups who saw in the Bill the perpetuation of privilege and the ill-treatment of animals left on the Forest all winter. The Bill

Stoney Cross, 1972: at that time, vehicular access to the open Forest was uncontrolled (Photo A. H. Pasmore)

survived Select Committees of both Houses and became law in July 1964 (Pasmore, 1974).

The *New Forest Act, 1964* extended the perambulation to include 1395 ha of adjacent commons, and retracted it elsewhere to conform to the convenient location of road grids. It provided for the construction and maintenance of perambulation grids and fences and for the fencing of the A35, which was completed in 1967. The added areas, mainly comprising Rockford, Ibsley and Hyde Commons on the west edge of the Forest, Hale Purlieu to the north and the Bramshaw commons to the north-west, became subject to the jurisdiction of the Verderers. The *Atlas of Claims to Common Rights* was re-opened to admit claims to rights of pasture over the added areas and their commoners thus became New Forest commoners. An anomaly persists in that registration was confined to pasture rights, leaving common of mast and other rights unaffected. Other provisions found their way into the Act. With the Verderers' consent, the Forestry Commission were enabled to make camp sites on the unenclosed Forest, and enclose land for 'creating new ornamental woods' – mercifully something not yet contemplated. The pannage season, previously 25 September to 22 November, became any period of not less than sixty consecutive days decided by the Forestry Commission after consulting the Verderers. Finally, both the Commission and the Verderers were to 'have regard to the desirability of conserving flora, fauna and geological and physiographical features of special interest'.

The conservation clause was a response to the growing awareness of the New Forest as an incomparable assemblage of natural habitats. This had been recognized in 1959 when The Nature Conservancy and the Forestry Commission signed an agreement which recognized what was described as the Forest's 'important nature reserve status', though on paper this amounted to no more than an agreement to consult over the management of a number of specially sensitive areas. Subsequently, however, The Nature Conservancy came to be closely involved in most management issues (mainly because of the conservation commitment of the Deputy Surveyor, Arthur Cadman) and in 1979 a new agreement formalized consultation between The Nature Conservancy (later the Nature Conservancy Council) and the Forestry Commission over management policies and work programmes for the Forest.

In 1971 the whole Forest was notified as a Site of Special Scientific Interest (SSSI) under the *National Parks and Access to the Countryside Act, 1949*, the effect of which was to require the local planning authority to consult The Nature Conservancy over planning issues affecting the area. In 1986 the SSSI was re-notified under the *Wildlife and Countryside Acts, 1981 and 1985*, making it necessary for owners and occupiers to give four months notice of intention to carry out any potentially damaging operations listed in the notification, and with provisions for compensation where appropriate. Thus, the Nature Conservancy Council (NCC) has come, since the 1950s, to represent a new element in an already complex management and administrative structure.

The most recent Forest legislation was precipitated by the *Countryside Act, 1968*, which conferred on the Forestry Commission a general power to provide recreational facilities in their forests but omitted to stipulate the necessity for obtaining the Verderers' consent in the New Forest. The Verderers were ultimately left with no option but to promote a remedial Bill to safeguard their guardianship role. This, in due course, became the *New Forest Act, 1970*. The 1970 Act reasserted the Verderers' control over the provision of recreational facilities and made two other important provisions. It provided for the fencing of the remaining A-class road through the Forest, the north–south A337 (fenced in 1973); and it extended the Countryside Commission's grant aid powers to enable them to assist with the Verderers' finances in appropriate situations, powers used in the 1970s to cover 75% of the cost of grazing improvement and the Steward's salary.

Planning for Recreation

The camp site clauses in the 1964 and 1970 Acts reflected rapid growth in the use of the Forest for recreation. By the late 1960s there was an acute need to decide how many people and their tents, caravans and vehicles were tolerable without environmental damage and to decide means of accommodating them. In the Forest before 1972, vehicles were permitted by default to penetrate

Surface damage to Forest lawns was extensive before protection against vehicles (Photo A. H. Pasmore)

wherever it was physically possible. They could be discovered in surprising places. With trivial exceptions, it was possible to camp or caravan anywhere on the unenclosed Forest. In the early 1960s the situation was already getting out of hand. Erosion scars and vehicle tracks were multiplying annually. The summer landscape was everywhere marred by the gleam of cars and caravans. The Forest was becoming tatty.

Forestry Commission figures for the numbers of camping permits issued for overnight stays provided a useful index of demand. The number of camper nights (= 1 camper for one night) increased at an average of 14% per annum (a staggering 25% in 1968) from 83,000 in 1956 to 485,000 in 1969. At the end of the 1960s there were more than 4000 tents and caravans on the Forest during the peak Bank Holiday periods. Most came from within 100 miles. An estimated 3.25 million day visits were made to the Forest in the year ending September 1969. The peak numbers of cars parked in the Forest at one time was about 6000, though up to 20,000 per day were estimated to drive off the highway on to the Forest at peak times.

Projections of these figures led many to question whether the Forest could survive to the end of the century and, indeed, *The New Forest – Can it Survive?* was the title of a leaflet later produced by the County Council. Without an imposed discipline, I doubt if it would have survived to the mid-1980s.

In 1962, a group, of which I was one, devised simple plans for car-free zones, to be closed to vehicles by ditches with locked barriers across tracks and small car parks at the periphery. Arthur Cadman was persuaded to somewhat cautiously embark on a car-free-zone policy, which at first met local hostility, particularly from the commoners. For a while barrier breaking became a local sport. However, several large tracts of Forest became free of vehicles for the first time for years and the notion gained support. By 1965, the Forestry Commission, Verderers, Nature Conservancy and Hampshire County Council were all alarmed by the potential for destruction in the continued uncontained growth of recreational use. In December 1966 they came together to form a New Forest Joint Steering Group comprising representatives of the four authorities, together with others from the New Forest and Ringwood and Fordingbridge Rural District Councils. The Steering Group appointed the inevitable Working Party to study the problems and make recommendations. I represented the Nature Conservancy on both.

Extraordinary though it now seems, it took four years to produce a report for public reaction. This, when it came, we called *Conservation of the New Forest*. It was essentially an environmental impact analysis from which management conclusions were drawn. We arrived, I fear, at a package of proposals which might have been derived intuitively at the start, but we were well armed with the supporting arguments. Inevitably, we proposed the exclusion of vehicles from most of the Forest by ditches and barriers; the provision of car parks at the edge of car-free zones; and the confinement of camping and caravanning to particular places. The planners among us invented euphemisms to disguise the simplicity of the proposals. 'Car-based day visitors' were to be 'channelled' to 110 'day visitor sites', nine 'viewpoint car parks' and twenty-one 'walkers' car parks'. Campers and caravanners were to be 'progressively' channelled to sixteen 'informal camp sites', two 'informal camping areas' and five 'equipped camp sites', with a back-up overflow camp site (New Forest Joint Steering Group, 1970).

The proposals survived public scrutiny remarkably intact. The final recommendations were published in November 1971 (New Forest Joint Steering Group, 1971) and the Minister of Agriculture agreed shortly after to finance their implementation by the Forestry Commission. By the end of 1976, the Forest had been transformed by the confinement of cars to car parks and campers and caravans to fifteen sites. The curtailment of individual freedom was sad but inevitable.

The levels of provision for camp sites and car parks decided in 1971 was reaffirmed in 1976 by the participants in the original study (Forestry Commission, 1976). The consensus then was that to increase provision would take it over the threshold beyond which serious damage would again occur, besides which it was extremely

Forestry Commission car park, one of over 130 provided after 1972

difficult to find further suitable sites for facilities. Thus, since 1971, the numbers of tents and caravans has been held at a ceiling of 4800, with a Bank Holiday overflow provision to 6300, and the number of car park spaces to 5500 (Forestry Commission, 1976).

The Woodland Crisis 1968–1971

As the New Forest Joint Steering Committee and its Working Party contemplated the problems of recreation, so a major controversy over the woodland management policies of the Forestry Commission was unfolding.

Ironically, by the 1920s, many of the 18th- and 19th-century Inclosures which had been such a blight when planted, were now valued and beautiful oakwoods. In addition, there were numerous areas of formerly unenclosed woods surviving intact behind the fences. In recognition of the scenic importance of the broadleaved Inclosures, section 6 of the 1877 Act had laid down management guidelines which were later to be cast repeatedly in the face of the Forestry Commission. Care was to be taken to:

'maintain the picturesque character of the ground and not wholly to level or clear the woods but to leave . . . a sufficient number of the most ornamental trees; and to keep the woods replenished . . . by protecting the self-sown plants or by planting trees in the vacant spaces, having regard to the ornamental as well as the profitable use of the ground'.

Section 8 of the Act stipulated further that the unenclosed woods of the Forest should be 'preserved'. Victorian sensibilities may later have been difficult to interpret in practice, but the message was clear.

There were extensive oak fellings during 1914–18, and afterwards the Forestry Commission, newly come to the Forest, embarked on a policy of steadily converting the broadleaved woods to conifers. In 1923, the partial felling of Burley Old Inclosure (a former pasture wood) precipitated a public outcry which temporarily halted the policy. In 1927 a local committee was formed by the Commission as a forum for discussing the management of the old woods and it functioned, if at times perfunctorily, until the Second World War.

In 1928 the Commission undertook that 60% of the Inclosures should remain under broadleaved trees, but by 1937 they had managed to reduce it to 54% and by 1963, when a new Working Plan was prepared, it was 42%. In 1972 it was 37% and in 1982, 36% (Small, 1972, 1983). The 1963 Working Plan, which remained a well-kept secret until leaked in 1970, proposed reducing it further to 25% over twenty years and eventually eliminating broadleaved trees except as meagre screening belts to conifer plantations. Conversion, however, remained slow until the sudden and dramatic departure of Arthur Cadman. In November 1968 he resigned as Deputy Surveyor and publicly announced in the Verderers' Court that he believed he no longer had the confidence of his masters. His preface to the Commission's Working Plan, written years before, had warned of the likely outcome of its policies. At the same court, the New Forest Association sought (in vain) a suspension of the broadleaved felling programme and the reconstitution of the old Advisory Committee.

The new Deputy Surveyor was uncompromising. Plans for extensive clear-felling became known. In 1969 began an attempt to commercially exploit the unenclosed pasture woods, starting with the 'thinning' of Rushpole Wood (SU3009). The tale of subsequent events has been vividly told by Anthony Pasmore, who like myself was a participant in many of its dramas (Pasmore, 1977). Neither arguments by biologists that it was unnecessary for the perpetuation of the woods (the claimed objective) nor protests that it was illegal and an affront to an unparalleled cultural heritage, immediately prevailed. However, before a second area of unenclosed woodland could be exploited, the public outcry reached a crescendo in early 1970 with the leaking of the 1963 Working Plan which revealed both the intention to nearly eliminate broadleaved trees from the Inclosures, and the commercial motive in exploiting the unenclosed woods. In September 1970, James Prior, the Minister of Agriculture, intervened. After visiting the Forest he imposed a temporary ban on broadleaved felling and early in 1971 issued a Mandate to the Forestry Commission which spelt out the policies which they must follow. It was to be reviewed after ten years, and was reaffirmed, unaltered, in 1982. It is an important document.

The Mandate declared that the unenclosed woodlands were to be 'conserved without regard to timber production objectives' and conversion of broadleaves to conifers in the Inclosures was to cease. The broadleaved Inclosures were to be managed on rotations of at least 200 years, with felling limited to single trees or groups of no more than one acre. These directions were prefaced by the over-riding requirement that 'The New Forest must be regarded as a national heritage and priority given to the conservation of its traditional character'. Open to interpretation though the traditional character may be, the sentiment is unmistakable.

A by-product of the woodland crisis was the formation in late 1970 by the Forestry Commission of the New Forest Consultative Panel, which was to act as a 'sounding board for local public opinion on the factors which need to be taken into account in the management of the Forest'. It has forty-six members from every statutory and voluntary organization associated with the Forest. Cynics have suggested that the intention was to weight it with parochial and marginal interests in order to dilute the voice of those who could speak with authority, but if this was the intention, it has not succeeded. The Panel has fulfilled a useful guardianship role and has killed off many potential problems at germination.

Conclusion

I have tried in this and the preceding chapter to show how the unique and complex administration and management of the Forest has evolved. In the 1980s it can seem a labyrinth of interacting organizations and interests in which the stranger can quickly become lost. I will attempt a brief explorer's guide.

The crown land within the perambulation is vested in the Minister of Agriculture, by section 4(5) of the Forestry Act 1945 and is placed at the disposal of the Forestry Commission by section 4(6) of the Act. The Commission is thus in the position of the crown's (or state's) agent. It is ultimately responsible for all matters which arise from ownership of the soil. Except for the owners of turbary and marl rights, and except for the statutory provisions for grazing improvement given to the Verderers, only the Forestry Commission has the right to touch the soil. It alone has the right to the timber or other produce of the soil, except insofar as the commoners may take it through the mouths of their animals. However, the Commission cannot grant licences or wayleaves for such purposes as cricket pitches, golf courses (of which there are three), pipelines, power lines and other public utilities (except accesses to houses) without the consent of the Verderers. The

Commissioners' bye-laws regulate the use of the Forest by the public, which enjoys access over it on foot or on horseback.

The Forestry Commission has powers to practise silviculture in the Statutory Inclosures within constraints imposed by aesthetic and biological considerations. With the consent of the Verderers they can carry out management work in the unenclosed woods, but only in order to ensure the perpetuation of these woods in their present form. They have a statutory obligation to carry out estate management work on the open Forest generally, including drainage and the clearance of scrub and encroaching pine. Finally, they have a duty to maintain the *Atlas of Claims to Common Rights*, though in practice this has been done by the Verderers at the Commission's expense. The Deputy Surveyor administers the Forest from The Queen's House, Lyndhurst.

The Verderers of the New Forest are responsible for the care, health and regulation of commoners' stock on the Forest through bye-laws, but they have no power to stint the number of animals turned out by individual commoners or in total. They employ a Clerk, and four Agisters who supervise the stock. In a general sense the Verderers are the guardians of the commoners and common rights. They are also the guardians of the Forest's landscape and natural habitats, a duty exercised through their power to veto development. The veto extends specifically to road construction or improvement by the highway authority; to the exchange of Forest land for private land (a facility provided for in the 1949 Act); to the enclosure of the extra 5000 acres (2024 ha) of unenclosed Forest for plantations; and to work in the unenclosed woods. The Verderers can also authorize limited enclosure and cultivation for pasture improvement, and with the consent of the Forestry Commission, they can carry out such pasture improvements as bracken eradication. Some of their powers and duties sit uneasily together.

The Verderers hold a bi-monthly open Court in the Verderers' Hall, Lyndhurst, at which they hear presentments from commoners, the public and local organizations about management and development proposals; from the Forestry Commission on matters of public interest; and from bodies such as the County Council seeking to construct or widen a road, or a water company wanting to lay a pipeline. Views on such matters are heard at a subsequent Court before a decision is made. From time to time, their bye-laws are prosecuted in the Court. The Verderers' Court is a good measure of the Forest temperature: if there is controversy it will surface there.

A wide spectrum of organizations influence the affairs of the Forest (witness the size of the Consultative Panel) among which day-to-day the most prominent are usually the New Forest Association which is concerned with the protection of the Forest landscape and its traditional uses; the New Forest Commoners' Defence Association, whose title says all that is needed about its history and purpose; and the NCC, the government agency with statutory responsibility for nature conservation. Hampshire County Council and New Forest District Council, as the local planning authorities, also have a critical role to play, for it must be remembered that in any event the powers and functions of Forestry Commission and Verderers are confined mainly to the crown lands, extensive though they are. Planning policies are strongly protective (chapter 16) but their success is paid for in vigilance, notably by the local branch of the Council for the Protection of Rural England, and the NCC.

The system is one of checks and balances. Excesses on the part of the Forestry Commission can be met by the Verderers' veto, and the reverse is partly true. In the event of the Verderers failing to act in defence of the Forest, as happened in the woodland crisis of 1968–71, there is a strong environmental lobby capable of exerting the pressure necessary to retrieve the situation. The consultations required with the NCC under the *Wildlife and Countryside Acts, 1981 and 1985* are another hurdle in the path of the potential transgressor.

Forest affairs are not all crisis and dissent. There is much common ground in the perception of the Forest and its management and in resistance to unwanted development threatened from outside. The environmental lobby, of which the NCC is one expression, the Verderers and the Forestry Commission, have an honourable recent history of collaboration in successfully resisting oil exploration, roadworks and pipelines on the Forest. Let it be admitted, however, that the various organizations with a common interest in protecting the Forest do not always agree about how it should be managed. There are, for example, inescapable differences between commoners and ecologists over the drainage of wetlands. On this and other aspects of management the Forest legislation does not provide clear guidance, but confines itself to generalizations permitting wide latitude in interpretation. Later chapters will testify that this leaves abundant scope for debate.

The Commoners' Rights

Around the Forest margins and in the pockets of enclosed land within it, there is a distinctive landscape dominated by small, hedged meadows and scattered dwellings, the generally irregular pattern of which testifies to its origin in piecemeal enclosure from the wildland. The Forest margins are often marked by linear settlements which have arisen from concerted phases of creeping encroachment. To much of this land, and indeed to some lands much further removed from the Forest, is attached the rights of common exercisable over the unenclosed Forest and its peripheral manorial wastes.

Forest edge holdings at Hyde, 1905 (Photo Phillip Allison collection)

Together with the deer, the ponies, cattle and other stock turned out by the commoners have been a potent force in the shaping of today's Forest, through their influence on the regeneration, age and species structure of the vegetation. I do not now recall who first described the ponies as the architects of the Forest scenery, but there is a strong element of biological truth in this, though cattle and in the past, perhaps sheep, have also played a part. Because the future of the commoners is inextricably interwoven with that of the Forest itself (and it is better to think of the two as part of one social and ecological system) it is important to understand the history and socio-economics of the commoners as a community, and to identify the factors controlling the numbers of animals they have depastured on the Forest.

Commoners and Crown

Much can be inferred about the importance of common rights in medieval and later times from the forestal documents (chapter 5) but the references are generally fragmentary and often indirect. Rather than attempt to reconstruct the commoners' economy and its fortunes from these sources, I propose simply to allow the graphic statement of the copyholders of Cadnam and Winsor in 1591 to stand proxy for the condition of the New Forest commoners as a whole.

The commons of this manor were small (40 ha) but adjoined the extensive (200 ha) commons of Wigley, over which the stock of the Cadnam commoners had customarily roamed. The Lord of Wigley, however, was attempting to exclude them, and in the resulting action in the Court of Chancery, they deposed

'that the said Complaynants were poore Coppieholders of the Manor of Cadnam and Winsor, and their whole estates and livynge depended upon the same, soo that if they should be abridged of their ancyent customs it would be their utter undoing'.

The commoners prevailed and the commons of both manors survive today as part of the group at Bramshaw which was brought within the Forest perambulation in 1964.

Interestingly, a late 19th-century attempt to enclose part of the Wigley Commons (Half Moon Common) by Hans Sloane Stanley, the then Lord of the Manor, was thwarted by an action taken by G. E. Briscoe Eyre in 1880. The earlier Chancery decree was called upon in aid of the case (Eversley, 1910).

Pre-17th century evidence is sparse, but the New Forest is probably unique for the wealth of later documents testifying to the importance of the common land in the local economy. In particular, there are successive registers of claims to common rights, the earliest dating from 1635. Then, and again in 1670, on the occasion of the forest eyres, registers of all claims to Forest rights and privileges were prepared. Probably, similar registers had been prepared for similar occasions before the 17th century, but if so, they have been lost. An abstract of the 1670 register was published in 1776 (Abstract of Claims, 1776) and an extended version in 1854 (Office of Woods, 1854), when commissioners were preparing the new register required by the Deer Removal Act.

In 1670, 307 claims were registered, but these refer to a much larger number of holdings because the lords of the larger manors submitted single claims covering all their tenants and copyholders. Most holdings specifically mentioned were between 1 acre (0.4 ha) and 50 acres (20 ha) in size. Most of the smaller ones were the manorial tenants and copyholders but there were many tiny freehold properties. There were also many holdings in the 50–200-acre (20–81 ha) range, often identified as assarts and usually occupied by 'Gentlemen'. Claimants sought to establish one or more of five rights of common – common of pasture (i.e., for cattle, ponies, donkeys and mules); common of mast (the right to turn out pigs in the pannage season); common of turbary (the right to take turf fuel and perhaps mire peat – though this has never been absolutely clear); common of estovers (the right to take fuel wood); and common of marl (the right to take marl from recognized pits in the Forest). Common of grazing for sheep was claimed for the lands formerly held by the Cistercian abbeys of Beaulieu and Netley, though it is uncertain if sheep were ever grazed in large numbers on the New Forest. There is no consistent acknowledgement of the fence month and no mention of the winter heyning.

Forest edge holdings at Ogdens, 1936; broadcasting the seed and harrowing it in. Most holdings grew some corn but depend mainly on stock-keeping (Photo Eric Ashby)

Most claims acknowledge the forestal rule of *levancy* and *couchancy*, that is, the limitation of the number of animals depastured in the Forest's growing season to that which the holding could sustain in winter. Turbary was sometimes interpreted to include

the cutting of 'fern, heath and furze'. Estovers were often specifically qualified to mean the taking of dead wood and 'decaying' trees.
Both turbary and estovers were supposed to be exercised only by
the 'view and allowance of the foresters'. That the local economy
was heavily dependent on the exercise of common rights in the
18th and 19th centuries is confirmed by the petitions lodged against
the 1698 Act.

An attempt was made to compile a further register of commoners
and common rights in 1792, probably as one of the preliminaries
to the eventual disafforestation and partition of the Forest proposed
by the Commissioners' report of 1789 (Stagg, 1983b). On this
occasion, each Keeper submitted a list of inhabitants and their
holdings in his Walk. For eight of the fifteen Walks, the lists are
clearly of commoners, with details of the rights they enjoyed. For
the remaining seven Walks, it is not clear if the lists are of commoners or of all heads of households. Some lists appear to include
recent encroachments, which would have been unable to claim
common rights, though their occupants probably exploited the
Forest illegally. Holding sizes are not mentioned. The document
identifies 2314 holdings or dwellings, and their occupants, many
of whom are recorded as tenants. For the eight Walks where common rights were recorded, the returns are specific as to the number
of loads of turf and wood fuel claimed, and the number of animals
depastured, though it is difficult to interpret the latter figures since
there was no stint on the number a commoner could depasture.
They may have been the numbers claimed to have been turned
out in 1972, or perhaps an order of scale guessed or estimated by
the Keeper.

From the end of the 18th century, the tacit official intention
seems to have been to reduce the value of the common rights so
that on eventual disafforestation, the commoners' share would be
minimal. This could be accomplished by increasing the area of silvicultural Inclosures and by attempting to enforce archaic forestal
restrictions on the exercise of the rights. Success in enforcement
was possibly less important than the reaffirmation of the legal
limits of the rights. Practically the only explanation for the failure
of the crown to seek disafforestation at an early date must lie in
recognition that the number of commoners (which included influential landowners) was so large and the rights so valuable, that
the crown allotment on disafforestation would have been un-
acceptably small.

The unsuccessful 1792 Bill and the successful 1808 Act (chapter
5) were followed in 1819 by a further assault on the common rights
in the shape of *An Act for Regulating the Right of Common of
Pasture in the New Forest*, which provided for the exclusion of
stock from the Forest during the winter heyning. It was presented
as no more than an affirmation of the Forest Law. The evidence

given to successive Parliamentary committees between 1848 and 1868 shows that as well as attempting to re-assert the forestal customs, it was the Office of Woods policy to reduce the value of the rights, by enclosing and planting as much of the most productive grazing land as possible, under the Acts of 1698 and 1808.

The preparation of the register of common rights in the 1850s (Office of Woods, 1858) must also have been as a preliminary to disafforestation, and it must have been disappointing to the Office of Woods to find that the Commissioners supported so many claims. However, though 1200 claims were allowed out of 1311 submitted, in not a single case did they confirm all the rights claimed. In addition, it was later said that many unlettered cottagers failed to claim the rights they had been accustomed to exercise, and thus forfeited them by default.

The commoners' slice of the Forest cake in the event of disafforestation was clearly a matter of some interest to the Select Committees of 1848, 1868 and 1875, as well as to the Commissioners of Woods. Witnesses before the 1848 Committee estimated that it amounted to about one half of the crown land area. In 1868 and 1875, it was suggested that it was between one half and two thirds, though as a result of the Inclosures made after 1851, the real value was admitted to have considerably depreciated. Indeed, it was suggested that if the Office of Woods exercised its claimed rolling power of enclosure to take in the remainder of the better grazing land, said to be about 11,000 acres (4453 ha), the commoners' share on disafforestation would be about one sixth of the Forest.

In the event, the New Forest escaped disafforestation, and both Forest and commoners received the protection of the *New Forest Act, 1877*. In the absence of a vigorous local economy in which the exercise of common rights was an integral and often vital part of the customary working of small farms and cottage holdings, the Forest could not have survived the 19th century except as a name on the map. The rights and their economic importance formed the legal foundation of opposition to silvicultural enclosure and disafforestation alike, even if by the 1870s the case was strengthened by a new, broadly-based environmental lobby. We owe an incalculable debt to those Victorian gentlemen who were the adversaries of the crown in the years before 1877, and who subsequently continued to play their parts in Forest affairs into the 20th century – W. C. D. Esdaile, the owner of Burley manor; G. E. Briscoe Eyre, of the Warren's estate, Bramshaw; Francis Lovell, of Hincheslea, which was an ancient vaccary; Charles Castleman, solicitor and a director of the London–Dorchester Railway Company; Lord Henry Scott, later Lord Montagu, owner of the Beaulieu estate; Henry Compton, owner of Minstead manor; and many others, besides a supporting cast of articulate small commoners. In their passing, they left us not only the New Forest –

the original albeit marred by the Office of Woods' plantations –
but also much information about the commoners' economy in the
late 19th and early 20th centuries.

The Commoners' Economy in the Late 19th and Early 20th Centuries

In evidence before the Select Committee of 1875, W. C. D. Esdaile
analyzed the claims to common rights allowed in 1858 thus:

'I find that the smaller commoners come out . . . 207 own 1 acre, 200 own
1–4 acres, 126 own 4–10 acres, 51 own 10–20 acres, 44 own 20–30 acres,
beyond which I have taken them to be larger holders.'

These figures excluded tenants. Of the ' larger holders' – i.e., the
balance of 571 claims allowed by the Commissioners – most owned
less than 80 acres (32 ha), but they included a number of the larger
estates which submitted block claims for up to 150 tenants, most
of which occupied holdings of less than 50, and usually less than
20 acres. The extent to which the 'small commoners' depended on
the Forest was central to the evidence given to the 1868 and 1875
Select Committees. It was said that grazing rights enabled a
commoner to maintain three times as many cattle as he could without them. Esdaile, in evidence before the 1868 Select Committee,
said that it was felt among the smaller commoners that:

'to lose the common rights . . . would be simply ruin; they would not be
able to manage their land in the way they do now . . . I have never been
able to find a smaller owner who would be willing to be compensated for
the right which he has'.

Others gave evidence supporting this statement. Disafforestation
and allotment between the crown and those with common rights
would leave so small a share to each commoner that they would
lose the livelihood which derived from their joint enjoyment of the
unenclosed Forest.

The rights of grazing and pannage reduced both overhead costs
of stock-keeping and capital costs of land purchase. Rights of
turbary and estovers, and the customary cutting of bracken for
bedding, and litter and gorse for fodder, reduced or eliminated
heating costs and kept down stock-keeping overheads. The combination meant that a family could live in modest and independent
comfort on a holding which elsewhere would not have supported
them. Many of the occupiers of the smaller holdings had two or
three sources of income, but their livelihood and way of life re-
volved around the exercise of the common rights. G. E. Briscoe
Eyre has left us an admirable study of the New Forest's late 19th-
century smallholding economy (Eyre, 1883), in which he describes
the Forest as:

'run with the mares, and in their fourth year breed a good colt. Brood mares are much valued and are rarely sold; a very good one will fetch £15'.

The open Forest, he says, is the 'cottager's farm', the source of his livelihood and of a modest capital.

Overheads were most reduced in the case of ponies, which required minimum labour and superintendence. 'The fillies', Eyre said:

'characterized by a moderate but widespread prosperity, even in these hard times, and by the low percentage of pauperism . . . and this can be distinctly traced to the judicious exercise of common right.'

He gives the average annual profit on a troop of five ponies as £20, with minimal annual outlay and little commitment of the holding's resources.

Most smallholders kept one or more cows, which depended more heavily on the holding, especially in winter. Heifers, on the other hand, could run on the Forest for much of the year where they were

'nearly as self-maintaining as pony stock, until they have their calf . . . in the spring they will be sold with calf at side for £10 to £14 each'.

The value of common of mast varied with the quality of the mast year, and with the capital available for buying in 'early and cheap as many pigs as he can hope to keep' until the pannage season. At the end of a moderately good pannage season

'they return bettered to the value of about 10s to 20s (50p–£1) a head, and fit for immediate sale'. In a good mast year, £5 thus laid out may be doubled in three months . . . cottagers have been known to make £20 a year by their pigs.'

Most holdings had turbary rights, each right being for a specified number of turves which were supposed to be cut 'by the view and allowance' of the Keepers. Individual rights averaged about 4000 turves and the right was allowed for about 1500 dwellings in 1858. Heath turf 'with its necessary complement of a few faggots or a little stump wood, keeps a cottager in fuel through the winter.' (Eyre, 1883). Fuel wood, or estovers rights by the mid 19th century, had been exchanged for the assignment of specific numbers of cords* of wood cut and stacked by the Office of Woods. The policy was to reduce the numbers of rights by purchase. Briscoe Eyre gives a total annual assignment of 376 cords comprising seven 'large' rights totalling 94 cords and a large number of 'small' rights of a few cords each. By 1915, the annual assignment had been reduced to 240 cords (Lascelles, 1915) and has since been reduced further.

*A cord is a stack measuring 8 ft (2.44 m) in length, 4 ft (1.22 m) in width and 4 ft in height.

The cutting of bracken for bedding and litter was a valued custom, exercised since time immemorial but not recognized as a common right, and at times regarded as an offence against the vert. According to Briscoe Eyre, 'fern' was sold by the Office of Woods 'under conditions generally considered to be prohibitive' in the late 19th century, but that it was bought 'chiefly from necessity'. It continued to be cut extensively until the 1940s, and a little is still cut today. Similarly, the cutting of gorse for fodder was widespread until the present century. Eyre (1883) refers to the gathering of 'furze tops' in winter, and in general it seems to have been the younger material which was usually collected from each bush. Crushing or pounding was sometimes necessary to improve palatability (though New Forest ponies experience no difficulty in dealing with it on the Forest) and, indeed, elsewhere in Britain and in northern France, gorse was cultivated as a fodder crop during and before the 19th century, and sophisticated milling machinery was developed to process it (Page, 1788; Elly, 1846). In the Forest, gorse faggots were also cut for firing local pottery and brick kilns, and the cutting and carting of 'furze and heath' faggots for the kilns and for broom making was a common sideline (Gilpin, 1791; Jebb, 1915).

The exercise of common of marl seems to have died out late in the 19th century. In the local context, marl was the calcareous marine clay (often highly fossiliferous) of the Headon Beds, which outcrops sparingly in the south of the Forest. Pits were dug, from which marl was removed to improve the soils of enclosed holdings, and probably for the construction of the locally ubiquitous cob buildings. The taking of marl from 24 'open and accustomed pits' was by 'view and allowance' of the Keepers, but none of the surviving Keepers' diaries and account books for the 1850s, 1860s and 1870s mention marl, though they do include receipts for 'turf tickets'. However, Williamson (1861) says that according to 'the New Forest financial accounts', 138 cubic yards (105.6 cu m) were excavated in the year ending 31 March 1860. If the 'financial accounts' still exist, perhaps they could throw further light on the last years of the practice. The customary marl pits are readily identifiable today, though time has healed their newness, and given them a mantle of thorn thickets and open woodland, whilst one series of pits was dammed to form Hatchet Pond (SU367015).

Twenty-four years after Briscoe Eyre's account, Jebb (1907) left a further snapshot in time of the commoners' economy, though his study is biased towards conditions at Warrens, from which he derived much of his information. Briscoe Eyre had come into the estate in 1887 and found difficulty in letting the larger farms, whose rental values were falling in the Depression. He subdivided them into smallholdings and enlarged some existing smallholdings to produce a land distribution 'which would meet the local needs of

Forest edge holding at Ogdens, 1937. Holdings were family affairs. Capital outlay was minimized by handwork (Photo Eric Ashby)

the population', and give a better rental return. In 1907, the 2700-acre (1093 ha) estate had sixty-eight holdings, of which only nine were over 50 acres (20 ha) and thirty-eight were under $12\frac{1}{2}$ acres (5 ha). 'Ordinary cottage holdings', says Jebb, 'average about 6 acres (2.4 ha). On these the men earn extra wages by carting etc.' Twelve acres (4.9 ha) were considered locally to be sufficient for an entire living, and many thought this the maximum size which could be profitably worked without hired help. Holding size was important and there was 'a certain acreage which is specifically adapted to the local requirements ... regulated by the amount of stock the wife and family can manage while the husband is out at work' in the case of cottage holdings, and 'the amount of land a man can cultivate himself with his family without hired help', in the case of smallholdings and small farms. The stock ran on the Forest, and the holdings were down to hay, with a strip or two devoted to roots, cabbage or potatoes. On larger holdings some land would be in cereals. The common feature was the relatively large head of stock which the use of the Forest enabled them to maintain.

Modern Times

The image of the New Forest which we glimpse in the writings of Briscoe Eyre and Jebb, and in the Minutes of Evidence of the successive Parliamentary committees which considered the Forest's destiny in the 19th century, are light years removed from the realities of the 1980s. Times have changed, and for the commoners they have changed most rapidly and radically since the Second World War. Until then, despite vicissitudes, the smallholding and cottage stock-keeping economy disintegrated only very slowly. Kenchington's description of the Forest and its commoners in the war years of the early 1940s and the preceding agricultural depression between the wars, is not so very different from those of Victorian and Edwardian times (Kenchington, 1944). Moreover, he was employed by the County War Agricultural Executive Committee and was in a position to be authoritative. He gives the number of agricultural holdings in New Forest parishes as 1195, of which 731 were under 5 acres (2 ha), 316 were 5–10 acres (2–4 ha), 274 were 10–20 acres (4–8 ha), 287 were 20–50 acres (8–20 ha), 178 were 50–100 acres (20–40 ha), and 218 over 100 acres. He estimated that about two-thirds of the holdings represented the main source of livelihood to their occupiers. Holdings less than 50 acres accounted for approximately 23% of the agricultural land, but represented 81% of the number of holdings. His description of them recalls those of Briscoe Eyre and Jebb:

'Many of these tiny holdings were equipped and stocked not as smallholdings proper but as miniature farms. Most engage in cattle keeping, either as cowkeepers or as rearers of young horned stock, using the holdings as a source of winter forage and pasturage, and a winter base for stock running on the Forest.'

In the decades before 1940, the smallholders of the New Forest found markets for much of their produce in the expanding urban areas of Bournemouth and Southampton, and among the affluent middle class who were coming to live in and around the Forest itself. In the 1930s, however, the local economy received successive blows from the loss of the farmhouse butter trade to wholesale imports from Australia and New Zealand, and from the importation of mass-produced Danish bacon. Nonetheless, the low overheads made possible by the use of the Forest, enabled the small commoner to get by, the profits of the holding often supplemented by part-time employment. Kenchington, describing the effects of the inter-war agricultural depression, commented that 'cheap corn and cake well suited the grazier, stockman, pigman, and poultryman side of the forester's agriculture'.

The accounts of Eyre (1883), Jebb (1907) and Kenchington (1944) all confirm that the major agricultural depressions, based on steeper falls in grain than in stock prices, tended to operate to the commoners' relative advantage. To some extent he was also buffered against disaster by the ability to retreat into a near-subsistence economy (provided rents were not extortionate) when prices for his products touched bottom. It will be remembered that Briscoe Eyre commented that 'the region is characterized by

a moderate but widespread prosperity, even in these hard times' – the hard times of the middle of the Great Depression. Jebb (1907) said that the average rental per acre for larger farms in the Forest had dropped by half in twenty years, whereas the rents for small-holdings had been maintained. The Forest system, in which the use of the commons reduced overheads, and which was essentially a mixed, stock-raising enterprise exploiting local markets, was well insulated against depression. It has proved less well able to survive the economic and social climate of the era which began in 1945.

Forest edge holding at Ogdens, 1937: carting the oat harvest. The pony-drawn general-purpose cart was ubiquitous (Photo Eric Ashby)

Since the late 1940s, Government agricultural policies and, latterly, government interpretation of the Common Agricultural Policy of the European Economic Community, have favoured large farms at the expense of small units. Price support systems, grant schemes and improved production techniques have raised production levels in all sectors of agriculture to unprecedented levels, but this has required investment by individuals or estates beyond the reach of the small farmer, whilst unit returns have diminished relatively. A spiral has been set up in which farm size and production levels have chased capital investment and loan charges. Economies such as those of the New Forest commoner have been left in a poor position. Cattle on the Forest make small live weight gains compared with those on modern improved pasture, and low overheads do not wholly compensate. New mass marketing methods for milk, butter, potatoes and poultry have compounded the smallholders' difficulties.

Haymaking in the 1920s – hay was the most important crop on most Forest holdings (Photo collection of Mr Bill Veal)

The decline of the age-old Forest economic system has been hastened by spin-offs from increased national affluence and by new perceptions of living. Greater affluence is to be derived from full-time employment than from operating a Forest holding. Concurrently, increased per capita income and mobility, and a desire to live in the country has sent house and land values soaring since the early 1960s: the New Forest has proved highly attractive to both commuters and the retired. To some extent, Government planning policies, which see the neighbouring area of south Hampshire around Southampton Water and eastward to Portsmouth as a growth area, are to blame for housing pressures on the Forest. The result is that house prices are beyond the reach of many of those with the closest ties to the Forest. For a quarter of a century, as Forest holdings have fallen vacant, many have fallen prey to high-salaried incomers. Circumstances are often such that Forest holdings fail to pass from one generation of commoners to another. Sadly, the inheriting relatives often prefer the capital to the farm.

Land values have followed house prices, a trend fuelled mainly by the demand for horse and pony grazing, and, in the 1960s and much of the 1970s, a proliferation of riding schools, trekking centres and livery stables. Now, in the mid-1980s, fields which might form a useful part of a Forest holding are selling for as much as £4–5000 per acre (£10–12,000 per ha), or even more in some localities. There are no means of recovering this kind of capital cost, plus loan charges, from a small farm, even with the benefit of common rights. High rents present similar difficulties.

These social and economic changes have transformed the context in which common rights are exercised. The numbers of commoners turning out cattle and ponies has diminished since the 1940s according to local testimony, though there are no data to confirm this and the trend had certainly halted by the mid 1960s. However, the numbers of commoners turning out pigs on the autumn seed crop has continued to decline into the 1980s, and the exercise of turbary rights has virtually died out. Between 1920 and 1970, the number of agricultural holdings in the Forest parishes was reduced by 50%; no less than 76% of the holdings under 5 acres (2 ha) were lost (Kiff, 1970). The mixed stock-keeping economy of family-run cottage holdings and small farms is of the past. Formerly, the Forest was the pivot around which the holding was managed. Today, turning out stock on the Forest is mainly a useful management option for small farms, and a spare- or part-time occupation for a community which draws on commoning to maintain its social ties and traditions. For many commoners, running ponies on the Forest is an unbreakable habit.

The scale on which commoning has declined this century is hard to quantify. There appear to be few records of the numbers of practising commoners before the Verderers began keeping them in 1965. The number of claims to common rights in 1670 (307), 1792 (2314) and 1858 (1311, of which 1200 were allowed) does not tell us how many commoners exercised the rights. However, my

The Forest edge today, Furzey Lodge

impression from reading the Minutes of Evidence of the successive Parliamentary committees which reported on the Forest, is that in the 18th and 19th centuries, a large proportion of the rights were exercised. The main decline in the numbers of practising commoners may have begun in the 1920s, and been hastened by poor market prices for cattle and ponies in the 1930s. In 1931 the Agisters gave a return of 541 practising commoners (Hampshire Record Office 3/M/75). Kenchington (1944) estimated 1300 commoners but he presumably meant potential and practising commoners. More recent information has emerged from a study carried out on behalf of the Countryside Commission in which a questionnaire was circulated to all practising commoners and a sample were interviewed (Countryside Commission, 1984). Between 1965 and 1981 the numbers of commoners turning out stock on the crown lands varied between 290 (1966) and 385 (1976); the mean was 333. The total numbers rose slightly but not significantly during the period. Data are only available for the adjacent commons since 1972, when marking fees first became payable for stock turned out there. Subsequently, the number of practising commoners varied between 35 (1972) and 74 (1981). Here, there was a significant increase in numbers, which may not be unrelated to the fact that marking fees for ponies remain at only 50% of the level imposed within the pre-1964 perambulation, and marking fees for cattle remain at only 12.5%. The Countryside Commission study suggested that there might be about 200 commoners turning out stock continuously on a long-term basis, and a much larger pool of about 300 who move in and out of commoning. I concur that some such order of size is near the truth.

Despite the overall reduction in the number of smaller landholdings in New Forest parishes this century, mainly through

Forest edge cottages, now desirable residences

aggregation and residential development in some of the villages, there remains a substantial bank of smallholdings from which common rights may potentially be exercised. There is also a large degree of tenurial fluidity in the New Forest which means that small parcels of land are constantly changing owners or tenants. Of 379 practising commoners who returned questionnaires in 1979, 230 had less than 10 acres (4 ha); forty-seven between 11 and 20 acres (4.5–8.1 ha); twenty-one between 21 and 50 acres (8.5–20 ha); thirteen between 51 and 100 acres (20–40 ha); five between 101 and 200 acres (40–80 ha); and three over 200 acres. Many of the smaller holdings were dispersed in two or more localities. Much of the land was held on grazing licences or informal tenancies, though half or more was owned. Of the holdings under 10 acres, 139 (60%) turned out only ponies, and some of these turned out numbers far in excess of that which could be accommodated on the holding should the need arise. 'Perhaps 100' obtained a full-time living from their holdings (though from my own experience this seems very unlikely): of the seventy-five commoners interviewed, nineteen (25%) claimed to do so, and seven of these claimed to depend on holdings of less than 20 acres (8.1 ha). It was estimated that 65–80% of practising commoners in 1979 came from families with a tradition of commoning, the remainder being comparatively recently-arrived professional, managerial or retired people.

The average number of ponies and cattle turned out by each commoner remains small, though it is undoubtedly much larger than in the late 19th century. Between 1965 and 1981, an average of 8.4 ponies and 5.3 cattle, or 13.7 animals, was turned out on the crown lands by each practising commoner. On the adjacent commons, the comparable numbers were 7.2 ponies, 9.2 cattle, or 17.3 overall. The relatively higher cattle numbers evidently reflected the much smaller marking fee payable to the Verderers in respect of the commons. The wide variation masked by averages is revealed in Fig. 8, which analyses the position in 1981.

The data in the Countryside Commission study suggests that despite adverse economic and social circumstances, the New Forest

Fig. 8.
Stock Depastured on the Crown Lands in 1981

Numbers of commoners depasturing	Numbers of stock depastured							Totals	%
	1–5	6–10	11–20	21–50	51–100	101–150	151–200		
Ponies only	141	55	29	15	2	0	0	242	77.8%
Cattle only	8	3	6	6	0	0	0	23	7.4%
Cattle and ponies	9	5	13	11	6	1	1	46	14.8%
Totals	158	63	48	32	8	1	1	311	

Countryside Commission, 1984

The total numbers of ponies depastured was 2550 and the number of cattle 1139.

commoners are far from a threatened species. I believe this would be a blinkered view. The pressures of high land values, high rents and poor markets leaves the community in a more precarious state than may superficially appear. Were it purely a matter of economics, I suspect that I would now be witnessing a slide into oblivion. As it is, the exercise of common of pasture survives more because it is a way of life and a part-time occupation bound up with a feeling for the Forest and for a tradition, than because it is an economic necessity. This is not the soundest basis for survival.

The Numbers of Commonable Animals Turned Out

The grazing and browsing of the commoners' ponies and cattle is a vital element in the Forest's ecology. Changes in their numbers are a barometer of vegetation change as well as of the fortunes of their owners. At no time in the Forest's history would there seem to have been any limitation on the numbers of animals a commoner might turn out, and it is important to know what factors limit stock numbers and on what scale the Forest has been grazed at different times. One would expect numbers to fluctuate in response to changes in livestock product prices, and, indeed, there is evidence that this has been so in the 19th and 20th centuries. In addition, numbers (and the relative effect on the vegetation) would appear to have been influenced by the periodic imposition of forestal restrictions.

There is a comparatively good record of the number of stock depastured on the Forest from the late 1870s to the present time. Earlier records, however, are few and are estimates rather than an accurate census, except for the 1792 document, and this gives information for only eight of the fifteen Walks. Figures 9 and 10 depict the available information about numbers of ponies and cattle depastured on the crown lands. There are no data for the manor wastes before 1964 when they were brought within the perambulation.

In the first half of the 18th century there were depressive factors at work. There are reasons to believe that for a time at least, the

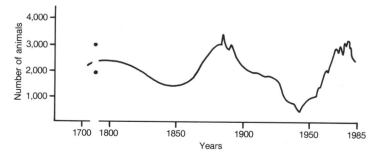

Fig. 9.
Ponies Depastured on the Crown Lands

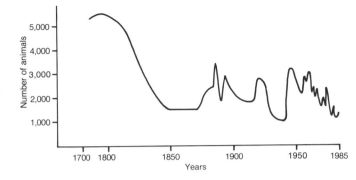

Fig. 10.
Cattle Depastured on the Crown Lands

winter heyning and other forestal restrictions were enforced. The national cattle plagues of 1714, and the 1740s and 1750s, are also likely to have depressed numbers. For the later 18th century there are indications of rising numbers of cattle and ponies, marked at the end of the century by two 1792 estimates. In the papers of the politician George Rose, whose home was at Lyndhurst, there is an estimate of 4680 cattle and 1590 ponies for thirteen of the fifteen Walks (Hampshire Record Office 2M30/669). The Keepers' returns of 1792 (Stagg, 1983b) give 2960 cattle and 1526 ponies for eight of the fifteen Walks. Assuming these to be the numbers turned out in 1792 and that the remaining Walks were stocked to the same levels, this gives 5550 cattle and 2861 ponies for the Forest as a whole. There is consistency in the cattle numbers (similar extrapolation would give a George Rose figure of 5400 cattle) but inconsistency in the pony numbers (extrapolation gives a total of 1835, or 36% fewer in the George Rose data).

The turn of the 19th century or soon after may have been a watershed beyond which stock numbers were depressed again. The diaries, notebooks and accounts of a number of Forest Keepers have survived for the years from 1845 to 1871, and they contain ample evidence that the 1819 Act providing for the removal of stock from the Forest during the winter heyning was enforced during at least parts of this period. Enforcement began earlier than 1845. In evidence to the Select Committee on the Woods, Forests and Land Revenues of the Crown, in 1848, Thomas White, the Lord Warden's Steward claimed that the 'average number' of cattle and ponies turned out was respectively 1500 and 1400, and that numbers of both had been much reduced 'in consequence of an Act passed in 1817 (sic) prevented them running in winter'. Spooner (1871) says that 'about 3000 ponies, heifers and cows' were turned out at that time, which is a similar figure to that given by the Steward twenty-three years earlier. From the late 1840s until at least 1869, the Keepers were constantly instructed by the

Steward to carry out drifts (round ups) to clear the Forest in the fence month and winter heyning. Correspondence between the Verderers and the Commissioners of Woods confirms the crown's determination to impose these forestal restrictions. Though their efforts sometimes met with mixed success ('The people about Fawley have turned out nearly all their Colts and have behaved very ill, and have given a great trouble all the past season, we must not be laughed at' complained the Steward to his Keepers in October 1846), they must have made life very difficult for the Forest edge communities.

The first stock census, instigated by the new Court of Verderers in 1878, gave 2903 ponies, 2220 cattle and 438 sheep. Pony numbers rose to a peak of 3194 in 1885 and then fell away to about 1500 in 1917. Cattle numbers held up until the 1890s and then followed pony numbers downwards to reach a low ebb around 1913–15. The high stock numbers of the late 19th century must in part represent a response to the relief afforded by the 1877 Act, but they are also consistent with the national trend towards live-stock during the agricultural depression, which was based on steeper falls in grain than in livestock produce prices.

This century has seen a succession of marked fluctuations in stock numbers which mirror market trends. During and immediately after the First World War, prices mounted rapidly and the numbers of stock followed, to peak at 4550 in 1920, after which there was a steady decline, following falling prices, until in 1940 only 571 ponies and 908 cattle were turned out (or at least, paid for – the data derives from the marking fee records). Thereafter, with rising prices for heifers and dairy produce and a new trade in horseflesh, numbers rose steadily. Pony numbers peaked at 3200 in 1978 and have declined since. Cattle peaked at 3000 in 1961 and have since fluctuated widely, with an overall downward trend.

The market for New Forest ponies has varied widely over time. In the 19th century, they found a market as working pack and saddle animals and, increasingly, in the collieries. Late in the 19th century, the breed succumbed to the Victorian enthusiasm for 'improvement', which seems to have sufficiently affected temperament and stature to have depressed the colliery market: hence the fall in numbers early this century. Light road transport continued to take the better-looking animals until the motor car became common in the 1930s. The rise in numbers during and after the Second World War was based first on the horseflesh trade and then on the burgeoning market for riding ponies which came in the wake of increasing middle-class affluence. New Forest ponies found markets in continental Europe as well as in Britain, but in the early 1970s, the riding pony market began to burn itself out. Too many of the better animals had been sold off the Forest and there were altogether too many in circulation. Prices declined after

1976 and in the late 1970s and early 1980s increasing numbers were sold, at poor prices, for slaughter.

In the circumstances it is surprising that the numbers of ponies on the Forest have not declined further. Not only have markets been poor but marking fees increased relatively steeply from £2 per animal per annum in 1975 to £10 in 1980, though it has since been held at that level. Profits are mostly marginal or nil and most commoners have other than wholly financial motives for depasturing ponies on the Forest. Most would probably claim that it was central to a way of life.

The absolute number of cattle turned out masks a trend away from dairy stock to stores since the 1950s. Today there are very few dairy herds or house cows turned out. The practice is usually to buy and sell in response to prevailing beef markets, though the margins are often low. Marking fees are, in general, likely to be of less importance than market prices in determining the numbers on the Forest, though it is noticeable that numbers on the adjacent commons (where only 12.5% of the Forest marking fee is payable) have been maintained since 1976, in contrast to an overall decline on the Forest. Similarly, numbers of ponies on the commons have levelled off since the downturn in prices, but have not actually declined as they have on the Forest. Viewed overall, however, this brief review of stock numbers and markets re-emphasizes the relatively precarious position of the commoners.

Finally, let me turn to the pig, to lament the decline in numbers turned out on the autumn seed crop. I think the New Forest remains the only locality in Britain where common of mast is still exercised, but the right has fallen victim to the socio-economic changes of recent decades. In the 19th century, 5–6000 were recorded as being turned out in good mast years. Since 1960, there have been only two years in which more than 1000 were turned out (1778 in 1962 and 1046 in 1968) and numbers have fallen progressively throughout the period (Fig. 11). As I write, the acorns

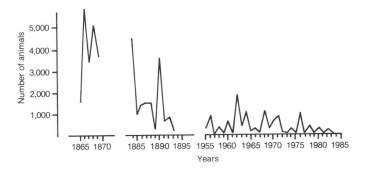

Fig. 11.
Pigs Turned Out on the Crown Lands in the Pannage Season

are as thick on the ground as I can ever recall them: yet few have though it worthwhile to turn out pigs to exploit the profligacy. Small-scale pig keeping is not worth the trouble in a climate which favours the large modern producer. Sadly, the decline of the mast rights is symptomatic of the changed circumstances of the New Forest commoner in the late 20th century.

Ponies, Cattle and Deer

Since at least medieval times, and probably long before, the New Forest has supported free-ranging domestic herbivores, besides the deer which it was the early purpose of the Forest to protect and encourage. How do these animals interact with their environment? How do they distribute themselves and what do they eat at different times of the year? How much of the annual production of their food plants do they consume and how does their grazing affect the composition and productivity of the vegetation? What limits does their environment set on their survival and productivity? These are among the questions which observation and research since the mid-1960s has set out to answer.

I have already discussed the history of pony and cattle populations insofar as it is possible to reconstruct it (chapter 7). Here, I also review information about the past number of deer and attempt to express the numbers of all the different herbivores as an index

Pony drift in progress
(Photo A. H. Pasmore)

which takes account of their various food preferences, food intakes and feeding behaviour. Such an index helps explain the age structure of populations of long-lived trees and shrubs, and assists in interpreting the composition of the Forest's vegetation as a whole.

Ponies and Cattle

I became interested in the social behaviour and ecology of the ponies and cattle on the Forest in the early 1960s. Most commoners had a good idea of the daily and seasonal movements of their animals, but there was speculation about the relative importance of different foods and it was often difficult to come to general conclusions about other aspects of the animals' ecology from the anecdotes of local people. I have remained an interested observer of the animals and the ways in which they exploit their environment. Others have carried out more ambitious studies of their social behaviour and ecology.

First, during 1965–8, Dr S. J. Tyler studied the social organization and behaviour patterns of the ponies. Stephanie Tyler's work concentrated on the pony populations of two widely-separated study areas – 780 ha of low-lying neutral grassland, deciduous woodland, glades and heath centred on Balmer Lawn, north of Brockenhurst; and 500 ha of heathland, wood and mire centred on Backley Plain re-seeded area which lies on one of the higher gravel terraces. In 1977, the NCC funded Dr R. J. Putman of Southampton University for a three-year study (1977–80) of the food and feeding behaviour of ponies and cattle in the New Forest. This study also concentrated on two study areas, one of 580 ha south-east of Lyndhurst, and another of 1200 ha west of Brockenhurst, both mainly on low-lying terrain with a wide range of habitat. The basic objective was to investigate the relationship between the animals and the vegetation, so measurement of the nutrient status, productivity and animal offtake of the different plant communities was as important to the work as the diet and movements of the animals themselves (Nature Conservancy Council, 1983).

The NCC study was part of a larger research 'package' which included the Countryside Commission socio-economic study (chapter 7) and a two-year study of the feeding behaviour and body condition changes of ponies financed by the Royal Society for the Prevention of Cruelty to Animals, and carried out by Dr J. I. Pollock (Physiological Laboratory, Cambridge University). Jon Pollock worked mainly in three areas, one at Fritham on one of the higher terraces; Stephanie Tyler's earlier Backley Plain area; and a third area on the lower terraces at Hill Top in the south-east of the Forest (Pollock, 1980).

The three studies between them covered a reasonable cross-

section of Forest habitats, so the results are probably more-or-less representative of the Forest as a whole. What is interesting, and a little chastening, is that much of the painstaking quantification has 'only' served to confirm much that has been common knowledge or opinion among commoners for generations. In some respects, too, the later two studies, by concentrating on techniques such as the repetitive recording of standard plots or transects in order to produce statistically usable data, have missed or under-recorded some aspects of behaviour which are clearly apparent to any observer familiar with the Forest and its animals. However, so long as we do not neglect the background of unquantified local knowledge, the three studies collectively provide a fascinating insight into the relationship between the commoners' animals and their environment.

Pony drift: portable pound in use at Fritham (Photo A. H. Pasmore)

Management and Social Organization

Visitors to the Forest readily accept that the cattle which they see grazing there are farm stock. In the past, most cattle depastured on the Forest were dairy herds, house cows, and their followers (mostly of a brindled Channel Island type) which came and went between feeding grounds and holding in daily peregrinations which often took them surprisingly long distances from home. Today, most cattle are stores, and with some exceptions, remain on the Forest for much of the year between purchase and sale. In some cases they may return to the holding, or close to it, for supplementary food, depending on their seasonal requirement. Less evident to the casual observer, the ponies are also individually owned and managed domestic animals.

The earliest clear descriptions of the ponies are those of Gilpin (1784) and Duncan (1840), who describe them as no more than 12–13 hands, full-bellied, slender-limbed, somewhat large-headed and long-necked. Duncan adds that their legs are short in proportion to the length of the body. Whilst deprecating their form, both writers extol their hardiness, strength and agility, and Gilpin tells us that they were then a principal commodity at local fairs, where they were purchased for 'every purpose to which a horse can be applied'. Ponies, he remarked, could represent a little fortune to a poor cottager whose mares bred tolerably handsome colts.

The breed, if there truly was one, was modified by the use of stallions of Arab and other origins in the late 18th and mid-19th centuries, and the introduction of other native pony breeds in the late 19th and early 20th centuries (Piggot, 1960; Pasmore, 1977; Russell, 1976). There has probably been a general increase in size, and the alien blood is clearly evident in individual animals, but the characteristics described by Gilpin and Duncan are still generally

The pony sale yard,
Beaulieu Road Station –
the main sale outlet
(Photo A. H. Pasmore)

apparent. Possibly the long neck and long head derive from selection pressures for efficient browsing. Similarly, perhaps, the slender limbs and light weight are adaptions to the need for agility in negotiating the mires, dense woodland and scrub of the Forest, habitats which are uncommon in the areas occupied by the other British pony breeds.

Whatever the origins of the New Forest pony population, it has been a managed resource since at least medieval times. Today, the age and sex structure of the population is grossly modified by management. There are annual drifts for branding, tail marking (to denote payment of marking fees the tail is cut to a shape which is distinctive for each Agister's district), worming and removal of colt foals and some other animals for sale. Although many brood mares spend their whole lives on the Forest, a high proportion of younger animals are removed, either at the drifts or during colt* hunts in which individual animals are hunted down by riders. A variable proportion of the population is removed during the winter and, indeed, the Verderers have powers to order off individual animals in poor condition or likely to become so. The number of stallions is small in relation to the total population. Since the 1950s or before, only about 130 (3–5% of the total) have run on the Forest in the breeding season. They are depastured free of marking fees but are supposed to achieve an acknowledged 'standard' and must be registered in the New Forest Pony Studbook. They must be moved at least every fourth year to avoid inbreeding.

Though not obvious when large numbers of ponies are assembled on a favoured grazing ground, ponies maintain close-knit social groups. Stephanie Tyler found that most groups simply comprised a mare and one or more of her offspring. Other groups consisted of two adult mares with varying numbers of offspring, and a small percentage of the ponies formed groups of three to six mares and offspring. Many mares were solitary, but this was because their foals had been killed (usually in road accidents) or removed. Changes between social units were frequent in young animals (and thus false family units could be recorded) but not generally among older mares. Young mares which left their mother's group either joined another group, became attached to a single mare, or remained solitary, to form the nucleus of a new social group. Large mare groups eventually split into smaller ones. Interestingly, both fillies and colts which left their mothers, retained a close relationship expressed in periodic 'visits home' and mutual grooming. Jon Pollock detected a similar social structure, although his sample size was much smaller (Fig. 12). Most stallions become attached to particular mare groups, but in the breeding season (May–August) they attract a number of groups into a harem herd which

*'Colts' in the Forest are young stock irrespective of sex, but 'colt hunting' extends also to the capture of older animals.

Source	Percentage of group in population			Total groups
	1 mare+ offspring	*2 mares+ offspring*	*3 or more mares+ offspring***	
Tyler (1972)*	61%	27%	12%	124
Pollock (1980)	68%	29%	4%	28

* average of three successive winters
** including false family groups

Fig. 12.
*Social Groupings of New
Forest Ponies*

at times may comprise as many as twenty to twenty-five mares. At this time they establish and defend well-defined territories.

Almost all colt foals are removed from the Forest in the first, or sometimes second, autumn. A few remain to become stallions or return to the Forest as geldings. Much smaller numbers of fillies are removed in their early years. The few colts which remain are tolerated by stallions until their third summer but not subsequently; were the sex ratio uncontrolled, bachelor groups would presumably form, much as in unmanaged horse populations studied in North America and the Camargue (Bruemmer, 1967; Wells & von Goldschmidt-Rothschild, 1979).

*Ponies at a summer
shade (Photo A. H.
Pasmore)*

Each social group has a well-defined home range, long known to commoners as its haunt or run, within which it confines all its routine activities throughout the year and to which adult mares usually remain faithful throughout their lives on the Forest. Home ranges of different groups coincide or overlap, and in Stephanie Tyler's ponies they varied in size between 82 ha and 1020 ha. The essential requirements of a home range are food, shelter, water and a 'shade'. The last requirement refers to the traditional places at which ponies and cattle assemble during warm summer days. A few shades are in woodland, but most are in the open, often on reseeded areas or lawns, and some are at roadsides where the animals will spill across the carriageway and block it to traffic. They mostly loaf and doze, standing head-to-tail, with constant tail movement. Shades are constant in exact location over decades and their main attribute is said to be relative freedom from the irritant insects in which the Forest abounds.

When all four requirements occur in close proximity, home ranges are small. At Balmer Lawn, Stephanie Tyler plotted home ranges of between 82 and 164 ha. For most groups there, the extensive lawn formed the focal grazing area; the surrounding woods provided shelter and much winter food; there was abundant water in a ditch system and pond; and there was a traditional shade. In

Winter feeding

Ponies on improved grassland, Latchmore Bottom

the extensive woodland to the north, where small clearings formed focal grazing sites, one group of ponies ranged over 330 ha, and elsewhere in the Balmer Lane study area, where heathland separated focal grazings from other requirements, home ranges were also much larger. In the Backley Plain study area, where the focal grazing area and shade was on a reseeded area on the terrace summit, and shelter, water and valley mire grazings were relatively distant, home ranges varied between 655 and 1020 ha. From my own observation, home ranges can be 5 km from end to end, especially if they are constrained by the narrow limits of linear greens among settlements, or by Inclosure fences, but most ponies do not travel that far in their daily progresses. Home ranges are deeply imprinted on the ponies, and every commoner has stories to tell of animals returning to their old haunt within a few days of release many miles distant. The mechanism by which they do so is quite unknown.

Most home ranges centre on an open grassland, such as a reseeded area or lawn, and this tends to split ponies, and also cattle, into more or less discrete populations. Few animals move between populations. An important ecological implication of this arrangement is that there is considerable local variation in grazing pressure such that it is greatest close to the grazing focus, where most home ranges overlap, and least at intermediate distances between such places.

The social organization of cattle on the Forest is grossly distorted by their management, but they appear to form social units which do not necessarily correspond in size to the herds turned out. Store cattle bought and sold in response to short term market trends tend to form smaller, less cohesive groups than well-established, structured herds. In either case, cattle, like ponies, occupy well-defined home ranges which vary in size according to similar requirements – food, shelter, water and a shade. Long-established herds, presumably with long, collective memories of the district, range more widely than others which have more tenuous links. Moreover, the former exhibit a propensity for making sudden changes in their established daily behaviour patterns, perhaps in response to locally-diminished food resources or to changes in the weather and thus the location of shelter.

Daily and Seasonal Movements

Within their home ranges, cattle and ponies follow daily patterns of movement which remain constant for long periods but show seasonal variations mainly associated with changes in food availability, the summer habit of shading and the greater need for shelter in winter. In general, most groups concentrate daily on the grassland forming the focus of their home range, arriving there from dawn through the morning, and leaving in the afternoon and evening. Stephanie Tyler found that the ponies arrived earlier and left later at natural lawns than at reseeded areas, and associated

Sussex cattle on the Forest: one of the few remaining old established herds

this with the poorer productivity of the latter. The daily movements of different groups were closely co-ordinated in summer, when they shaded together, but showed much variation in winter. The length of time spent grazing on the focal grasslands was longer in the growing season of the vegetation than in the winter when the grasslands were very bare.

Between leaving the grasslands in the afternoon and arriving there again the following morning, Stephanie Tyler's ponies grazed in valley mires, on heathland and in woodland and gorse brakes, tending to spend much of the night in the shelter of the woods and gorse. This general pattern has many variations. Notably, in July–September, up to six hours may be spent shading, individual animals leaving the shade only briefly to drink or graze. At this time, afternoon movements are often modified to include a considerable detour to drink. The colder the weather, the less pronounced the daily movements. In very low temperatures, or when the chill factor is high, many groups remain all day in the woods or the depths of the gorse, conserving energy by minimal movement. At all times of the year strong winds and heavy rain reduce the time spent in the open. There are variations on the general theme. Some groups remain in woodland throughout the year. Some spend a high proportion of their time, day and night, on roadside verges and in hedged lanes.

Cattle exhibit comparable daily and seasonal behavioural rhythms to the ponies but spend more time on the local grasslands, graze the heathlands more extensively but generally avoid the valley mires. The Southampton University study suggested that individual groups used heathland and woodland reciprocally at

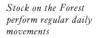

Stock on the Forest perform regular daily movements

night: on calm, and especially moonlit nights, they remained in the open, but sought the shelter of the woods in rain and high wind.

In the autumn, a proportion of the cattle are removed from the Forest and many of those which remain are fed to a variable extent with straw. Supplementary feeding greatly alters their behaviour pattern and often results in the herds concentrating on and around the feeding site for much of the day, irrespective of how much straw remains. Thus, the animals may be distracted from natural foraging and the provision of only modest amounts of straw is probably counter-productive, especially considering its often poor quality.

Feeding Strategy and Food

The effects of the different herbivores on the vegetation are related to their different feeding strategies as well as to the numbers present. Ponies are large bodied and non-ruminant and obtain nutrients by a high throughput of food which is poorly digested and includes much fibrous material. This strategy requires long periods of continuous feeding. In the Southampton University study, it was found that the New Forest ponies spent 75%–88% of their time feeding. They feed throughout the day and night, though there is a tendency to spend longer periods resting at night than in daytime. They consume much woody growth and leaves browsed from trees and shrubs, and their large upper incisors also enable them to crop very close to the ground. In contrast, cattle and deer are ruminants. They consume smaller amounts of food in relation to their size, and digest it more efficiently with the assistance of rumination. Thus, feeding periods are shorter than those of ponies. In the New Forest it was found that cattle fed for about 60% of their time in summer, and even less in winter, almost wholly in daylight, the night being spent mainly at rest and in rumination. Cattle, moreover, take less fibre than ponies, browse less, and cannot crop the ground so closely. The diet of the deer is described in a later section, but browse is important to all four species present in the Forest, though three, including the numerous Fallow Deer, are heavily dependent on grass. There are no estimates of the proportion of their time they spend feeding but it is probably around 50% or less, mostly at night.

The main ecological implications of these feeding strategies is that individual ponies make greater demands on the vegetation than individual cattle or deer. Not only are they larger animals but they require larger amounts of food per unit weight and take a wider range of food plants. Moreover, they are able to crop the sward more efficiently than either cattle or deer. Among the herbivores the ponies thus play a dominant role in the ecosystem.

The amount of time spent by ponies and cattle on the main

Browsed holly – the cone shape is characteristic, a leading shoot eventually escaping upwards

vegetation types comprising the unenclosed Forest is depicted in Figs. 13 and 14, which are derived from the Southampton University study. In general this reflects the relative importance of each type of vegetation in the diet, though food was not the sole determinant of animal distribution. While the wet heaths and mires were used exclusively for feeding, gorse brakes and woodland were of great importance as shelter, while from about mid–June to early September, the animals were shading for much of the time spent on the neutral grasslands. So although both ponies and cattle occurred on neutral grasslands in more than 50% of observations for most of the year, the contribution these areas made to the total food intake was much less than that. Wet heaths and mires were especially important food sources for ponies. Heathland was a more

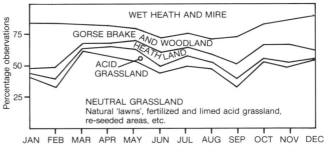

Fig. 13.
The Use of Different Vegetation Types by New Forest Ponies

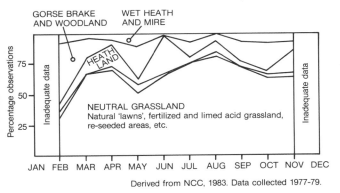

GORSE BRAKE
AND WOODLAND

WET HEATH
AND MIRE

HEATHLAND

Inadequate data

NEUTRAL GRASSLAND
Natural 'lawns', fertilized and limed acid grassland,
re-seeded areas, etc.

Inadequate data

Percentage observations

75

50

25

JAN FEB MAR APR MAY JUN JUL AUG SEP OCT NOV DEC

Derived from NCC, 1983. Data collected 1977-79.

Fig. 14.
*The Use of Different
Vegetation Types by
Cattle*

important food source for cattle than ponies, and is certainly more
important to cattle in the Forest as a whole than the results from
the study areas suggested. The same is true of acid grasslands,
which were not well represented in the study areas. The data are
probably also biased towards the more easily-observed groups of
animals which spend a high proportion of their time in the open.
Thus the importance of the gorse brakes and woodlands into which
so many ponies simply vanish in winter has been largely missed.

Figs. 15 and 16 (also from the Southampton University work)
depict the seasonal diet of ponies and cattle revealed by dung
analysis. Cattle diet showed no dramatic changes through the year.
The amount of grass eaten varied from about 65% in mid-winter
to 80% in mid-summer, though this included supplementary straw,
which was not distinguished in the analyses. The grass was derived
not only from the favoured neutral grasslands but from heathland,
acid grassland and heath. Heather formed 20% or more of the

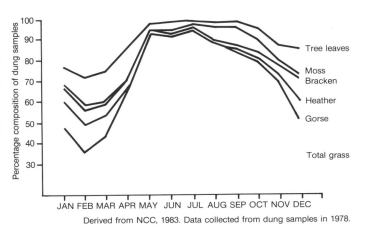

Percentage composition of dung samples

100
90
80
70
60
50
40
30

Tree leaves

Moss
Bracken

Heather

Gorse

Total grass

JAN FEB MAR APR MAY JUN JUL AUG SEP OCT NOV DEC

Derived from NCC, 1983. Data collected from dung samples in 1978.

Fig. 15.
The Ponies' Annual Diet

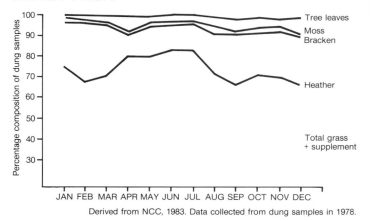

Fig. 16.
*The Annual Diet of
Cattle*

Derived from NCC, 1983. Data collected from dung samples in 1978.

diet in winter and 10% in summer, which I believe generally under-represents the importance of heather to cattle in the Forest. Similarly, tree and shrub leaves and seedlings, brambles, wild rose species and other browse do not appear in the analyses, though cattle take these foods extensively in woodlands, and wood edges and along the lanes. Show a cow a good mixed hedge!

The dietary pattern of the ponies showed a more definite seasonal pattern. In May, June and July, grass comprised more than 90% of the diet, derived from wet heaths and valley mires as well as the neutral grasslands. After August, the grass percentage declined to less than 40% in February, before starting to rise again. It was replaced between September and May by gorse, tree leaves and twigs (notably holly), moss, heather and (in August–September) surprising quantities of bracken fronds.

Comparison of the production of different kinds of vegetation with the amounts removed by ponies, cattle and deer together, is illuminating (Fig. 17). Data collected during the Southampton University study in 1978–9 showed that most of the annual production of the vegetation was removed during the growing season. An astonishing 94% was removed from re-seeded areas, and the proportion was little less for acid grasslands and mires. Important sources of forage remaining at the end of the growing season included rushes (which have a high food value), bramble leaves, and purple moor grass (though the last is deciduous, and the dead straw in midwinter is practically useless as forage).

The summer offtake figures must be used with caution because the study was carried out during dry, dessicating summers when grass growth was poor except in the mires. The percentage offtake in the growing season will be smaller in wetter summers with better production on the drier sites, and, of course, when (as in the mid-

| | **Growing season** | | |
Vegetation	Production (tonnes/ha)	Offtake (tonnes/ha)	Offtake as % production
Re-seeded areas	2.14	2.04	94
Limed/fertilized acid grassland	3.18	2.72	86
Stream-side lawns	4.76	3.14	66
Acid grassland	1.53	1.31	91
Valley mire (all vegetation)	4.47	3.99	89
Purple moor grass			
on heathland	2.19	1.05	48
in valley mire	4.81	3.52	73
Rushes	11.89	8.53	72
Bramble leaves	3.09	0.75	24

Nature Conservancy Council (1983).
All data are for 1979 except for the valley mire site, which is for 1978; purple moor grass and rushes are calculated as though they were at 100% cover; and bramble was measured by surface of bush rather than unit area of ground.

Fig. 17.
Vegetation Removed by Herbivores by the end of the Growing Season

1980s) herbivore numbers are below the very high levels of 1978–9 (Figs. 9, 10 and 20).

Let us follow the year through. Summer is a time of plenty, and the animals accumulate fat reserves which they can mobilize during winter and early spring when least forage is available and temperatures are lowest. To the ponies in particular, the wet heaths and mires may be nearly as important a source of grass (mainly purple moor grass) as the neutral grasslands, besides providing a range of other food plants among which jointed, sharp-flowered and bulbous rushes are particularly important. Some pony groups are heavily dependent on grass and other herbs found in woodland clearings and glades. Browse is least important at this time, though ponies and cattle take quantities of green leaves, twigs, bramble and other climbers and shrubs: it is a puzzle to know how these foods were missed in the faecal analyses.

As the summer wears into autumn, so the animals turn increasingly to the acid grasslands dominated by bristle bent (*Agrostis curtisii*) and purple moor grass. The former species is relatively unpalatable, but in September, October and November, most of the summer production is removed. Concurrently, browse becomes increasingly important and the cattle take increasing amounts of heather, which is selectively removed from the community – neither cross-leaved heath (*Erica tetralix*) nor bell heather (*E. cinerea*) appear to be palatable to cattle, ponies or deer. Then, and throughout the winter and early spring, the ponies selectively graze dwarf gorse (*Ulex minor*) from the same dry heath community. The autumn pattern of feeding is grossly modified by an abundant seed harvest. Then, ponies and cattle will concentrate on the acorn crop almost to the exclusion of other foods including most other fruit – crab apples can lie thick and unheeded beneath the trees, and I have never seen berries taken.

By December, the ponies are turning to their staple winter foods – gorse, holly leaves, twigs, and tree leaves, and moss 'hoovered' from the woodland floor. All the small twigs of fallen trees are eaten, as indeed would be the foliage in summer – a habit which occasionally results in an animal becoming trapped in the prostrate canopy. Fig. 15 shows an increase of browse in the winter diet but the collective wisdom of commoners, and my own observations, suggest that the analysis grossly under-represents its importance. During December–March most ponies are probably heavily dependent on just two foods – gorse and holly – and cattle are similarly dependent on heather.

In mid and late winter, the ponies conserve energy by restricting movement. Many remain deep in the woods and gorse brakes: the depths of the gorse are both food and stable at this time and the gorse brakes are a vital element in the survival strategy of the animals. Gilpin (1791), and some later writers, say that the ponies crushed the gorse with their forefeet to make it more palatable. If

Hedges are well trimmed in the Forest

1. △

2. △

3.
◁

4. ▽

1. Ridley Wood from the edge of Berry Wood, January 1982

2., 3. & 4. Butterflies like the white admiral (2. & 3.) and the silver-washed fritillary were once common in the forests, but are now reduced almost to rarity/ chapter 11 (*Photos: 2. F. V. Blackburn; 3. Paul Sterry; 4. Anthony Wharton; Nature Photographers*)

5. △   6. ▽

5. Pasture woodland, Eyeworth Wood, October 1984. Fallen timber is as important a biological resource as the standing trees/chapter 9

6. Woodland in retreat; relict hollies after fire, Acres Down, March 1982/ chapter 4 *et seq.*

7. The New Forest is one of the few places where the magnificent stag beetle remains common /chapter 9 (*Photo: Paul Sterry, Nature Photographers*)

7. △

8. The New Forest Cicada – the Forest woods support the only known population of British cicadas/chapter 9 (*Photo: Paul Sterry, Nature Photographers*)

9. The Southern damselfly – a national rarity, with many colonies in the New Forest/chapter 14 (*Photo: Bob Gibbons*)

8. △   9. ▽

10. △

11. ▽

10. Amberwood Inclosure, December 1985: a 19th-century oak plantation with little shrub layer/chapter 11

11. The pannage season, December 1984/chapters 7, 8

12. Dockens Water, Queen North Wood, November 1983

13. Marsh gentian in tussock heath/chapter 12 (*Photo: Robin Fletcher*)

14. The wild gladiolus – confined in Britain to the New Forest/chapter 12 (*Photo: S. B. Chapman*)

12. △

13. ▽ 14. ▽

15. △

16. ▽

17. △ 18. ▽

15. Alderhill Bottom, Amberwood Inclosure beyond, October 1980/chapters 1, 2

16. Balmer Lawn 'hummock-scape' derived from tussock-heath, November 1982/chapters 12, 13

17. New Forest mare browsing gorse; there is little to eat on the adjoining reseeded area/chapter 8

18. Unenclosed oakwood: Frame Wood/chapter 9

19. △

20. ▽

Browse line on isolated yew

they did so then, they do not now: certainly, they appear to treat it gingerly (as they do holly) and as far as I can tell (and I have watched the process often) they try to lay the spines along the tongue both in biting sprays from the bushes and in mastication. They are not always successful.

Inevitably, the animals lose weight in winter, and for this reason, relatively few cattle are left out. Extreme weight loss in ponies is usually due to heavy loads of internal parasites or poor adaptation to Forest conditions, or both. There have been times when such animals were common in early spring and gave rise to understandable public protests. However, most of the periodic criticism of pony condition is poorly-informed, and in general, weight loss is probably no more or less than is to be expected in a population of free-ranging herbivores relying on a strategy of accumulated energy reserves and lowered winter food intake. Low productivity may be a further necessary environmental adaptation. Most New Forest mares produce a foal only once in every two or three years (Pollock, 1980).

Spring is the critical time. If it is late and cold, the animals can be in trouble. The timing of the first flush of grass is vitally important, if not always to survival, certainly to successful foaling. It comes first on the streamside lawns and then in the valley mires, occasionally late in April, more often in May. After that the other

Colour plates opposite:

19. The wooded catchment of the Lymington River, from Acres Down, March 1982/ chapters 1, 2

20. The hobby – one of the few lowland heath birds that isn't under threat in the New Forest/chapter 14 (*Photo: F. V. Blackburn, Nature Photographers*)

In the early spring the Forest floor provides scant forage

grasslands begin to flush, the animals begin to gain a little weight and the yearly cycle is complete.

The Deer Population

Medieval documents bear ample testimony to the conservation and exploitation of New Forest deer. The court rolls record offences against the venison; there are references which suggest culling to supply meat for court and military; and it is evident that by the 17th century the animals were sustained by winter feeding. There is no particular evidence that the deer were shot (with arrows), and other medieval forestal sources suggest that most catches were made by driving deer into nets. I suspect the ultimate sophistication in medieval deer-catching can be detected in the wasted, but massive, surviving boundary banks and ditches of Lyndhurst Old Park in the New Forest.

The Old Park was first mentioned in 1291 but was not then new. By 1300 it had been extended from about 146 ha to about 200 ha. It was disparked sometime between 1490 and 1597. Its shape is probably unique among medieval deer parks and closely resembles that of the Heligoland traps employed at bird observatories (Fig. 18). From the wide end it narrows and curves in an angular half circle into a long funnel. There is no evidence that the wide end was originally closed by a bank and ditch and I speculate that the deer were drifted gradually into the park and eventually into the funnel to be netted, or if it was a sport day, shot. The calendar of Patent Rolls for 1428 nearly confirms this idea when it tells us of

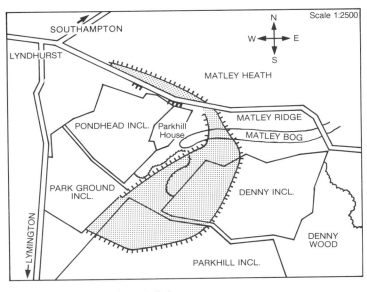

Fig. 18.
Lyndhurst Old Park

⊔⊔⊔⊔⊔⊔ Park bank and internal ditch

the Old Park that 'it was wont to afford excellent sport when the king came there and it was most convenient to be appointed for a drift to be made there every year'.

Red and fallow deer are referred to in the medieval documents but the latter were clearly the most numerous by the 13th century. I have found no medieval references to roe deer in the New Forest,

The New Forest fallow deer are thought to be descendants of those originally introduced by the Normans, and unlike English park herds undergo a consistent annual colour change (Photo Michael Leach, Nature Photographers)

Lyndhurst Old Park bank

but the species seems to have been rare in England by the 13th century and probably extinct by the end of the 14th century. Roe reappeared in the late 19th century, presumably deriving from re-introduction elsewhere. Sika deer were introduced in the 20th century.

Information about past numbers of fallow deer is collected in Fig. 19. The earliest census is for 1670 when the Regarders made a return of 7593 fallow deer and 375 red deer (Lascelles, 1915; Insley & Clarke, 1975). The 18th- and 19th-century data derive from the Commissioners report of 1789, Office of Woods annual reports and

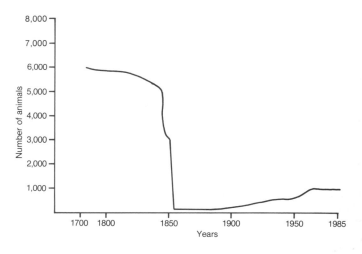

Fig. 19.
Fallow Deer Populations 1669–1984

the reports of successive Parliamentary Committees on the Forest. The graph shows a dramatic decline after 1839 and a crash after the *Deer Removal Act 1851*. Within a few years few deer remained, though many sought refuge on neighbouring estates on some of which they were tolerated. Once the money allocated to extermination dried up, numbers began slowly to rise again and by 1900 they were estimated at about 200 (Lascelles, 1915). The subsequent rate of increase was suppressed by culling, but numbers increased gradually to roughly 1000 in the 1950s. It has since been held at about that level by an annual shooting plan based on census' at the end of each winter (Whitehead, 1964; Insley & Clarke, 1975).

Kenchington (1944) suggested that before numbers were reduced in the 19th century the fallow deer population may have fluctuated between 8–9000 and 13–14,000 according to the incidence of severe winters. The latter figures seem highly unlikely, but the former are close to the 1670 census and may represent the periodic upper limit of numbers in the old deer forest. It is doubtful if this could have been achieved without supplementary feeding.

For at least three centuries before 1851 it was the practice to 'harbour' the deer around the Keepers' Lodges, where they were fed hay and browse cut from trees and shrubs, especially holly in winter. Eyre (1871) vividly described the feeding of the fallow deer in the evenings at Bramblehill Lodge in the 1840s, just before the deer forest was lost forever. As in other royal forests, artificial feeding resulted in overstocking and periodic dramatic winter mortality. The Commissioners' report of 1789 claimed that in just two of the Forest Walks, 500 deer died in the severe winter of 1878–9, and that 'the Forest is so much overstocked with deer that many die yearly, of want, in the winter'. If it was overstocked at 5900, how much more overstocked had it been in 1670 at 7593?

Fallow deer remains are absent from pre-medieval archaeological contexts, though the species was present in Britain in the last interglacial period. It is generally considered to have been reintroduced by the Normans, though I know of no unequivocal contemporary documentation and introductions have occurred since. The New Forest fallow deer are thought to be the descendants of the 'original' reintroduction. Their pelage is distinctive in that unlike English park herds they undergo a consistent annual colour change. In summer the pelage is chestnut with white spots, but in October changes to dark grey, or mulberry. Both coats provide excellent camouflage, especially the summer coat, in the dappled sunlight of woodland or among the deep bracken where many does have their fawns, while the winter coat is a remarkably close match to the dun colours of the Forest at that season. White animals are relatively numerous and both menil and black forms occur: all are probably derived from park stock which found their way to the Forest this century.

The red deer population has been small for at least 400 years and has been sustained by periodic introductions. The 1670 figure of 357 may or may not have included about sixty stags imported from France to the Forest in that year (Insley & Clarke, 1975). In the 19th century, numbers given in contemporary Keepers' notebooks and diaries suggest a population of 100 or less. How many of these were killed after 1851 is not known. A small population seems to have persisted in the south of the Forest since the late 19th century, supplemented by at least three introductions, and today centred on the woods south of Brockenhurst. A second population was established when in 1962, a three-year old stag, six hinds and five calves were released from Old House, north of Burley. A further stag was released in 1973. In the 1980s, this group has numbered sixty to seventy animals which collectively occupy a broad, central belt of the Forest including the main blocks of Inclosures and the surrounding heaths. Concurrently, a small herd of unknown origin has become established immediately north of the Forest and sometimes penetrates south.

Roe do not appear to have become firmly re-established until the 1920s. They then increased steadily to around 300 in 1961. Subsequent annual Forestry Commission census' showed a steady increase to 620 in 1970, followed by a steady decline to 264 in 1984. The early part of the decline, to 435 in 1973, was at least partly the result of a reduction policy, but after that the cull was greatly reduced and the decline was probably the result of significant habitat changes in the Inclosures (chapter 11) (Lascelles, 1915; Whitehead, 1964; Forestry Commission, unpublished).

The present population of sika deer are said to derive from two pairs released on the Beaulieu estate in 1904 and 1905. By the 1920s they were widespread on the estate and in the neighbouring Forest as far north as the main London-Dorchester railway line, beyond which they have never become established. Numbers were severely reduced in the 1930s, and again in the 1960s; by the mid-1970s the population was being controlled at about seventy animals (Insley & Clarke, 1975). This has since increased to 150 or more.

Deer Food and Feeding Behaviour

The annual diet of roe deer and fallow deer in the New Forest was determined by John Jackson from the analysis of the rumen contents of culled animals and road accident victims between November 1970 and March 1973 (Jackson, 1977a; 1977b). The diet of fallow deer (325 animals) was dominated by grasses, which comprised more than 50% of food from March to September and more than 20% in the remaining months; that of roe (105 animals) was dominated by bramble and rose, which formed 30–40% of the diet year-round, peaking in December. Three main phases in the annual diet of the fallow deer could be distinguished. From about March to September, grasses were the main food, with other herbs and broadleaf tree and shrub leaves and twigs also forming important foods. In October, the amounts of grass consumed declined as the animals turned to the autumn seed harvest, concentrating especially on acorns in years when they were abundant. Bramble and rose also became significant in autumn and there was a gradual shift to a varied winter diet dominated by browse – bramble, rose, heather, bilberry, holly, ivy, dead leaves, bark and conifer foliage. During this period the deer evidently mobilized fat reserves, and by late February they were in poor physical condition. However, fallow deer are able to pick up condition again earlier than the ponies because they feed extensively on farmland where the first flush of grass is earlier than on the Forest.

Roe showed no such definite dietary cycle. Bramble and rose dominated throughout the year. The winter and early spring diet included large proportions of conifer foliage, heather, and ivy, with small amounts of grasses, herbs and fungi. From May until the autumn, grasses and herbs became increasingly important and in August, collectively accounted for 25% of the diet. The new, tender growth of broadleaf trees and shrubs, holly and bilberry were also important. In the autumn, like the fallow deer, the roe concentrate on the seed harvest, especially acorns, though these did not account for more than 15% of the diet in a succession of autumns in which the crop was abundant (Jackson, 1980).

Though the range of plants eaten by fallow and roe deer was wide, they largely avoided some dominant New Forest vegetation. Like ponies and cattle, they avoided cross-leaved heath and bell heather in the heathland plant community, and bog myrtle (*Myrica gale*) which is abundant in the Forest wetlands. Unlike the ponies but in common with cattle, they seldom took gorse; and in contrast to ponies and cattle, they seldom ate bristle bent or purple moor grass, preferring the finer grasses of the neutral grasslands and farmland. Bracken was seldom recorded in the analyses (Jackson, 1977a; 1980).

There are no comparable published data on the diet of red or sika deer in the New Forest, but it would appear to resemble that of fallow deer much more closely than that of roe. Thus, to summarize, three of the four species present are mainly grazing animals to whom browse is important, especially in winter; and the roe is mainly a browsing animal which consumes grass in summer.

Roe are usually solitary or in groups of male, female and young. The three grazing species tend to form larger groups with females, young and immature males usually segregated from mature males except in the rut. However, from recent work on fallow deer in the New Forest by N. A. Rand (unpublished) it seems that the groups are less coherent than first appearances suggest and that the basic units of social organization are the doe and fawn and the buck, each occupying a well-defined and comparatively small home range which is shared with or overlaps that of many other deer. This arrangement becomes modified in the rut, when male deer establish and defend territories to which they attract females.

The composition of groups is constantly changing, though at any one time a buck or doe will accompany others of the same species and sex. The home range of each animal includes extensive cover with abundant browse, and one or more areas of higher quality grassland. Deer tend to spend most of the day at rest or feeding spasmodically in small groups in the woods, gorse brakes or other cover, and to make their way to open grazing grounds towards dusk, joining other groups as they go. On some sites, large herds assemble at dusk, returning to cover early the following morning unless the site is particularly undisturbed. Favoured crepuscular or nocturnal feeding places include the reseeded areas, natural lawns and Inclosure rides, and importantly, pasture on farmland. In a few places (notably Boldrewood Farm, where there is a public hide made irrelevant by the tameness of the animals) the deer are tolerated or encouraged on Forest edge holdings, but they are mostly unwanted guests especially on new leys and cereals, and many pay the inevitable penalty. However, though difficult to measure, it is probable that a high percentage of the grass in the diet of red, sika and fallow deer in the New Forest, especially in spring, is derived from farmland. Roe depend much less on farmland. The sika probably depend on it most; it is possible to count nearly the whole Forest population in the space of an hour or two as they return on a narrow front from farmland into the Forest Inclosures where they disperse in groups for the day.

Grazing and Browsing Pressure

Numbers of commoners' animals and fallow deer are shown in Figs. 9, 10 and 19, but these, even if numerically combined, cannot wholly reflect the pressure on the vegetation. First, the diet, size and feeding strategies of ponies, cattle and deer are different. Second, the area available to the deer has always been larger than that of the other herbivores, because the deer have ranged over farmland and fenced Inclosures as well as the unenclosed lands. Moreover, the area available to commoners' stock has been further reduced since 1964 with the gridding and fencing of the perambulation and main roads. Thirdly, commonable stock have not necessarily been on the Forest for the whole year. Fewer animals (especially cattle) have been out in winter than in summer and between 1819 and 1877, the fence month and winter heyning was enforced to at least some effect. Finally, before 1851, the deer population was sustained by supplementary feeding.

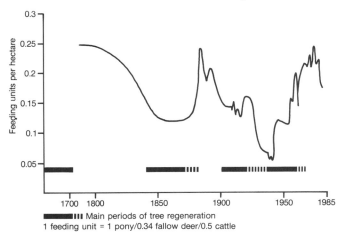

Fig. 20.
*Grazing and Browsing
Pressure, and Tree
Regeneration Phases*

Fig. 20 attempts to overcome some of the problems. Numbers of animals have been converted to feeding units where 1 feeding unit = 1 pony = 0.5 cattle = 0.34 fallow deer. This is based on an ultimately subjective judgement of the differences in diet, size and feeding strategy. The resulting figures have then been adjusted to reflect the different area available to deer and stock at different times, though it does not take into account the closure of the perambulation after 1964. In my earlier book on the Forest (Tubbs, 1969) I attempted a similar exercise in which 1 pony = 5 feeding units: 1 fallow deer = 3 feeding units; and 1 cattle = 1 feeding unit. The curves of the two graphs are not very different, but I have learnt much since the 1960s and believe the conversion used to produce Fig. 20 is more accurate. It does not accommodate the supplementary feeding of the deer before 1851; the exclusion of stock from the Forest in the fence month and winter heyning before 1877; or the confinement of stock within the perambulation after 1964. Taking the first two of these factors into account, it is likely that grazing and browsing pressure before 1877 would in effect be lower than the graph suggests. Since 1964 the effective index must be higher than the graph suggests, because of the more limited area available to stock. The modest numbers of red, sika and roe deer, which have not been incorporated into Fig. 20, must also have contributed to this.

The general conclusions to be drawn from Fig. 20 are that the impact of the large herbivores on the vegetation was high before 1800, diminished to a low point in mid-century, rose steeply to a high towards the end of the century, fell again, recovered somewhat during and after the First World War, fell to all-time low in the 1930s, rose to another peak in the late 1970s, and in the mid-1980s is declining again.

CHAPTER 9

The Ancient Woodland

The 3671 ha of unenclosed woodland in the New Forest, called
'Ancient and Ornamental' in the 1877 Act and so known today,
have all the classic characteristics of ancient pasture woodland.
Many of the trees have been permitted to live their natural life span
and there is an abundance of old, senile and decaying trees which
support an exceptionally rich fauna of beetles, flies, and other insects
which spend part or all of their life cycles in dead wood. Hole- and

*The beechwoods in places
spread onto the plateau
gravels (Bratley Plain
adjoining Slufters
Inclosure)*

crevice-nesting, insectivorous birds, are particularly numerous. There is a wealth of epiphytic lichens and mosses associated especially with the older trees. Ecological diversity is enhanced by the variety of growth forms, which reflect the diversity of local circumstances in which the trees arose. The herb and shrub layers, however, are impoverished of all except the least palatable species because of the long sustained grazing of deer and stock. The woods are therefore poor in insects which require low cover or which feed on nectar. Most of these characteristics are shared by 285 ha or more of former pasture woodland which became trapped behind the fences of 18th and 19th-century Inclosures.

Now, as in medieval times, and probably long before, the woods are grazed by cattle, ponies and deer, and pigs are turned out on the mast. In the past, pollarding and shrouding were common practices in the woods, and the timber suffered such vicissitudes of exploitation that it is sometimes a wonder the woods survived.

The ecology and history of the woods was first studied by George Peterken and myself in the 1960s (Peterken & Tubbs, 1965; Tubbs, 1968), and in the 1970s by Small & Hackett (1972) and Nicholas Flower (Flower, 1977, 1980a, 1980b, 1983), with whom I collaborated in preparing conservation management policies (Flower & Tubbs, 1982). I have attempted here to synthesize these studies, together with unpublished data of my own, into a brief account of the ecology of the woods.

General Characteristics of the Woods

The unenclosed woods extend across the Forest area in a discontinuous mosaic. Tracts of uninterrupted canopy alternate with abundant glades, clearings and wet flushes, and belts of mixed riverine woodland or alder carr follow the drainage system. In most of the woodland there is reasonably abundant surface water and there are networks of gutters and runnels everywhere. Humidity within the woods is noticeably high year-round. The composition of the woods is summarized in Fig. 21 and their distribution is shown in Fig. 2.

The woods are dominantly beech and oak (mostly *Q. robur* but sometimes *Q. petraea*, and often a bewildering range of intermediate forms), with a shrub layer mainly of holly. Beech-dominant woods tend to occur on free-draining, often degraded or podsolic soils, and are a consistent feature of sandy knolls and the edges of the gravel terraces. Oakwoods and mixed oak-beech woods tend to occur on more slowly permeable soils and on the less impoverished parent material. There is a sharp contrast between the acid mor humus beneath most beechwoods and the rich mull humus beneath most pure oakwoods.

Besides beech and oak, small numbers of birch, ash, yew (*Taxus*

Fig. 21.
*The Composition of the
Unenclosed Pasture
Woods*

Stand type	hectares
>90% oak, 0–10% beech in canopy; ash local, some birch, occasional yew; holly shrub layer	637
50–90% oak, beech sub-dominant; ash local, some birch, occasional yew; holly shrub layer	834
>90% beech, 0–10% oak in canopy; holly shrub layer	488
50–90% beech, oak sub-dominant, yew occasional, ash rare; holly shrub layer	1048
birch, oak, some Scots pine (up to 150 years old)	338
Holly 'holms', sometimes with oak 'core'	174
alder carr	152
TOTAL	3671

*The moss carpet beneath
beeches*

Derived from Flower and Tubbs (1982) and subsequent information.
Note: this table excludes approximately 285 ha of former pasture woodland which survives behind the fences of Silvicultural Inclosures.

baccata), field maple (*Acer campestre*), crab, and rowan occur, but seldom form a significant proportion of the canopy. Crab (*Malus sylvestris*) and rowan (*Sorbus aucuparia*) are confined mainly to wood edges, glades and clearings. Ash occasionally forms as much as 10% of the canopy and exceeds that level in some riverine localities. Field maple is a major constituent of part of Brinken Wood (SU282052). In a few places (e.g., Pinnick Wood SU193078 and Brinken Wood SU285052) hawthorns (*Crataegus monogyna*) are more abundant than hollies in the shrub layer. Other widespread but never abundant shrub layer species include alder buckthorn (*Frangula alnus*), guelder rose (*Viburnum opulus*), sallow (*Salix einerea*), blackthorn, bramble, field rose (*Rosa arvensis*), dog rose (*R. canina*) and honeysuckle (*Lonicera pericymenum*). Ivy is common but occurs (like honeysuckle) on less than 10% of trees, though a notable feature of the woods is the relatively frequent occurrence of very old ivy stems, which sometimes achieve a girth of 0.5 m or more.

The riverine woods, on enriched alluvial soils which are often winter-flooded, are normally oak–holly dominated, but ash trees are numerous and the shrub layer is often species-rich and (for Forest conditions) prolific, with blackthorn thickets and abundant climbers. Alder is common along streamsides and forms linear carr where peat replaces alluvium, to be replaced in turn by sallow carr in the less-enriched upper reaches of drainage systems. Most alder

Self-sown Scots pine on the open Forest, Sandy Ridge

carr have been coppiced. Curiously, holly is abundant in many of the less frequently flooded carr, forming a community with the alder which is rare in Britain. In the wider carr, holly tends to occur mainly at the margins and in this situation it can be a component of a mixed woodland dominated by alder, holly, birch, ash and oak. This forms a discontinuous zone in which the number and abundance of species other than alder increase laterally to the carr axis.

Birch, oak, scots pine and holly are the usual pioneer trees in the New Forest. Birch, or birch–oak, readily infills clearings and spreads outwards from woodland and margins when herbivore numbers are low. Birch, and often oak and holly, are also nursed and protected by gorse brakes on the heaths and if they do not succumb to the fire which usually destroys the gorse, they ultimately survive as isolated tree clumps. Scots pine, which is little-eaten by herbivores, is widespread on the heathlands (from which it is periodically cleared) and is often common in a matrix of colonizing birch in glades and clearings.

Locally, holly is a heathland invader. It can form dense monospecific stands which often assume a roughly circular shape and are known locally as 'holms' or, formerly, 'hats'. Often the holms include abundant whitebeam (*Sorbus aria*) (indeed, this is nearly confined to holly holms in the Forest), rowan, yew and sometimes a central group of oaks which eventually spread their crowns over the holly canopy. Holly holms are a characteristic feature of the Forest and occur widely on the better-drained parts of terrace edges and sides.

Andrew's Mare, a characteristic New Forest holly holm

Several generations of trees are distinguishable in the pasture woods but a consistent feature is the large number of trees over

250 years old – including many beech, and a much smaller number of oak at or near the end of their lives, and thought to be of pre-1650 origin. Besides the age of the oldest trees, there are several pointers to long continuity of woodland on most sites which support mature woodland today. Among the most convincing, is that brown forest soils are common beneath pasture woodland in the Forest on parent materials similar to those which have developed podsols beneath acid grassland and heath following forest clearance (Dimbleby, 1962). Acid grasslands often exhibit intermediate states of degeneration today (chapter 12). The persistence of the little-leached soils beneath woodland argues for its continuity of cover presumably since the Atlantic period or earlier.

Not all Forest woodland soils are so little modified. Oak, beech, holly and birch are all capable of colonizing very degraded soils in the New Forest, and woodland of these species may thus be secondary. However, some soils may have degraded beneath deciduous woodland as a result of some past combination of circumstances which tipped the balance between the supply of nutrients to the soil from trees and rain, and the natural process of leaching in especially acid parent material. There is a close association between beechwoods and podsols in various stages of development. Some beechwood soils exhibit a 'micropodsol', in which there are successive bleached and dark brown enriched layers at the top of the mineral soil in an otherwise argillic (clayey) brown earth. This association of beechwoods with podsols cannot be coincidental, and the raw, acid litter produced by beech on base-poor soils may be responsible. If so, podsolisation beneath the beechwoods may be a comparatively recent phenomenon, for beech has only achieved its present level of representation in the Forest in recent centuries. In sum, an unleached or little-leached brown soil beneath woodland in the Forest is probably a good indicator of ecological stability and woodland continuity; but a leached, perhaps podsolic soil is not necessarily an indicator of woodland retreat and recolonisation.

A further indication of the antiquity of the woods is the persistence of a remarkably rich flora of epiphytic lichens. Old-forest lichen communities generally and many species individually, have relict distributions and appear incapable of colonizing new woods which arise in the wake of felling under today's conditions of discontinuous forest. They persist only in comparatively few places where, as in the New Forest, there has been continuity of woodland habitat from one generation of trees to the next. Similarly, the rich invertebrate fauna of dead wood in the Forest is a strong indication of long-term habitat continuity. Many species are not adapted to wide dispersal. Moreover, in the absence of a continual supply of dead wood, which in turn requires that a high proportion of trees are permitted their natural span, they would not survive. The dead wood invertebrates, like the Forest woods themselves, appear to be relics of the primaeval woodland ecosystem.

Several writers have suggested that certain herbaceous plants are indicators of ancient woodland because they have poor powers of dispersal. Peterken (1974) listed such indicator species, but few occur in pasture woods because the ground flora has usually been impoverished by grazing. However, Flower (1980a) regarded the occurrence of butcher's broom (*Ruscus aculeatus*), wood spurge (*Euphorbia amygdaloides*), wood anemone (*Anemone nemorosa*) and dog violet (*Viola riviniana*) in association with undisturbed brown earths and a mull humus, as indicative of woodland continuity in the New Forest. What is interesting is that the various indications of ancient woodland – an unleached brown soil, a mull humus, a rich epiphytic lichen flora, a rich dead wood fauna and the occurrence of abundant butcher's broom and wood spurge (*Ruscus* and *Euphorbia*), tend to occur together, notably in most woods where a generation of old trees, especially oak, is well represented. This cannot be coincidence and lends support to the notion that such woodland has a long pedigree.

Woodland Dominants and their Palatability

As late as Saxon and perhaps early medieval times (say 700–1100) the woods were mainly of oak and hazel, with alder well represented, probably mainly in linear carr along watercourses. However, the woods also included birch, holly, beech, often lime and probably very locally, elm and hornbeam (chapter 4). Since then, hazel has been replaced by holly as the dominant shrub; beech has become as important as oak; elm and lime have become extinct, and hornbeam nearly so. Scots pine has also become common since its reintroduction in the early 19th century (chapter 11).

Lime, elm and hazel are consistently absent from pasture woods in Britain. Their common characteristic is their palatability to stock – the bark and leaves of elm and lime were once widely used in Europe as fodder. Their absence from pasture woods is most likely the result of preferential browsing by domestic herbivores, and in forests by the deer, since land use and settlement stabilized in Saxon times. Progressive decalcification of the base-poor soils may have contributed to the demise of calcicoles like lime and elm.

Hazel forms 20% or more of the pollen in the New Forest's premedieval buried soils, but this falls to 5–10% in medieval soils, and lower still in modern surfaces. By the 16th century, it was probably only abundant in the Forest in coppices where it was protected against herbivores, and the end of the coppice system probably signalled that of the remaining hazel (chapter 10). Hazel persists in few pasture woods today and then only very locally and at a low density or as occasional stools, mostly heavily browsed and often moribund. In sharp contrast, it occurs in neighbouring private woods as a continuous shrub layer which was formerly coppiced for hurdles, wattle and other produce.

Documentary and pollen evidence suggests that holly was common in the Forest in medieval and early modern times, and probably before. The word 'holm' is probably of Anglo-Saxon derivation. It became dominant in the shrub layer probably over the long span from early deer forest times to the present century. Certainly it responded to periods of diminished grazing pressure from the mid-19th century onwards, and probably did so during similar episodes in earlier times. Holly has an advantage over more palatable deciduous shrubs, where there are large numbers of grazing animals. Peterken (1966) found that mature hollies in the New Forest exhibited relatively high rates of photosynthesis throughout the winter (except in freezing conditions), and that the species had a high rate of productivity which was channelled mainly into leaves and shoots rather than trunks and boughs. Further, the dark green leaves absorb a relatively high proportion of the incident light, which also tends to increase productivity. As a result, holly carries a large leaf mass throughout the year and its rate of production can keep ahead of animal offtake. Moreover, it is highly resistant to fire, and even old trees readily regenerate from root stock.

The pollen record shows that the dramatic rise of beech to codominance with oak is fairly recent; documentary evidence shows that it has taken place since late medieval times (Flower & Tubbs, 1982). It seems mainly to be an artefact of preferential exploitation of oak and is thus best seen in the context of the management history of the woods (chapter 10).

The native small-leaved lime (*Tilia cordata*) was sufficiently common in comparatively recent times to leave several place names, probably of Saxon origin, including Lyndhurst and several Linwoods. Today, apart from an experimental planting in Gibbet Wood in 1979 and several planted in 1984 at The Queen's House, Lyndhurst, I know only one small-leaved lime tree in the Forest, and that is in a Lyndhurst hedgerow. Elm persists more widely as a hedgerow tree, but I don't know a single individual in the pasture woods or Inclosures.

I am uncertain of the relative palatability of hornbeam. There is no evidence that it was ever a major component of the Forest woods and probably no more than three small populations persist today: a mature tree and abundant saplings in a patch of oak–holly pasture wood trapped in Foxhunting Inclosure (SU390050); several mature trees in Pinnick Wood (SU191073); and ten trees (eleven until one was inexplicably felled in 1985), at the Bench, Lyndhurst's village green.

The fragmented national distribution of wild service tree (*Sorbus torminalis*) may owe much to palatability. In the Forest pasture woods, there is an uneven-aged population among oakwood at King's Hat (SU307052) and scattered trees elsewhere. The closely-related rowan is highly palatable but, anomalously, remains relatively common in the Forest, albeit mainly as scattered individuals. Few seedlings survive and reachable foliage is heavily browsed, so rowan must owe its relative success to its consistently prolific production of berries. These are distributed widely by birds, ensuring that some seedlings survive in the protection of dense gorse, holly and other cover. Unfortunately, the pollen of the various *Sorbus* species cannot be differentiated and are not recorded in pollen diagrams. Hence, it is not possible to say anything of the past history of either of these two species in the Forest.

The Herb Layer and Epiphytes

Like the tree and shrub layers, the herb layer of the woods has been impoverished by centuries of grazing, though the acidity of the soil (pH 3.5–5.0 in the upper horizons of most soils) in any event limits the number of species which might occur. In the beech-dominated woods, the situation is exacerbated by low light levels beneath the dense summer canopy and the extremely acid litter which the trees produce. In most woods the ground flora not only comprises few species, but plant density is low and there is much bare ground. The most species-rich localities are on the inherently less impoverished clays, mainly in the south of the Forest, and on the stream-side alluvium of valleys and gutters.

Excluding rarities or very localized plants, about forty-five species of higher plant and a few ferns occur fairly consistently in the woods. The bryophyte flora is richer, especially in deeply-shaded old beechwoods, where the woodland floor is often bare except for deep, hummocky moss carpets of *Dicranum majus, D. scoparium, Hylocomium splendens, Hypnum cupressiforme, Leucobryum glaucum, L. juniperoidum, Plagiothecium undulatum, Pleurozium schreberi, Rhytidiadelphus viticulosa*, and sometimes other species including the brown mosses *Bazzania trilobata, Saccognya viticulosa* and *Scapania gracilis*. Such moss carpets are a beautiful and characteristic feature of the Forest beechwoods, and form particularly about the exposed roots of the trees. They are generally associated with bilberry, which in more open beechwoods often forms a continuous, close-cropped sward in which common cow-wheat (*Melampyrum pratense*) is consistently present. Bracken is common where light levels permit.

The flora increases in diversity and density with increasing light levels, in turn dependent on the proportion of beech and oak, and with increasing soil nutrient status. In oak dominant woods, wood anemone, wood sorrel (*Oxalis acetosella*), wood spurge, butcher's broom, yellow pimpernel (*Lysimachia nemorum*), dog violet and bluebells (*Hyacinthoides non-scripta*) occur consistently at low densities. Bracken is often abundant. A few oakwoods on richer soils yield a longer list though densities remain low. Here we can add primroses (*Primula vulgaris*), bugle (*Ajuga reptans*), lords-and-ladies (*Arum maculatum*), enchanter's nightshade (*Circaea lutetiana*), wood avens (*Geum urbanum*), common twayblade (*Listera ovata*), barren strawberry (*Potentilla sterilis*), sanicle (*Sanicula europaea*), germander speedwell (*Veronica chamaedrys*), wood speedwell (*V. montana*), woodruff (*Galium odoratum*), greater stitchwort (*Stellaria holostea*) and a few others. There are two particularly notable absentees – dog's mercury (*Mercurialis perennis*) and great woodrush (*Luzula sylvatica*), which are usually common in ungrazed woods on similar soils.

The direct effects of grazing and trampling are apparent everywhere. The commonest species – wood anemone, wood sorrel, wood spurge and butcher's broom – are more or less unpalatable to herbivores. Wood spurge in particular is carefully avoided. Butcher's broom possibly persists because of its defensive armoury of stiff, spiked leaves which look as though they ought to deter most animals, although some ponies browse even this intractable looking plant. Most of the remaining widespread species must be relics of once larger populations. It is not difficult to find evidence in support of this notion. In oakwoods adjoining the Forest and on similar soils the same species, and many others, occur in populations which are orders of magnitude larger than in the Forest. Moreover, such woods have abundant bramble and roses in the shrub layer and a profusion of trailing honeysuckle and other climbers, in contrast to the paucity of these shrubs in the Forest: all are avidly browsed by deer, ponies and cattle.

Perhaps one of the most conspicuous contrasts is provided by the bluebell. The shimmering blue carpets common in enclosed coppices are confined in the Forest to a few places in stock-free parts of Inclosures. In Broomy Inclosure (SU214116), the boundary fence was relocated in the late 1960s, leaving open to grazing half of an extensive, and until then protected, bluebell carpet beneath the 1809 oaks. Within two years in the area thrown open to stock the density of plants had been reduced by more than 30%, the density of flowering stems by 50–75%, and individual plants had become smaller and more prostrate. In contrast, the plants remained vigorous in the ungrazed area. Equally compelling examples of grazing effects are provided by plots which for one reason or another have been fenced against herbivores in the unenclosed woods. Invariably, the numbers of individuals of the species present increases quite quickly, though an increase in species diversity is slower. Presumably the herb layer, low shrubs and climbers have made a general recovery in the woods whenever herbivore numbers have been particularly low in the past, but the long-term direction must be towards impoverishment, particularly as the distribution of the more sensitive, less vigorous species becomes progressively more fragmented.

If the woodland floor is sparse in higher plants, the cryptogamic* flora of the woods is exceptionally rich. The trees themselves, and especially the older oaks and beeches, support what Francis Rose and Peter James (1974) believed to be an almost intact representation of the epiphytic* lichen and moss flora of the primeval Atlantic forests of 5000 years ago. The large number of oaks, beeches and hollies of great age and girth and varied form; the irregularity of the canopy, and the consequent pattern of deep shade alternating with well-lit glades; and the great extent of the woods, affording shelter from dessicating winds and maintaining some semblance of the high humidity which must have characterized the primeval woods, combine to provide conditions for an epiphytic flora thought to be unequalled in the lowlands of western Europe.

Both the trees (and especially those which are senile and decaying) and the woodland floor are also rich in fungi. Ferns however tend to be sparse, though lady fern (*Athyrium felix-femina*), hard fern (*Blechnum spicant*), broad buckler fern (*Dryopteris dilatata*) and male fern (*D. filix-mas*) are widespread. The epiphytic common polypody (*Polypodium vulgare*) is abundant wherever the branch structure of the trees permits it a hold. Three much rarer species persist in the high humidity of riverine woodland and alder carr. Royal fern (*Osmunda regalis*) occurs in twenty or thirty such localities and also sometimes colonizes artificial drains, where it is then in danger of eradication during maintenance. Beech fern (*Phegopteris connectilis*) is known from a single, 1.5 km-long carr, where it is almost continuous over 0.75 km where the carr is wettest and the valley most deeply incised. Marsh fern (*Thelypteris thelypteroides*) is known from six carrs, four of them in a fairly close group. Possibly both of the latter species are more widely distributed than present records suggest. The scattered distribution of all three species may owe much to Victorian fern collecting.

The epiphytic bryophytes *Dicranum scoparium, Homalothecium sericeum, Frullania dilatata, F. tamarisci, F. fragillofolia, Hypnum cupressiforme, Isothecium myosuroides, I. myurum, Metzgeria furcata, Neckera complanata, N. pumila, Orthotrichum lyellii* and *Zygodon viridissimus* are abundant on trunks and larger limbs of mature oaks and beeches, and *Porella platyphylla* is common on beech. Often the mosses cover the moister south-western side of the tree, whilst the remainder is richly encrusted with lichens. The thicker carpets of corticolous bryophytes may in turn provide a holdfast

*Cryptogram=plant without stamens or pistils and thus no true flowers or seeds, e.g., ferns, mosses, lichens etc.
*Epiphyte=plant which grows on another but not necessarily (or usually) parasitic.

for luxuriant growths of common polypody. Further assemblages of bryophytes are characteristic of wet flushes, alder carr, rotting logs, decaying stumps and other micro-habitats. The richest communities, however, are consistently associated with the older generations of trees, whether they are terricolous, as with the luxuriant bryophyte turfs beneath the old beeches, or epiphytic on living bark or dead wood.

A high proportion of epiphytic lichens have very poor powers of dispersal and are confined to woodlands with a continuous history of tree cover. Old trees would appear to be vital to their persistence and many ancient woods which have been systematically cropped, for example in coppices, are poor in lichens. Ancient wood pastures preserve the richest floras. The New Forest has the richest of any woodland in lowland western Europe: 278 species of corticolous and lignicolous lichens have been recorded by Francis Rose and Peter James since 1967, including many whose main British population occurs here (e.g., *Porina hibernica, P. coralloidea, Rinodina isidiodes, Phyllopsora rosei, Bombyliospora pachycarpa, Thelopsis rubella, Parmelia reddenda, Schismatomma niveum* and *Agonimia octospora*)and two species at present unknown elsewhere in Britain (*Parmelia dissecta* and *Catineria laureri*). The six richest woods in the New Forest have more than 130 species/km^2, with a maximum (in 1983) of 174 species/km^2 in Busketts Wood (SU308109). Many quite small woods have densities which approach these and the flora is continuously rich throughout the pasture woodlands, including most of the fragments of former unenclosed woodland trapped behind Inclosure fences. Moreover, some species characteristic of pasture woodland have colonized adjoining 19th-century oak plantations (Rose & James, 1974). There are ancient woods in Britain with comparable numbers of species to the richest Forest woods but they are all small and isolated and none support as many species or so many rare species as are present in the Forest. No woods with more than 150 species are yet known in the lowlands of continental western Europe.

Rose & James (1974) provide an important ecological account of the epiphytic lichen flora of the New Forest. Oak and beech provided the main substrates for 85% of the 259 species then recorded, but ash and holly were also important and supported rich and characteristic assemblages. The relatively few thickets of old blackthorn also bore a characteristic lichen community, dominated by several species of the conspicuous *Usnea* genus. On the other hand, alder and birch woods were generally poor in lichens. Probably most carr were periodically coppiced until comparatively recently, and most birch fail to achieve an age or girth sufficient to permit colonization by extensive lichen floras. Pinewoods in the Forest are also noticeably impoverished.

Five main groupings of epiphytic lichens and associated bryophytes were distinguished, forming a developmental sequence from pioneer communities on smooth-barked trees of small girth and with low bark pH to a climax community on mature trees of great age and girth, and with rough bark of high pH; and a 'post climax' group of species characteristic of ancient, and often senile oaks. Two further groups of species occurred locally. Eutrophic communities were occasionally found in the path of nutrient seepages from tree wounds and among branches used by roosting pigeons; and in some patches of sheltered, wet woodland, leaching had increased bark acidity to produce a community with affinities to those commonly found in upland Britain under much higher rainfall. Finally, in some places nearest the Southampton Water industries, aerial pollution had left impoverished communities of a relatively few species known to be tolerant of sulphur dioxide.

The climax community, rich in bryophytes as well as lichens, was characterized by the occurrence locally of the large, foliose *Lobaria* (notably *L. pulmonaria*, *L. laetevirens* and *L. amplissima*) and the moss *Homalothecium serviceum*. Rose & James (1974) considered this a near approach to the lichen community of old, undisturbed natural forest. Its persistence on the New Forest may be attributable to the high humidity maintained beneath the extensive and relatively undisturbed broadleaved canopy. However, many species are rare and fruit irregularly, and the most complete expressions of the climax and post-climax communities occur on comparatively few trees. This suggests that the lichen flora of today, though rich, is the relict of a much richer flora, impoverished by felling and the changes in microclimate induced by felling and perhaps drainage.

The Age Structure of the Woods

Most woods consist of two or more distinct generations of trees, the age of which has been established by counting the annual growth rings of fallen or felled trees. The oldest (A) comprises mainly oak, beech and holly of large girth which are either pollarded or have large spreading crowns suggestive of growth in relatively open conditions. A-generation yew also occurs locally and probably, the occasional massive crab tree is from the same period. Some coppice stools of alder are also probably very old. The A-generation can be separated into an older sub-generation of mainly open-grown, commonly pollarded trees; and a younger unpollarded sub-generation which arose in gaps among the older trees or in places from which they had been removed. In the oldest sub-generation, which includes many senile and decaying trees, oaks are scarcer than beech, but they are less so in the younger sub-generation. Holly, both pollarded and unmutilated, occurs in both.

The largest surviving oaks, all pollards, are 5–7 m in girth at

A-generation pollard beech, Bratley Wood

breast height. Flower (1983) listed thirty-nine such trees, and I can add at least three more, but there are many times that number of old pollarded oaks 4–5 m in girth, and some maidens, which I believe are of similar age. Only four oaks are known which exceed 7.0 m girth: the largest is 7.4 m, which is not large for old oak trees on richer soils and reflects the low growth rate achieved in the Forest. The oldest oaks dated by counts of annual growth rings (mostly from fallen trees subsequently sawn at the butt) date from 1640–50, but these were comparatively vigorous maidens free of rot, which post-dated the older, usually more degenerate trees. The latter I thus deduce to be of late 16th- or early 17th-century origin. The oldest and largest trees are massive, but few survive intact. Most have lost limbs and are dying back, confirming that not much more than about 400 years is the maximum life of an oak in the poor New Forest soils.

The A generation in Bratley Wood, where successor generations are mainly absent

The earlier sub-generation of beech are of smaller girth and presumably younger than the oldest oaks. Flower (1983) listed ten beeches over 6.2 m in girth, the largest of which was 7.4 m (Queen Bower SU288043). Beeches, mainly pollards, of 4–6 m girth, however, are still abundant and there are numerous pollards of 2.8–4.0 m which clearly grew up with the larger trees and are thus similar in age. The difficulty in obtaining growth ring counts from most old beeches is that they are usually rotten in the centre, but the oldest sound beech counted was 347 in 1963, thus dating from 1616. A further nineteen trees proved to date from 1616–60.

The oldest holly was 254 years old in 1963 and thus dates to about 1709. Many counts were of stems dating from 1709–65. However, the oldest hollies are clearly coppice stems arising from stools of much greater age and commonly 3–4.5 m in girth, whereas the largest stems are 2–2.5 m girth. It would seem that stools coppiced in the 17th century regenerated and were pollarded in the 18th century. I strongly suspect that the oldest holly stools and root systems, like the oldest alder stools, are of 16th-century age or earlier, for the plant seems nearly indestructible in its capacity to regenerate from rootstock after felling and fire.

The younger, non-pollarded element of the A generation mainly comprises beeches and oaks 2.5–4.0 m in girth. The range in girths among trees which clearly arose simultaneously has proved considerable, depending on local soil variation and the vagaries of competition within the stands. However, the form and cohesiveness of the later A-generation stands make them a distinctive element in the woods.

The B generation is much younger and arose at woodland margins and in places where it can be conjectured the older A-generation trees had died or beeen felled after the establishment of the later part of the A generation. Most B-generation oak and beech are in the girth range 1–2 m but there are many exceptions and some overlap with the A generation. The B generation is biased in species-composition towards those locally dominant in the A generation, but birch is frequent (though often now moribund), ash occurs on richer soils, notably in valley bottoms, and yew, Scots pine, crab, rowan, whitebeam, willow and hawthorn are widespread. Hawthorn and blackthorn scrub, mostly now disintegrating with age and stock damage – the interior of thorn thickets are much used by ponies and cattle for shelter – colonized alluvial valley floors.

The C generation is younger still, and is similarly species-variable. It represents the further colonization of gaps, glades and clearings and expansion of woodland margins, mainly by birch and oak. The paucity of species in the A generation compared with those which arose subsequently is mainly explained by its age, which exceeds the life span of most species available for colonization except oak, beech, holly and yew.

Although the species composition of a generation tends to be biased towards that of the older generations in the same place, there has been an increasing trend from beech to oak in the B and C generations. In the A generation, beech dominates the canopy in about half the woods, but in the B generation this position is most often reversed and in the C generation oak is dominant, usually to the exclusion of beech.

The interior of the woods shows great variation in the representation of the generations. In places (notably Bratley, Ridley, Berry and parts of Mark Ash Woods) the A-generation canopy remained closed until recently and excluded the B and C generations, so that the woods are mainly composed of old trees. Elsewhere, a B generation became established which largely excluded the C generation; or the pattern of death and regeneration has resulted in all three generations being present in the wood. Commonly, groups of A-generation beech have died since the mid-1950s but the C generation has not become established in the gaps they have left, though it is abundant at the woodland edges. Thus, there is a recurrent pattern in which there is a core of open beech wood within an expanding ring of young oakwood. The factors which have inhibited the appearance of a C generation within the wood are not clear, though the acid litter produced by beech growing on base poor soils, the rejuvenation of a dense holly shrub layer, and

B- and C-generation oak and beech, Mark Ash Wood

the concentration of grazing herbivores on the clearings, may all be important.

The holly-dominated holms may be fitted into the generation structure observed elsewhere. Areas of unshaded holly, often with oaks emerging from or over-topping the canopy, are features of all three generations. These holms appear to have arisen from the direct colonization of heathland by holly. Dimbleby & Gill (1955) showed that holly can form a mull humus on podsolic soils, apparently assisting oak regeneration and resulting in small oakwoods becoming established within an expanding zone of holly. Occasionally beech gets in before the oak. If neither colonizes in the 20–30 years before the holly canopy closes, succession is arrested until the holly degenerates, perhaps 2–300 years later, and much will then depend on grazing pressure. Most often, the holms come and go: many places which are now open heath have 'holm' or 'hats' place names, and there are many open groups of ancient, often moribund, hollies and oaks, which are holms in the final stages of decay: often they have succumbed to fires which have swept the heaths. Ring counts of ancient hollies are seldom satisfactory, because of decay and the fusion of multiple stems, but I guess many moribund groups must be of at least early 17th-century origin.

It is less easy to fit the alder woods into the generation structure. Most have been coppiced and ring counts yield only the approximate date when this last occurred. To ring-count stools is impractical. Stools of 2.5–4.0-m girth are common and stools of 4.0–6.0 m are frequent. The latter usually occur in groups and may be very ancient, perhaps exceeding the age of the oldest remaining oaks, for coppicing is said to greatly extend the life of a plant. In the few small uncoppiced carr, the largest trees are 2.5–3.0 m in breast–height girth which, remembering the rapid growth rate achieved by alder, may represent the B generation.

The Age of the Generations

From 189 ring counts made in 1963 and 1964, George Peterken and I dated the periods of most active regeneration since the early 17th century to 1663–1763, 1858–1923, and post 1938 (Peterken & Tubbs, 1965; Tubbs, 1968). Since then the number of counts has been increased to 530. This larger number confirms the 1660–1760 regeneration period but places the B generation mainly during 1840–70 and the C generation between 1900 and 1960, with least regeneration during 1920 and 1935. Fig. 20 shows these regeneration periods in relation to grazing and browsing pressure. Considering the inadequate data on herbivore numbers before 1884, the relatively small number of ring counts, and the subjective judgements involved in arriving at a grazing and browsing index, Fig. 20 supports the relationship surprisingly well. It suggests that regeneration ceases generally at an index of 0.16 grazing units per

Oak–birch expansion of woodland margin, Wood Crates

C-generation oak ; A-generation beech in background, Wood Crates

hectare. The anomalous check in regeneration between 1920 and 1935 appears to derive from widespread closure of the B- and C-generation canopy at this time (Peterken & Tubbs, 1965).

In the 1960s it was clear that the most recent regeneration phase was coming to an end. Few seedlings escaped grazing and most saplings were suppressed. A survey of C generation trees and shrubs in 1983 and 1984, illuminated the position more clearly. I examined birch, oak, beech, thorns, alder, alder buckthorn, crab and willows which had colonized glades and woodland and margins; and hawthorn and blackthorn with emergent oaks and ashes which had colonized alluvial lawns. Ring counts of 110 cut samples confirmed that the glades infilled mainly after 1930. The youngest trees proved to be mainly heavily browsed moribund birch 0.5–1.4 m high and between fifteen and twenty-three years old. A class of vigorous birches up to 8 m high proved to be of similar age. Some had got away and some had not. Ring counts of large samples of hawthorn, blackthorn and oak stumps left after clearance from parts of alluvial lawns (Dockens Water SU2503; Warwick Slade SU2706; Brinken Wood Lawn SU2705) confirmed that thickets had established at various times between 1932 and 1961. Older groups of oaks and some ashes fell into a somewhat older age group dating from 1904–20 which had arisen through thorn thickets of which only vestiges now remain.

Tree and shrub regeneration effectively ended by about 1970. The effects of browsing are plain today. Deciduous saplings are annually stripped of leaves and twigs; there is a well-marked browse line on older trees and shrubs; and holly and gorse bushes are commonly 'topiarized' into rounded or conical shapes. Despite browsing, the hollies eventually escape upwards and the gorse bushes gradually expand their canopy, but these processes are slow.

The Woodland Fauna

Of roughly 30,000 invertebrate species (excluding Protozoa) in Britain, more than half are thought to depend on deciduous woodland. The New Forest pasture woods are known to possess an exceptionally diverse invertebrate fauna, perhaps of the order of 5–10,000 species. This fauna exhibits certain definite characteristics related to the structure of the woodland. Groups dependent on nectar sources, a well-developed herb layer (including tall grasses), or a dense shrub layer of the sort provided by bramble, are poorly represented because these elements of the woods have been removed. Thus, for example, butterflies, day-flying moths, shrub-dwelling crickets and grass-dependent grasshoppers, are absent or occur in small and scattered populations. In contrast, the invertebrate fauna of the trees themselves and especially of old timber and dead wood, is exceptionally rich.

The total number of species inhabiting dead wood in the Forest is unknown, nor is it likely that a definitive total will ever be determined, but entomologists agree that the Forest is the richest place in Britain for this element of our invertebrate fauna. Probably 75–90% of the 600–800 species inhabiting dead wood in Britain occur here, including about 200 species of flies (*Diptera*), 400 species of beetles (*Coleoptera*), 30 species of bees and wasps (*Hymenoptera*), an unknown number of micro-moths and modest numbers of woodlice, millepedes and centipedes. Not all occur in every decaying tree and, indeed, each stage of senility and decay possesses its own distinctive fauna. There is thus a need for a wide range of trees in different stages of decay within relatively discrete parts of the woods in order to maintain the maximum invertebrate diversity.

The combined resource of mature and decaying trees is believed to be one of the richest invertebrate environments in Britain. It supports the majority of the 1540 species of beetle and 1200 species of moths recorded in the Forest as a whole and each of these totals in turn represents about half the respective British lists. It supports the largest known British assemblage of Diptera dependent on old timber. It is particularly rich in species whose survival depends on long term continuity of old timber; at least fifty-two species of beetle accepted as indicators of this condition are known to occur, which is the second highest for a woodland in Britain. The fauna of the woods includes many beautiful and spectacular insects. It must be one of the few places where that most spectacular animal, the stag beetle (*Lucanus cervus*) remains common: it is entirely dependent on rotting wood in its larval stages.

The old trees provide abundant nest sites for honey bees (*Apis mellifera*) and social wasps. Hornets (*Vespa crabro*), which usually nest in tree holes and hollows, are abundant and frequently transfer their attentions to houses, outbuildings and sometimes such inconvenient places as pillar boxes, suggesting that populations in some years may be at or near the optimum in the woods. Both the common wasp (*Vespula vulgaris*) and German wasp (*V. germanica*) are common throughout the Forest except on open heathland, but densities in the pasture woods, especially where they are broken by glades and clearings, appear particularly high. Though usually ground nesters (often in the bases of trees), both species also use trees here. The remaining British social wasps – the red wasp (*V. rufa*), (again usually a ground nester), tree wasp (*V. sylvestris*) and Norwegian wasp (*V. norvegica*) also occur in the woods.

The easily-studied woodland crickets and grasshoppers (Orthoptera) provide a good example of the relationship between vegetation structure and species composition of the insect fauna. In high summer the characteristic sound in the woods is the ventriloquial chorus of wood crickets (*Nemobius sylvestris*) (which incidentally has deluded many a bird watcher into believing the place was overrun with grasshopper warblers (*Locustella naevia*)), which inhabit the leaf litter. They are abundant throughout the Forest and, indeed, the area is the centre of their very limited distribution in Britain. Contrarily, the grasshoppers which might be expected – the woodland grasshopper (*Omocestus rufipes*), and in clearings the common green (*O. viridulus*) and meadow grasshoppers (*Chorthippus parallelus*) – occur only patchily and in small numbers, presumably because their food and cover (mainly grasses) is removed by herbivores. Similarly, the dark bush cricket (*Pholidoptera griseoaptera*) and speckled bush cricket (*Leptophyes punctatissima*), which depend on bramble and other low shrubs, occur only very locally, but the oak bush cricket (*Meconema thalassinum*), which inhabits the lower parts of the tree canopy, including holly, is common. Ragge (1965), in describing the Orthoptera of the Forest woods, clearly implies that the grasshoppers and bush-dwelling crickets were commoner then than now. Brown & Searle (1974) describe both crickets as very common in the Forest in 1972. I am thus led to suppose that the subsequent increase in grazing and browsing pressure has removed their habitat. It may be that many invertebrates, like many plants, have passed through cycles of abundance dependent on fluctuations in the numbers of large herbivores.

Predictably, one of the rarest New Forest insects is one of the best studied, the bug *Cicadetta montana* (Hemiptera-Homoptera) – the New Forest cicada. It was discovered in or near the Forest in 1812 and has since been known only from the pasture woods of the New Forest and from the woods around Haslemere in Surrey. By 1941 it had been recorded in about sixteen New Forest locations (Morley, 1941) but by then was thought probably extinct. It was rediscovered in the New Forest in June 1962 and has since been studied intensively there by J. A. Grant. There are still no certain records beyond the area of the rediscovery and today, the Forest woods support the only known population of British cicadas.

Cicada eggs are laid into the stems of trees and shrubs and on emergence the larvae fall to the ground and begin a subterranean existence lasting three to seventeen years, during which they feed on root sap, eventually emerging onto the aerial parts of the plant to complete the cycle. The adult stage lasts only six to eight weeks, and is also sap-feeding. Part of Jim Grant's research has aimed at elucidating the factors which limit the population. Intriguingly, though oviposition has been seen on many host plants in the study area, the favoured species in much of central and eastern Europe (where most studies have taken place) is the small-leaved lime. Can it be that this insect, which must have entered Britain before the last land bridge was severed, in times when lime was commoner, has since dwindled with its favoured host plant and has only partially adapted to others? Is its survival in the New Forest an indication of the recency with which the limes have gone from the Forest woods? Small-leaved lime (*T. cordata*) has now been planted experimentally in part of its main locality, and it will be interesting to see if the insect population responds. In view of the insect's long subterranean life, we may have to wait many years.

From invertebrates, let us turn to the woodland bird community. During the 1970s and 1980s six widely spread sample areas have been censused annually in the pasture woods as part of the British Trust for Ornithology Common Bird Census Scheme. Fig. 22 compares the percentage of species (excluding woodcock (*Scolopax rusticola*), woodpigeons (*Columba palumbus*), cuckoos (*Cuculus*

Fig. 22.
*Percentages of Bird
Species Associated with
Different Elements of
a) Six New Forest
Pasture Woods
b) Six ungrazed woods
in Southern England*

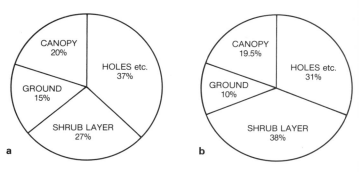

canorus) and birds of prey which are not best censused by the
methods used) nesting in different structural elements of the pasture
woods, with data from a similar number of woods of native deciduous trees with no known history as pasture, elsewhere in southern
England. The distinctions are small, though the Forest woods
have fewer shrub layer species (27% compared with 38%), more
hole and crevice nesters (37% compared with 31%) and rather
more ground nesters, even though the analyses excluded woodcock, which are common in the Forest. If, however, we turn to
comparisons of the numbers of territories (Fig. 23), the distinctions

Fig. 23.
*Percentages of Bird
Territories Associated
with Different Elements of
a) Six New Forest
Pasture Woods
b) Six Ungrazed Woods
in Southern England*

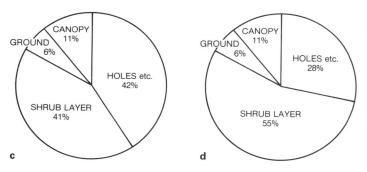

are larger, with a much greater percentage of hole and crevice
nesters (42%) in the Forest woods than elsewhere (28%). The
percentage distribution of both territories and species among
structural elements in all woods was consistent from year to year,
which encourages confidence that the results were representative.
They show that in the pasture woods, species favoured by old
timber are numerically dominant but that those associated with
the (impoverished) shrub layer are depressed both in numbers of
species and numbers of territories.

In the New Forest census areas, forty-seven species were recorded breeding at an average density of 903 pairs/km². This

compared with 700 pairs/km^2 in the plots elsewhere in southern woods. In the Forest the most numerous species (in order of declining abundance) were blue tits (*Parus caeruleus*), wrens (*Troglodytes troglodytes*), robins (*Erithacus rubecula*), chaffinches (*Fringilla coelebs*), then blackbirds (*Turdus merula*), great tits (*Parus major*) and coal tits (*P. ater*) in approximately equal proportions. Elsewhere, the consistent dominants were robins, chaffinches, blackbirds, wrens and blue tits.

In the Forest woods, the hole and crevice nesters comprise mainly green woodpeckers (*Picus viridis*), great spotted woodpeckers (*Dendrocopes major*), lesser spotted woodpeckers (*D. minor*), tree-creepers (*Certhia familiaris*), nuthatches (*Sitta europaea*), starlings (*Sternus vulgaris*), four species of tits, stock doves (*Columba oenas*), jackdaws (*Corvus monedula*), spotted flycatchers (*Muscicapa striata*) and redstarts (*Phoenicurus pheonicurus*); wrens can often also be included in this category. Pied flycatchers nest occasionally. Of this assemblage, lesser spotted woodpeckers and redstarts are distinctly local in occurrence. Both are highly characteristic of old timber, as is the stock dove. Redstarts appear not to tolerate a dense shrub layer, and thus favour grazed woodland. Extrapolation from the census areas suggests that the total redstart population of the Forest pasture woods has fluctuated in the range 400–1100 pairs which is probably a significant percentage of the British breeding population. The whole assemblage of old timber birds is probably better represented in the New Forest than elsewhere in the English lowlands.

Chaffinches, robins and wrens together form more than 70% of the shrub layer birds in all New Forest plots, the remaining 30% of the community comprising blackbirds and song thrushes (*Turdus philomelos*) which occur at low densities in the absence of a shrub layer other than browsed holly; and long-tailed tits (*Aegithalos caudatus*), bullfinches (*Pyrrhula pyrrhula*), dunnocks (*Prunella modularis*), chiffchaffs (*Phylloscopus collybita*), blackcaps (*Sylvia atricapilla*), garden warblers (*S. borin*), greenfinches (*Cardualis chloris*), goldfinches (*C. cardualis*) and linnets (*Acanthus cannabina*), all of which, except long-tailed tits, occur at very low densities. The main woodland floor species are woodcock, tree pipits (*Anthus trivialis*), willow warblers (*Phylloscopus trochilis*) and wood warblers (*P. sibilatrix*). The wood warbler, like the redstart, has a curiously disjunct distribution in Britain, but it is consistently present (though at varying densities) in both the pasture woods and broadleaved Inclosures of the New Forest. Tony Prater and Glynne Evans (unpublished) found 5.16–10.68 territories/km^2 in Forest woods, with an average of 280 m between nearest neighbours. In 1981, an incomplete survey of about half of the Forest woods, including broadleaved Inclosures, yielded 235 pairs. Extrapolation from the census plots suggests an average of around 350 pairs in the pasture woods alone, and I estimate that the total may reach two or three times that number at the peak of population cycles. This is likely to be a high proportion of the British population.

I suspect that the wood warbler (like the redstart) has been favoured by the long-term effects of grazing. The species is usually absent from woods with a dense shrub layer and appears to require relatively open conditions beneath a canopy of mature broadleaved trees. This the Forest, and especially the pasture woods, provides in abundance, the low, sweeping branches of the oaks and beeches, just above browse height, providing their characteristic song perches, and the deep litter layer among old roots providing nest sites. The songs of wood warblers and redstarts among open beech-woods fresh with emerging leaf is an indelible image of spring in the Forest.

Besides hole- and crevice-nesting birds, the old timber should be rich in bats. Over this group, however, hangs a question mark. Until recently, little was known about them, probably because they operate at inconvenient hours, but enough information emerged in the 1960s and 1970s to suggest a decline through pesticide con-tamination (via insect prey and timber treatment of roosts in house roof cavities), a general diminution of prey insects through more intensive farming which destroyed invertebrate habitats, human antipathy and the destruction of roosts in old trees and buildings. Now as the 1980s mature, things are hopefully changing, largely the indirect result of the *Wildlife and Countryside Act, 1981*, which protected all bats and gave an impetus to interest in their distribu-tion, numbers and ecology. However, our knowledge of bats tends to be biased towards populations and species using roosts in buildings, tunnels and caves, because these are most easily found and most often threatened.

However, bats are essentially woodland animals which have adapted to alternative roosts and hibernacula. Little is known about the bats of the old woods of the New Forest but it is probable that they may be among the most important areas for the group in Britain because of the abundance of suitable holes, hollows and crevices, and the fact that the Forest has been little affected by the factors which have reduced the absolute density of prey insects over so much of the English lowlands. Such information as there is (and this derives mainly from my friend and former colleague Michael Blackmore) suggests that at least nine of the fourteen British species occur in the old woods, including the very rare Bechstein's bat (*Myotis bechsteini*), which has been found at tree roosts in the Forest by both Michael Blackmore and S. C. Bisserot. Beyond the confines of the woods, the newly-awakened interest in bats has revealed what seems to be a high density of the commoner species in the Forest area, and it would be surprising if the pasture woods and their environs did not have a share in this wealth.

Woodland Use and Abuse

Long before the Inclosure Act of 1698, parts of the woods were managed as .coppices. Shrouding and pollarding were common practices until the 18th century, and from the 16th to 19th centuries, the woods were exploited for navy timber. In recent times they have been subjected to some unfortunate 'management' experiments. The 'natural' pattern of distribution has been much obscured by the Silvicultural Inclosures. To what extent have these historical episodes affected the structure – the 'naturalness' – of the woods? Though protected now, their recent history has been traumatic. What of their prospects?

Early Management

The early encoppicements (chapter 5) would have modified the woods at the time, but how many coppices were there and what legacy have they left? The names of twenty-nine coppices can be retrieved from documents, and the location and area of twenty-eight are known. Wasted banks and ditches with the characteristic irregular alignment indicate the locations of at least another six. There are doubtless others as yet unfound. The twenty-eight coppices of known size total 713 ha. Four (96 ha) are now heath or acid grassland; eighteen (526 ha) are beneath plantations in statutory enclosures; and six (91 ha) are within surviving pasture woods. It is only possible to guess the area of the remaining six coppices, because their boundary banks are incomplete, but they probably total around 60 ha: all but one are in the pasture woods of today. Thus, at least 141 ha or 4% of the pasture woods were at some time encoppiced. In my earlier book I concluded that the proportion was much larger, but the evidence does not support this. However, scattered fragments of irregular banks, mostly on open heath or grassland, may commemorate other, perhaps shortlived or abandoned attempts to raise a crop of underwood.

Few coppices were functional at any one period. Except on a few sites whose names occur repeatedly in the documents, encoppicement seems to have been an ephemeral episode in the history of individual woods. This is further suggested by the means often employed to protect them. Coppices were usually protected by a boundary bank and pale with an external ditch, a substantial structure which excluded deer as well as stock. That the coppice system had only a tenuous hold in the New Forest, however, is suggested by a frequent substitution of this arrangement with a quickset hedge or simple pale in 17th century coppice plans.

From the documents it is clear that hazel was the main underwood crop and probably the coppices prolonged its survival in the Forest woods. However, the long-term ecological consequences of encoppicement on the scale practised in the New Forest can only be slight and very local. Today, I cannot distinguish the coppices from other parts of the pasture woods by any characteristic of tree or shrub age structure or species composition, and any legacy of an enriched ground flora left by enclosure against stock has long since been dissipated. Certainly there is nothing to support the later claims of foresters that the pasture woods owed their origin to medieval silviculture. Nicholas Flower claimed to identify lines of widely-spaced A-generation oak in part of Pinnick Wood (SU 197078) which he suggested were planted (Flower, 1980b). I cannot detect planting lines there and the dispersion of trees is random. The grove of twenty-five massive, mainly maiden, oaks are clearly of similar age (though they range in girth from 2.8 m to 5.3 m) but they are probably no older than the 17th century, and there is no mention of a coppice there in the abundant documentation of the time.

Early management was not confined to encoppicement. There are occasional references to the coppicing of 'aldermoores', and from their structure almost all the alder carrs in the Forest have been coppiced at some time, most recently in the past 100 years. This century, alder charcoal, which is very fine, helped sustain the Shultz Gunpowder Mill at Eyeworth Lodge, Fritham, and in the Second World War, alder was cut to provide charcoal for gas mask filters. The resurgence of coppicing for these markets coincided with low herbivore populations, hence the present vigorous condition of the carr, which regenerated prolifically during the period before the recent increase in grazing pressure. Periodic coppicing accounts for the poor lichen flora of the carr, but the bryophytes and ferns, which form luxuriant carpets on and around the coppice stools, appear able to survive such trauma until the humid microclimate is restored by regrowth of the trees.

Two other 'management' practices were formerly common in the Forest. Pollarding amounted to coppicing a tree above browse height, and was intended to produce abundant branches of a size conveniently cut for deer to browse, or firewood. Shrouding was the lopping of lateral branches. In the Forest, shrouding was always frowned upon, but pollarding was permitted to provide deer browse. Inevitably, it was abused to provide firewood, and from 1583, attempts were made to suppress it as ruinous to potential timber. The 1698 Inclosure Act prohibited the pollarding of oak and beech and from the evidence of growth ring counts, the Act was surprisingly effective. Seventeenth-century pollards are rare,

Alder carr, Matley Bog, last coppiced in the 1950s

but they are abundant in that part of the A generation which arose before 1700. These old trees are a characteristic element of the pasture woods today, but they are disintegrating now, and I wonder if many will survive beyond my lifetime.

The 1698 prohibition did not extend to holly. This was the most useful of all browse species because it is winter-green, has the highest calorific value of all the plants taken by herbivores in the New Forest, and is relatively nutrient-rich (NCC, 1983). It becomes especially palatable (bark and leaf) a few days after cutting. The cutting of holly for deer browse remained common practice until the demise of the deer forest in 1851, and has periodically occurred since. Regeneration from rootstock after fire has continued to produce multiple stemmed trees and since the late 19th century, much commercial cutting for Christmas decoration has taken place (Lascelles, 1915). Thus, there are few individuals with a morphology unmodified by fire or the saw.

The cultivation of holly as a fodder crop was widespread in England and Wales between the 13th and 18th centuries and its origins are probably lost in even greater antiquity (Radley, 1961). The practice has left a legacy of 'hollin' place names in the Pennines, Cumbria and the Welsh Marches, and 'holm' place names more locally in the south: 'hollins' were often specifically the enclosures which protected holly groves (Spray & Smith, 1977). Groves of holly pollards, reminders of the former economic importance of the tree, are now known to survive in only about ten localities, and the New Forest is easily the most extensive.

Nicholas Flower (1980a) makes the interesting suggestion that some attempts may have been made to supplement natural re-generation in the Forest woods by sowing acorns. In support, he draws attention first to an early 17th-century enjoinder (not specific to the New Forest) to forest officers to

'caste acornes and ashe keyes into the straglinge and dispersed bushes; which (as experience proveth) will growe up, sheltered by the bushes, unto suche perfection as shall yelde times to come good supplie of timber' (J. Nordon: PRO/LR/2/194 f174).

Secondly, he calls in aid a late 18th-century account of the sowing of acorns in Forest Inclosures 3 ft (0.914 m) apart in triads, the ground then being strewn with haws, holly berries, sloes and hazel nuts to form a nursery thicket for the young trees. Thirdly, he observes that in most woods there are pairs and sometimes triads of (mainly) oaks whose bases are roughly 3 ft apart and whose girths are generally similar. Fourthly, he shows that the distance between trees comprising pairs or triads is consistently about 1 metre, and he deduces that they were sown in the fashion described in order to fill gaps beneath the canopy. However, there seems no reason why they should not, equally, have arisen naturally, two or three in a close group in the protection of a bramble or thorn, even as they can be seen to do today. In the absence of documentary support the point remains unresolved, but pairs and triads of beech or oak, or sometimes a mixture, are a recurrent feature of the woods in all three of the main generations. Whatever their origin, their number is tiny compared to the total number of contemporary trees, and if sowing took place, it had little influence on the sub-sequent structure of the woods.

Exploitation for Navy Timber and the Ascendance of Beech

The exploitation of the pasture woods for ship-building timber from the early 17th and early 19th centuries was a significant episode in their history (Tubbs, 1968; Flower, 1980a). Until about

1630, the amount of construction timber of any kind supplied by the New Forest was modest. The nearby ports of Southampton, Redbridge and Lymington built only a small tonnage of merchant shipping between them, and Portsmouth built no ships between 1509 and just before the civil war in 1642, when five frigates were ordered to be laid down there. The first, *Portsmouth*, was launched in 1650. At the declaration of the commonwealth in 1649, the Royal Navy had about 21,000 tons of shipping. By 1685, it had increased to 103,558 tons and by 1702 to 159,017 tons. Much of this was built on the Hampshire coast at Portsmouth, Southampton, Bursledon, and after 1698, Bucklers Hard, on the Beaulieu estuary. Shipbuilding demanded large volumes of oak timber within economically transportable distances of the yards, much of it of odd shapes and sizes. The oak of the New Forest and other Hampshire woodlands largely sustained this industry for nearly a century, and continued to supply it on a diminished scale until timber became obsolete in ship construction. In the 17th and 18th centuries much of the timber supplied by the New Forest came from the unenclosed woods.

Surveys of all the crown woods were carried out between 1604 and 1612. That for the New Forest (1608) pictures the woods just before the navy purveyors cast eyes on them. It recorded 123,927 'Timber trees'; and enough 'Fyrewood and Decayed' trees to yield 118,072 loads, which I calculate from somewhat later equations, to be probably 79,000 trees. Anything smaller than 'timber trees' was not recorded, but there clearly were younger generation trees present, for some individuals survive today, and many more provided navy timber in the 18th century. There were eighteen coppices totalling 1304 acres (528 ha), most of which a survey of the following year described as derelict and unenclosed; and 92 acres (37 ha) of 'aldermores'. The woods were 'for most part oake, and some small quantetyes of Beech and Ash' and 'all the said trees are very old and in great Decaye'. The 'Fyrewood and Decayed' trees probably represented a generation which arose in the late 12th century, whilst a few of the youngest trees present in 1608 may be among the most ancient pollard oaks standing today. It is uncanny that it is possible to reach so far back into history in the lives of two oaks.

From 1612, oak was felled in the forest for the navy yards at Deptford and Woolwich and from 1632 also for Portsmouth and other local yards. Felling for the navy continued for the remainder of the century and, periodically, during the 18th and into the 19th century. Besides oak, small amounts of beech and large numbers of 'doddards' (probably moribund oak, that provided big limbs, crooks and knees) were also taken.

Most of the A generation arose in the mid and late 17th and early 18th centuries in the wake of oak exploitation, much of it in the unshaded conditions left by the felled trees. It is described in the Regarders' return for 1670 which gives the condition of fifty-three woods: fifteen were 'decaying' and thirty-eight were 'prosperous' or 'very prosperous'. There is some confirmation of both regeneration and the effects of exploitation in a timber survey of 1707. This recorded only 12,476 oak 'fit for her Majesty's Naval Service', which by then effectively meant a large crowned oak 150 years old or more. Of these it was thought 300 could be felled annually for forty years 'there being so many young trees which are not of sufficient Bigness' that the Forest would be at least as well stocked after forty years as in 1707. There were also about 4000 large beeches, of which 100 could be felled annually and a 'large number' of old oaks 'from the limbs of which might be picked some useful parts'. These must have been survivors of the old trees recorded in 1608.

Further surveys of 1764 and 1783 reported successive increases in oak fit for the navy, to 19,836 and then to 41,792. The 1764 survey also recorded 7104 beech fit for the navy and the 1783 survey 18,996, though there is no definition of what was meant. In all the surveys, the number of navy oak recorded represent an unrealistically low density in the pasture woods (no more than about five oaks/ha in 1783). I can only conclude that the surveyors were highly selective in identifying what was suitable for the navy, or that the surveys were incomplete, and in either case that they can be no more than a crude index of the position. The 18th-century surveys and independent observations all report an abundance of young trees, and though there are no definitions of what size trees were meant, nor how many were within the 18th-century Inclosures (which would not have supplied navy timber that century), it is clear that it is the younger part of the A generation which is being described.

The A generation spanned a long period (1660–1760). Regeneration cannot have been continuous during this time but ring counts are too few to distinguish sub-generations which may have arisen during periods when herbivore numbers were low, or the winter heyning and fence month enforced, and exploitation of the Forest controlled. Both fence month and winter heyning were specifically reintroduced by the 1698 Act. I strongly suspect that at least periodic enforcement of forestal restrictions and controls, and possibly deliberate reduction of deer numbers (perhaps the 1670 census was a prelude to control) were important factors in the origin of the A generation. Such a hypothesis requires at least the periodic ascendance of the Surveyor General over the Lord Warden.

There is some support for such a hypothesis. In some other royal forests, a similar regeneration phase also occurred. The seventeen *Reports of Commissioners to Enquire into the Woods, Forests and*

Land Revenues of the Crown, 1787–1798 (of which the New Forest formed the 5th Report) include the testimonies of witnesses which describe it. Thus, for example, in Alice Holt, Hampshire:

'The trees now standing are mostly oak, some beech, and a few ash; and I judge them to be nearly all the same age . . . which I suppose to be about 115 to 120 years' growth; and I cannot discover the traces of either banks or ditches . . . or any appearance whatever of . . . inclosures.'

In Bere Forest, just inland from Portsmouth and exploited intensively by the navy yard, there was a similar generation which had arisen 'principally from a stock of timber nursed up and protected during the latter part of the last century' without benefit of Inclosure. In the Forests furthest removed from shipyards, where there was the least incentive to conserve timber, the regeneration phase was absent. Thus, in Sherwood, the timber recorded in the 1604–12 surveys had been felled and nothing remained except within recent Inclosures. Though the reports may be over-simplifications, they consistently attribute the regeneration of the Forests closest to the yards to enforcement of the winter heyning, and restraint on deer numbers and the cutting of scrub and young trees for faggots and fuel wood. The failure of regeneration after about 1750 is attributed to the 'relaxation and neglect of the officers of the department of the Surveyor-General'.

The main effect of more than two centuries of periodic exploitation, mainly of oak, was to adjust the species composition of the woods in favour of beech. Astonishingly, their essentially natural characteristics persisted and, for example, disturbance was evidently insufficient to eliminate such sensitive elements as the old-forest lichens and dead-wood insects, presumably because the scale of exploitation at any one time was small in relation to the scale of the woods. But how much richer they must have been, and how much more complete their flora and fauna, before the navy purveyors found them.

The pollen analyses from Church Moor, Barrow Moor and Warwick Slade mires, all within an area which has probably remained well wooded since the Boreal period, show steep increases in the amount of beech pollen in roughly the past 500 years (Barber, 1981; Flower & Tubbs, 1982). Similarly, in four out of five woodland soils investigated by Dimbleby & Gill (1955) the percentage of beech pollen increased rapidly in the upper horizons from near absence to 8–50% of arboreal and Ericaceae pollens. An indication of the relative abundance of oak and beech in the 16th century can be gained from a survey of 1565 (Roger Taverner, *The Book of Survey*), which gives the area and composition of 141 woods totalling 2074 ha, besides eleven coppices totalling another 230 ha (Fig. 24). The areas are clearly rough estimates or guesses, and the list does not include all Forest woods known at the time. The list looks like

	Oak	Oak, some beech	Beech, some oak	Beech	Holm, thorn, with oak	Under-wood ±oak	'destroyed' or 'utterly destroyed'	Totals
Number of sites	60	22	8	22	18			130
Area (hectares)	947	442	155	174	151			1869
Coppices								
Number of sites	2					5	4	11
Area (hectares)	30					67	105	203

The Book of Survey, Public Record Office LRRO/5/39. Areas in the original were expressed in acres.

Fig. 24.
Species Composition of New Forest Woods in 1563

the transcribed returns of the Regarders, in turn derived perhaps from the Forest officers, though it is in the name of The Queen's Surveyor. However, the document confirms the dominance of oak, and also shows that beech was already abundant in the Forest.

The dominance of oak in the early 17th century is confirmed by the surveyors of 1608, who reported that 'All the said trees are for the most part oak, and some small quantetayes of beech and ash.' The 18th-century timber surveys show a decreasing ratio of oak to beech, thus:

$$oak:beech$$
$$1707 \quad 3.2:1$$
$$1764 \quad 2.8:1$$
$$1783 \quad 2.2:1$$

A survey of the pasture woods by Nicholas Flower in 1978 gave a ratio of 1:1 (Flower & Tubbs, 1982). Fig. 25 provides a further measure of the change by comparing the 1565 and 1978 surveys. Gilpin (1791) and the surveyors who prepared the map accompanying the 1789 report (RPO F/20/48) described the clearance of oak for the navy from several woods in the Forest, most of which are now mainly beechwoods. The navy took little beech. The ratio of oak to beech delivered to the yards in 1783–91 was 7.6:1 (cf above) (Flower & Tubbs, 1982).

The implication is that preferential removal of oak left beech with a competitive advantage, though from the 1565 survey, and from pollen analyses, it is apparent that beech was increasing before the era of oak-felling, which possibly only accelerated an existing process. It is also not wholly clear why oak failed to regenerate in the gaps left by the felling, for there cannot have been any lack of seed sources.

The long period of oak exploitation has left few 17th-century oaks today, whereas there are abundant beech of that age. Today,

	Percentage of areas of different species composition				
Year	Oak dominant	Oak; beech sub-dom.	Beech; oak sub-dom.	Beech dominant	Holms etc.
1565	50.6	23.6	8.3	9.3	8.1
1983	20.0	26.2	32.9	15.3	5.5

See Figs. 21 and 24. Percentages for 1983 are calculated by excluding the alder carr and 'birch, oak, some Scots pine' categories in Fig. 21.

Fig. 25.
Species Composition of Unenclosed Woodlands in 1563 and 1983

beech is dominant in about half the woods (Fig. 21), a position which it achieved during the establishment of the A generation. However, oak is generally dominant in the B and C generations, suggesting that beech dominance will be a temporary phenomenon. The deaths of many beeches in the long, dry, hot summer of 1976 suggest, too, that the species is at the limit of its climatic tolerance here, and that a small change in average summer rainfall will place it at a disadvantage. I estimate that 4500 beeches were killed or severely affected by the 1976 drought. Large numbers died in the succeeding years, and further dry summers in the late 1970s and early 1980s maintained the elevated death rate. The disintegrating hulks of drought victims are common in the woods, though large numbers were felled after 1976 as a safety measure. Though the period of beech dominance may be waning, the degraded soils beneath most pure beechwoods in the Forest suggest that it may leave a legacy of soil impoverishment, especially on the more siliceous parent materials. The navy purveyors of the 17th and 18th centuries have much to answer for.

After 1877

Cutting of navy oak outside the Inclosures petered out in the early 19th century, and the 1877 Act conferred a degree of protection on both the pasture and broadleaved woods in the Inclosures (chapter 6). The 1877 Act, however, was insufficiently robust to prevent the destruction of many of the pasture woods behind Inclosure fences, nor the low-key exploitation of the unenclosed woods. The 1949 Act, moreover, was to include a provision which led to a period of more systematic felling of the latter.

First, let me briefly record the Victorian ornamentation of the woods. Between 1884 and 1887 nearly 3000 'ornamental' trees were planted on the unenclosed forest. They were mainly oak and beech but included chestnut, sycamore (*Acer pseudoplatanus*), limes (*Tilia × vulgaris* and *T. platyphyllos*), Turkey oak (*Quercus cerris*), red oak (*Q. borealis*), maples, various conifers and probably other species. Most were planted near roads and villages but some, mainly

Turkey oak, limes and sycamore, were planted out in the woods. In two places, in Matley Wood (SU333077) and Denny Wood (SU 332067) vigorous sycamore regeneration has since occurred. In one locality, Freeworms Hill on Fritham Plain (SU225129) a mixture of exotic species was added to a holly holm and is today known as Fancy Piece, or Fancy Trees.

The first documented loss of the wood pasture relics in the Inclosures after 1877 was the 8 ha of Burley Old Inclosure (SU2402) felled in 1923 (chapter 6). The next major assault was not until 1958–9, when most of Denny Inclosure (SU3206) was destroyed, an event to which I was a helpless and appalled witness. Denny was 44 ha of undisturbed, uneven-aged beech–oak woodland, with abundant 17th-century trees. In a few months it was reduced to timber stacks, mud and ruts. Only a 100 m-wide transect, for which The Nature Conservancy paid the Forestry Commission compensation, was spared. In the succeeding decade many more enclosed pasture woods were whittled away piecemeal. Many were scarred by new gravel roads built to service intensified management, and time after time driven through knolls of old beech pollards and small, discrete woods which, with greater sensitivity, could have been avoided. The same road programme destroyed Romano-British pottery kilns and boiling mounds. Puckpits Inclosure (SU2509), once a roughly circular wood dominated by A-generation beech and mantling the edge of a gravel terrace, was first slashed by a new gravel road, then partly felled and replanted with conifers. Like other woods, its aesthetic and biological identity and its microclimate were thus destroyed even though much of the wood remains standing.

From 1877 onwards, the unenclosed woods were over-shadowed by the persistent threat of 'management'. Successive foresters from Gerald Lascelles (Deputy Surveyor 1880–1915) onwards insisted that they derived from medieval or later plantations and that the trees had arrived simultaneously at senility without younger generations to replace them. Thus, the argument went, the woods required silvicultural treatment to survive. In 1875 Kenneth Howard, Chief Commissioner of Woods, claimed of Mark Ash Wood that it would be a treeless waste in less than 100 years. It is not. Indeed, all the contentions fail before the evidence in the field. However, the foresters' picture of the woods was so cherished and handed on that it gained an authority which set aside the evidence. What is astonishing is that it did so during a period when the woods were rapidly regenerating and expanding. *The Report of the New Forest Committee, 1947* records that the committee 'visited some of the woods and found the process of disintegration very conspicuous', though in fact they seem only to have been taken to Mark Ash Wood where the dominance of old trees is particularly obvious. The report (written mainly by the Deputy Surveyor, committee secretary) was persuasive about the altruistic motives of the Forestry Commission and the sensitive means that could be employed to 'regenerate' the woods. The result was Section 13 of the *New Forest Act 1949*, which enabled the Forestry Commission, with the consent of the Verderers, to enclose areas of up to 20 acres (8 ha) and carry out 'such forestry operations as appear to the Commissioners to be requisite' for 'preserving and regenerating' the woods. The lie was given to the motive by a later assertion by David Young, the Deputy Surveyor, that the Act 'gave us an opportunity at long last of putting these woods into production' (Pasmore, 1977).

The 1949 Act 'A & O' Inclosures as they became universally known, were an ecological disaster. Between 1951 and 1961, fifty-four Inclosures totalling 367 ha were punched into the established canopy of the woods. Most were clear-felled save for belts of timber left to testify to their earlier grandeur. Much of this died back from the sudden exposure. Seven Inclosures were in pure oakwood: five were planted with beech and two with beech and conifers. Forty-seven were in oak–beech woodland: four were left unplanted; seven were planted with oak and beech; twenty-five with beech alone; five with beech and conifers; one with oak, beech and conifers; and five with a mixture of beech, southern beech (*Nothofagus*), cherries and other exotics (Flower & Tubbs, 1982). Only four enclosures were deer-fenced, and few others remained pony-proof for long. Few fences were maintained and much planting failed. However, the crucial point is that the Inclosures were

Brinken Wood, 1967, during thinning of the ancient woodland – an ecological disaster (Photo A. H. Pasmore)

unnecessary for the conservation of the woods, which was the alleged purpose of the work. Uneven-aged woodland was replaced by even-aged groups, the continuity of the canopy was broken, and the structure of the soils destroyed by extraction. Sites on heavier soils were drained. This, together with the drainage of many woodland clearings in the 1960s and 1970s, further modified the woodland ecosystem.

This episode was followed in the 1960s by some more convincingly altruistic attempts to assist regeneration by the establishment of small fenced enclosures and individual trees in cages, beneath small gaps in the canopy of some A generation-dominated woods. More disastrously, in 1967, Brinken Wood (SU2706) was thinned, ostensibly to encourage regeneration and give the remaining trees more room. I believe this led directly to the deaths of most surviving beeches in the succeeding decade culminating in the drought year of 1976, which administered the *coup de grâce*. Practically no regeneration has occurred because of the grazing pressure.

Power to undertake the Brinken Wood felling derived from a clause inserted in the *New Forest Act 1964* which permitted the Forestry Commission, after consulting the Verderers, to carry out 'silvicultural maintenance'. It was on this that the Commission relied to justify the commercial aspirations of the 1963 Working Plan, which resulted in extensive felling in 120 ha of Rushpole

'Management' of Rushpole Wood, 1969 – a crisis in the Forest's history

Wood in 1969 (chapter 6). The wood suffered much structural damage and its glades and rides were reduced to quagmires.

The spurious or misguided attempts to assist nature in the 1951–70 period were not the only sources of damage to the woods. Until about 1920, trees were felled in the pasture woods to satisfy estovers rights (Lascelles, 1915). Subsequently estovers were satisfied mainly with cordwood from the Inclosures, but it became the practice to sell trees in the unenclosed woods for firewood on the grounds they were 'dangerous'. This formulae was stretched to its limits to satisfy demand. Many old pollard beeches, both in Inclosures and in the unenclosed woods, remote from public places and as sound as any other tree in the woods, were felled for firewood. I particularly regret the passing in this fashion of a fine assemblage of pollards felled in the driftway between Parkhill and Denny Inclosures (SU325059) in 1969, an event which fuelled the growing crisis. Mercifully, the intervention of the Minister of Agriculture in 1970 brought this abuse, as well as the more ambitious plans, to an end.

With the Minister's embargo on felling in September 1970 there was a pause for breath, in which I recall an enhanced pleasure in the woods because their survival was more assured. A new Management Plan was published in 1972, which among other innovations, suspended activity in the pasture woods until the NCC could carry out a detailed survey and propose new policies (Small, 1972). This was completed in 1982 (Flower & Tubbs, 1982). The basic proposal was a policy of non-intervention save for some argued exceptions. We were convinced that the woods had suffered more than enough intervention, and in particular we were persuaded that to deliberately break the canopy with 'regeneration fellings' grossly disrupted the ecosystem by increasing exposure, lowering humidity and attracting heavy grazing and trampling. However, it was thought prudent to propose the temporary enclosure (but not the felling) of the few areas where the A-generation canopy was beginning to open up and younger trees were absent. We also proposed the removal of the non-native and inappropriate trees planted in the A & O Inclosures. There were suggestions for experimentally re-introducing some of the lost tree species and for limited pollarding. The non-intervention policy and the other main proposals were subsequently enshrined in a revised Forestry Commission Management Plan for 1982–91 (Small, 1982). Even this enlighened document, however, could not resist describing the pasture woods as deriving from early silvicultural inclosure. The assumption that trees cannot grow without the aid of foresters dies hard.

Besides the policies adopted in the Management Plan, a code of conduct for the removal of fuelwood from the unenclosed woods was agreed between the Forestry Commission and NCC in 1974, in order to safeguard a crucial part of the ecosystem often lost to

Wind-thrown beech: the butt remains, the rest has gone for firewood.

woodland. Individual fallen trees and limbs had traditionally been sold for fuelwood where they were accessible, and increasing demand in the 1970s had resulted in large-scale removal. The code, which remains operative, stipulated that 20%, later increased to 40%, should remain in situ; that trees should not be removed where access would cause damage; and that no wood at all should be sold from 1231 ha of inviolate woodland. I speculate that the dead wood resource may be healthier today than at most times in recent centuries, during which, as the 1789 report confirms, the woods were scoured for fuel by local inhabitants and Forest officers alike.

The Cartographic Record

The earliest map showing the distribution of the Forest woodlands is Isaac Taylor's map of Hampshire and the Isle of Wight published in six 1 inch to 1 mile sheets in 1759. The 1789 report on the Forest was accompanied by a beautiful and detailed map at 4 inches to 1 mile based on surveys by Thomas Richardson, William King and Abraham and William Driver in 1786–7. The Old Series Ordnance Survey, published at 1 inch to 1 mile in 1811 and based on 3 inch to 1 mile drawings produced in 1797, clearly relied on the 1789 map for woodland distribution, as did most other maps, until a new survey in 1866–74 (mainly 1867–8) for the 1st edition OS New

*Dead beech – a 1976
drought victim, still
standing in 1983*

Series. Successive editions of the OS 1:10,560 (latterly 1:10,000)
sheets from then to the present time form the remainder of the
cartographic record.

The distribution of woodland on Isaac Taylor's map is similar
to that on the 1789 map. From the latter (Fig. 26) I estimate that
the area of unenclosed woodland was then 5466 ha, an approxima-
tion which takes no account of demonstrable or probable survey
errors (which were perpetuated on some later maps including the
Old Series OS). Of this, about 2227 ha were absorbed into 19th
century Inclosures, of which about 1800 ha were felled and replanted before the 1877 Act. Most of the woods which were enclosed formed part of an irregular pattern of wood and heath in the
catchment of the Lymington River, the woods mostly occupying
the higher parts of the eroded landscape and often comprising

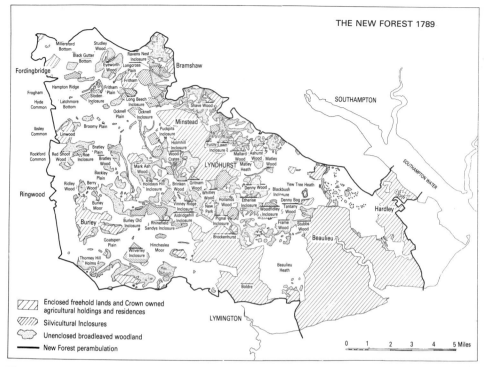

Fig. 26.
*The New Forest in the
Late 18th Century*

groves of pollards, some of which survive today among the plantations. Other pasture woods were lost within a scatter of Inclosures
along the north-east margin of the Forest. In both areas, parts of
the 1789 pattern survive (compare Figs. 2 and 26).

Between 1789 and 1868 roughly 200 ha of woodland was lost on
the unenclosed Forest as woodland margins retreated and clearings appeared, presumably as pockets of old A-generation trees fell
or were felled in places where successor generations had been unable to establish beneath a hitherto closed canopy. Many small
woods, perhaps holly holms, also disappeared from the heaths
during this period notably in the south-east of the Forest, presumably through fire, felling and grazing. These losses were bal-
anced after the mid-19th century by woodland expansion. Small
& Hackett (1972) calculated from comparison of successive OS
maps that the woods increased by 517 ha between 1867 and 1963.
Most of this comprises the 338 ha of 'birch, oak, some pine' in
Fig. 21, and the remainder is infilled parkland and glade.

How does the woodland area in 1789 compare with what may
be inferred for earlier times? In my earlier book I concluded that
it was considerably greater at the time of the 1608 timber survey
than in the late 18th century, though the evidence is slight. Sig-

nificantly, however, of about 100 woodland place names in 17th-century documents, only about ten are lost and all but four were still woodland in 1789, though doubtless many boundaries had changed somewhat. This argues for relative stability of distribution during the 17th and 18th centuries. I suspect that woodland retreat was only gradual during the earlier history of the deer forest. The fragments of coppice banks on acid grassland and heath can be seen, perhaps, as periodic pre-17th-century attempts to check the process.

A Speculation on the Future

For the immediate future at least, the pasture woods will remain free of ill-conceived intervention. The appearance of future generations of trees, however, will depend mainly on future numbers of commoners' stock and deer. These I cannot predict. The future of the old trees and rich flora and fauna dependent on them, is marginally less conjectural.

The density of living A-generation trees varied from 10–120 trees/ha in thirty measured plots in 1984. There is such enormous local variation that it is difficult to measure the resource without huge numbers of samples or a complete enumeration. However, density was usually in the range 20–50 trees/ha, of which between five and twenty trees were of pre-1700 origin. In 1984 I calculated that there were 60,140–150,350 A-generation trees, of which 15,035–60,140 were pre-1700. There was also a large resource of standing and fallen dead trees, ranging from 0–20 fallen and 0–28 standing dead trees/ha. Roughly half were contributed by the A generation. During the 1970s and 1980s this generation was contributing to the dead wood resource at an estimated 200–300 trees/year, excluding from this the large beech kill of 1976.

Assuming the natural span of oak on New Forest soils to be 400 years and beech 350 years, the 1650–1750 oak should die between 2050 and 2150, and the beech between 2000 and 2100, if they are not felled or wind thrown first. Arithmetically, windfall deaths at 200–300/year will not shorten the life of the generation, either of oak or beech. In practice, few oaks are windthrown, though it is a common cause of beech mortality. If these calculations are correct, the oldest B-generation trees will be old enough (oak 300 years, and beech 250 years) to adopt the biological role of today's A generation before its last trees die. However, the overlap between generations may not be long enough, and may not involve enough A-generation trees, for the more sensitive lichens dependent on old trees to persist. Also, although the supply of dead wood is likely to favour its invertebrate inhabitants until the 21st century, the supply will presumably diminish towards the end of the A-generation's life and a time-gap in supply may put part of this fauna at risk. These ideas are speculative, but suggest that 100 years is as long a time gap between tree generations in spatially limited woodland as it is prudent to accept if it is possible to plan otherwise. One management implication is that limited enclosure – but without felling – is an option to which it would be wise to resort. What must be guarded against, however, are further fellings such as occurred in the 1950s and 1960s in the name of conservation, an important effect of which was to diminish the resource of A-generation trees and thus increase the vulnerability of the woods to long-term impoverishment.

The pasture woods of the New Forest remain a unique and rich biological system. However, biologists who have studied the woods agree that they would be richer in plants and animals and closer to natural woodland in structure, had the saw been employed more sparingly, or not at all. The common practice of cutting drainage ditches from the 1949 Act enclosures and elsewhere has probably adversely affected the microclimate for many epiphytic lichens, bryophytes, insects and other forest organisms. The Inclosures have obscured part of the natural pattern of distribution, and most of the woods trapped within the Inclosures have since been destroyed or modified. The maltreatments of the past must never be permitted again if the woods are to survive and perhaps recover some of their lost riches.

The Forest and Forestry

The Silvicultural Inclosures comprise three main elements: the relicts of plantations established after the Acts of 1698, 1808 and 1851; the products of mainly 20th century replanting or natural regeneration which succeeded the harvesting of the earlier crops; and such trapped pre-Inclosure woodland as has escaped the saw. Much of the 18th- and 19th-century plantations have been felled in this century and mostly replanted with conifers. The so-called Verderers' Inclosures added further to the conifer plantations when they were planted on open heathland in the late 1950s and early 1960s (chapter 6).

Save for the element of pasture woodland, the broadleaved Inclosures are, in general, poorly-endowed with epiphytic lichens and bryophytes, nor do they possess sufficient senile, dying and fallen trees to support a particularly rich dead-wood insect fauna. The density of breeding birds, and especially of hole- and crevice-nesters, is lower in the oak and beech plantations than in pasture woods. On the other hand, the exclusion of stock from most Inclosures for most of the time, allowed a luxuriant shrub and herb layer to develop wherever light levels were high enough. The Inclosures came thus to be nationally renowned for their butterflies, moths, and other nectar-seeking insects. Sadly, and for reasons which I explore here, this is no longer so. Their loss is a major symptom of a more general biological impoverishment taken up again in later chapters.

The Legacy of Enclosure

Most of the 18th-century Inclosures included existing pasture woodland which survived behind the fences and in some cases survives today. However, most of this, and most of the plantations dating from the 18th century, were felled in the late 19th and the 20th centuries and replaced with conifers. Parts of the 18th-century plantations have survived in six Inclosures (North and South Bentley, Pitt's, Sloden, Raven's Nest and Long Beech), and pasture woodland enclosed in the 18th century has persisted in at least seven (Burley Old, Ocknell, Puckpits, Coppice of Linwood, Sloden, Raven's Nest and Woodfidley).

The oldest surviving 18th-century plantation is in the Bentleys, cleared and sown with acorns in 1700–3 (Flower & Tubbs, 1983). Those acorns are now widely-spaced, large-crowned oaks beneath

which there is a holly shrub layer and abundant natural regeneration of oak in gaps left by selective felling. All but 0.85 ha of North
Bentley were coniferized in the 1930s and 7 ha of South Bentley
were clear-felled and planted with Douglas fir (*Pseudotsuga
menziesii*) in 1967. The Minister's Mandate came just in time to
save the remaining 15.23 ha.

Only fragments of the 1775 oak plantations remain in Pitt's and
Raven's Nest Inclosures: all but 2.02 ha of Pitt's Inclosure was
coniferized this century, much of it in the 1960s, and most of
Raven's Nest was felled and replanted with conifers in 1967 and
1970, leaving only cosmetic belts of 18th-century trees. The 1787
survey (chapter 10) mentions old oaks in Raven's Nest at the time
of planting and some of these pre-Inclosure trees survive in the
belts today.

The 27.09 ha of 18th-century Sloden is more diverse. A discontinuous 1771 oak plantation is diversified with abundant yews
and hollies, and many ashes and hawthorns. Nowhere else in the
Forest are yew and ash so abundant in the woodland canopy. From
their size and open-grown form, some of the oaks pre-date Inclosure
and so, probably, do many hollies. The ash may derive from pre-
Inclosure trees: Sloden Coppice, which was within the later
Inclosure, was described in 1565 as comprising ash, holm and
thorn, and ash was also present there in 1609. Yew, however, is
not mentioned in the pre-18th century documents. A ring count
from the butt of a yew felled in Sloden in 1963 showed that it dated
from about the time of Inclosure and it seems possible that the
abundance of yew, holly and thorn derives from the method used
to establish the oak crop: in the Commissioner's report of 1789, a
witness describes how she was employed in the sowing of acorns
followed by the broadcasting of hawes, holly berries, sloes and yew
berries destined to form a nursery for the young oaks.

The Sloden yews were once more extensive. The present area
of 18th-century woodland (and it has remained unenclosed since
late in the 18th century) is less than one-third that of the original
Inclosure. The remainder, described in evidence to the 1877 Select
Committee as having comprised beautiful old yew thickets, was
cleared and replanted after the 1851 Act. Since the 1950s, dieback
and death have been slowly claiming many of those which remain.

Long Beech Inclosure, which was open ground in 1752, was
planted in 1775, thrown open in 1815 and partially re-enclosed,
clear-felled and planted with conifers in the 1960s. However, 32.86
ha of unenclosed woodland derived from the 1775 Inclosure remains, comprising even-aged stands of beech and oak with local
B- and C-generation development, on the upper slopes of a gravel
terrace penetrated by a network of small valleys containing alder
carrs and B- and C-generation beech and oak. Though little of Long
Beech appears to derive from pre-Inclosure woodland it is now a

beautiful and impressive wood of considerable ecological interest.

The pasture woods enclosed in the 18th century and still surviving, are ecologically comparable to those on the open forest but
their age structure has been influenced by their history of Inclosure.
Thus, Burley Old (24.74 ha) includes pre-Inclosure beeches; a
generation of oak and beech which arose after Inclosure in 1700,
and then, at intervals, perhaps as oak was removed for the navy,
until the Inclosure was thrown open in 1807; and another generation which arose on re-Inclosure in the 1850s. Closure of the canopy
has since prevented further development. Ocknell Inclosure (70.44
ha) has a generation of beech and oak dating from Inclosure in
1775. It has remained unenclosed since the late 18th century, but
the closed canopy limited B-generation development and the C
generation is confined to woodland margins. Puckpits (5.8 ha),
enclosed in 1700, was open for much of the 18th and 19th centuries
until re-enclosed in the 1860s. It, too, is dominated by 18th-century
beech, with some oak, whose canopy, combined with grazing,
prevented further regeneration until localized felling earlier this
century resulted in prolific oak regeneration. Finally, the 5.7 ha
ridge-top beech wood in Woodfidley (another 1700 Inclosure) contains a post-enclosure generation of beech; some 19th-century oak
probably deriving from re-enclosure in the 1860s after a long period
open to stock; and a C generation of beech which has arisen as a
result of fencing the wood against deer in 1962. Both Woodfidley

*Even-aged 19th-
century oak plantation
(North Oakley
Inclosure)*

Charcoal burning in the 1920s, using cordwood from a thinned oak plantation

and Puckpits were described in the report of the surveyors who prepared the 1787 map, as being full of young oak, the subsequent removal of which evidently led to beech dominance, as it did in so many pasture woods in the Forest.

Under the 1808 Enclosure Act, 5558 acres (2250 ha) were enclosed and planted between 1808 and 1823 and 1472 acres (596 ha) between 1830 and 1848. After the 1851 Act, 7347 acres (2974 ha) were enclosed between 1852 and 1870 and many of the older Inclosures which had been long thrown open were re-enclosed. With the 3252 acres (1317 ha) enclosed in the 18th century, the total area of silvilcultural inclosures was thus 17,629 acres (7910 ha) by 1870, of which, after 1877, only 16,000 acres (6478 ha) could be behind fences at any one time. In the 20th century the 2005 acres (812 ha) of 'Verderers' Inclosures' have further increased the enclosable area.

The earliest 19th-century Inclosures were mainly of pedunculate oak, with some chestnut. However, from about 1820, Scots pine and probably larch were used widely as nurses for the oak and as Inclosure-edge belts (Report of the Commissioners of Woods, Forests and Land Revenues, 1823). Most were removed during successive thinnings. Lascelles (1915) claimed that Scots pine was first planted in the New Forest in 1776 at Ocknell Clump (SU 250118), where a group of pines (certainly not of 18th-century origin) persists today. However, his source is unknown, and the first written reference to pine in the New Forest appears to be 1823.

For most of the 19th century, the oak plantations appear to have been thinned on a short rotation, a major inducement being the high price obtained for tan bark, which was stripped on the ground.

Early, heavy thinnings were also intended to promote the development of the large crowns which would yield the 'crooks' and 'knees' sought by the shipwrights. By the time the later plantations were maturing, however, the bottom must have dropped out of the market for ship-building timber and comparatively few of the oaks planted in the 19th century, supposedly to supply the naval yards, can have reached such a destination. Many survive as a legacy to the late 20th century of widely-spaced, even-aged oak plantations which collectively form a distinctive feature of the Forest.

Until 1851, planting had been restricted to trees which would produce navy timber. However, the 1851 Act extended planting to trees of any kind, which opened the way for conifer afforestation of the poorer soils which were not thought to yield oak or beech of reasonable quality.

'Instead of the varied intermixture of moor and wood and groups of oak, beech and holly scattered over the open spaces between the pervious woods, monotonous plantations of Scotch Fir are gradually overspreading the soil and obliterating its undulations' – G. E. B. Eyre (1871).

Even Lascelles, Deputy Surveyor from 1880 to 1915, observed with regret that much of the 'old Forest' had gone forever beneath the new Inclosures. In describing the 1851 Act Inclosures, he says that oak was planted wherever the soil was thought good enough, with alternate rows of Scots pine and larch nurses. However, planting

'went far to exhaust the oak-growing soil of the Forest . . . and quickly they came to the bad heath lands which could only carry Scotch fir, and that none too well' – Lascelles, 1915.

Besides Scots pine, Corsican pine (*Pinus nigra*), Weymouth pine (*P. strobus*) and Douglas fir were planted. Some survive today. The 40–50 m-high Douglas fir in Boldrewood Grounds (SU243083) and the ride-side rows which occur elsewhere, are hardly the New Forest but they are conspicuous skyline features.

The 1852–70 Inclosures included large areas of pasture woodland, whilst Puckpits and Burley Old Inclosures, first enclosed in the 18th century and subsequently thrown open, were re-enclosed. Many areas have been cleared and replanted, but besides part of Puckpits and most of Burley Old, parts of such ancient woods as Denny (SU3206), Ramley (SU358023), Knightwood (SU2606 and 2706), Wick (SU262092), Oakley (SU219049) and Vinney Ridge (SU 259052) survive, besides numerous small groups of old beeches and other scattered survivors of the pre-Inclosure Forest, all enclosed after 1852. Most of these woods show some evidence of a regeneration phase which followed enclosure. Lascelles (1915) commented on this and claimed, improbably, that the intention in

*Many old pollards
survive in the Inclosures*

enclosing these old woods was to 'serve as an object lesson to the
public' in how to perpetuate them. He chose to ignore the felling
and replanting which had already taken place.

Fig. 27 shows the present composition of the Inclosures. The
19th-century conifers bore the brunt of the heavy 1914–18 fellings,
and much of what remained, together with pre-1914 replantings,

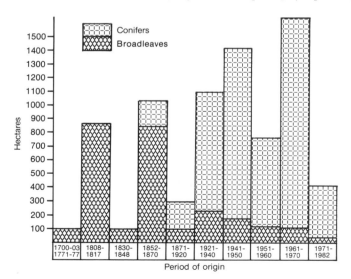

Fig. 27.
*Age Classes and Areas of
Broadleaves and Conifers
in the Statutory
Inclosures*

NB. Pasture wood, unplanted areas and some woodland of uncertain date
are excluded. Constructed from Forestry Commission information.

was felled in the early 1940s. Thus, most of the conifer plantations, mainly comprising Scots and Corsican pine, Norway spruce, Douglas fir and larch, derive from the replanting of felled conifer crops and the conversion of broadleaved woods after 1920 and again between 1940 and 1970. They include also the conifers of the new Verderers' Inclosures. Although extensive 19th-century oak and beech plantations survive, there are few broadleaved stands of 20th-century origin in the Inclosures. Most derive from natural regeneration. The Minister's Mandate of 1971 ended conversion to conifers and stipulated a rotation of at least 200 years for broad-leaved woods. In 1984 the Forestry Commission and the NCC agreed a policy for the pasture wood relicts in the Inclosure which was broadly similar to that for the unenclosed woods, and in which intervention would be confined to encouraging regeneration with-out the felling of mature trees. Since 1971, the area of beech has been increased by felling the conifer from mixed stands. Many oak and beech plantations have been thinned; a few of the oldest stands have been group felled to produce small clearings, and in Pond-head Inclosure a heavy ('shelterwood') thinning was tried, to promote regeneration. Before 1971 all these areas would simply have been clear-felled and replanted with conifers.

Many 19th-century oak plantations pose a particular dilemma. Such extensive, even-aged, 19th-century oakwoods as Amberwood, Islands Thorns and Broomy Inclosures are a remarkable habitat and possess a distinctive aesthetic quality simply because of their uniformity and extent. From within the woods, the widely-spaced trees stretch in continuous vaults to the limits of vision. There is little regeneration or shrub layer. Whatever is done to promote regeneration it can only be at the expense of the peculiar aesthetic appeal and spatial continuity of the woods. There are those who suggest that such a price may be so high that it would be better to permit them to go on untouched, to senility and decay 200 years hence.

The Field and Shrub Layers

Almost by definition, Inclosures were made to exclude the animals which suppressed tree growth, although their banks and ditches also formed indisputable legal boundaries. Before 1851 it was necessary to fence against deer as well as commoners' stock, but since then, fences have only been designed to exclude ponies, cattle and pigs. Individual Inclosures have not been continuously enclosed. From 1808 to 1848, the proportion of Inclosures thrown open grew from 24% to 44% as the trees grew beyond browse damage. It rose to 83% in 1851 in anticipation of the exercise of the rolling power of inclosure under the 1851 Act, but then fell steadily to below 40% in the 1870s as new Inclosures were planted and old ones thrown open. There it remained until the transfer of authority to the Forestry Commission in 1923, since which it has been maintained at 80% or more. Not all the Inclosures nominally enclosed were necessarily stock-proof at one time, but until the late 1950s commoners' animals found within secure Inclosures were impounded and released on a fine.

In recent history, the numbers of ponies increased steadily until 1978 (Fig. 9). After 1965, the density of stock increased sharply with the closure of the perambulation, which denied access to several thousand hectares of road-sides and greens which hitherto supported probably 20–30% of the stock turned out. Unsurprisingly, the sharp increase in grazing pressure led to the widespread penetration of stock into the Inclosures. In 1969 the Forestry Commission decided that in the absence of young, broadleaved plantations, the burden of controlling stock trespass could best be lightened by removing the locks from the gates and tacitly permitting the animals access, thereby incidentally saving the cost and trouble of continually replacing padlocks. The fences round six large Inclosure blocks were removed altogether between 1970 and 1974. Ponies in particular, rapidly penetrated everywhere. The ecological effects have been dramatic.

These events do not appear to have a precedent in the sense that all the Inclosures have before been open to stock; nor have a high proportion been open during a period of comparable grazing pressure. From the early 19th century, the Inclosures provided a reservoir of lightly-grazed woodland for plants and animals which were at a disadvantage on the more heavily-grazed, unenclosed Forest.

In the 1950s and early 1960s, sallow, bramble, roses, thorns, honeysuckle and other shrubs and climbers grew commonly at ride margins and wherever felling had opened up the canopy. The rides were linear, acid grasslands in which there was a profusion of small herbs, most of them common in acid grassland on the unenclosed Forest but here flowering unsuppressed. Drifts of thistles and other adventitious invaders of disturbed ground, were common. The ungrazed rides were periodically mown, a practice unnecessary after about 1970. The vascular flora of the Inclosures was formerly rich, and included many locally-distributed plants, mostly species of moist woodland streamsides and wood edges. At ride edges, the flora included plants derived from both woodland and grassland habitats and in moist localities on richer soils, the diversity was greatly extended. Here, woodland elements such as wood anemone, wood sorrel, primroses, pig-nut (*Conopodium majus*) and bugle could be found side by side with acid grassland plants such as self-heal, common milkwort and tormentil. In damp places and rideside ditches, plants such as great horsetail (*Equisetum telmateia*), common helleborine (*Epipactis helleborine*), bush grass (*Calamagrostis*

Hard-grazed ride, North Oakley Inclosure 1986

epigejos), yellow archangel (*Lamiastrum galeobdolon*) and columbine (*Aquilegia vulgaris*), occurred.

The richest Inclosures were those in the south of the Forest on Headon Beds and Barton Clays. Here, there were important populations of three, nationally-rare plants – lungwort (*Pulmonaria longifolia*), whose national distribution centres on south Hampshire and the Isle of Wight; bastard balm (*Mellitis melisophyllum*), which has a highly localized westerly distribution and is at the eastern limit of its range in the Forest; and heath sedge (*Carex montana*), which has a southerly distribution and for which the Forest is, or was, one of the most important localities.

Since 1969, grazing and browsing, mainly by ponies, has almost removed the shrubs and climbers and reduced the rides to bald, close-bitten turf. Little is permitted to flower in rides or at ridesides. Superficially at least, the formerly rich flora has gone, though doubtless most species survive in residual, non-flowering populations. These changes had begun in the mid-1960s, but after 1969, they were completed remarkably quickly.

The fate of the nationally rare species is uncertain. Heath sedge (*Carex montana*) is likely to have survived best (indeed, small colonies are known from the unenclosed Forest) but it appears to have gone from some former localities. Lungwort, whose blue flowers once sprinkled many ridesides in spring, is now very rare. Bastard balm persists in only one or two localities.

The field layer beneath native broadleaved trees in the Inclosures now closely parallels that in the unenclosed woods. The best-developed woodland plant communities are those of oak plantations

Extraction damage and machine regrading destroys the soil profile and tends to impoverish the ride flora

on brown forest soils which were at least partly wooded before Inclosure. Light levels beneath the oaks are relatively high and though localized, such places formerly supported a rich, acid oak-wood flora dominated by spring carpets of bluebells, wood anemones, wood sorrel, common dog violet and pig-nut, with abundand wood spurge and butcher's broom. Today, this flora survives in a sparse and degraded form, owing to grazing and trampling by stock. The ground flora of most oak plantations is sparse and dominated by grasses, though this is often attributable as much to impoverished soils as to herbivores: on slowly permeable, very acid clays, mostly planted in the 1850s and 1860s, purple moor grass is practically the only plant apart from the oaks. The shrub layer of most oak plantations is confined to variable densities of holly and, locally, hawthorn and is best developed in the earliest Inclosures where shrubs were encouraged as nurses for young trees. Other species are now sparse. Bramble and roses are common only in least heavily-grazed places on richer soils where growth rates can keep up with offtake. I recall some such Inclosures dense in low-growing shrubs in the early 1960s.

Mainly because of the low light levels, beech plantations are usually impoverished, irrespective of grazing. Most have a holly shrub layer and a field layer of bilberry, common cow-wheat and moss carpets, with much ground bare save for leaf litter. A further extreme of improvement occurs in the conifer plantations which, at their worst, are nearly sterile, and at best have a sparse field layer of grasses.

Epiphytes

Except in the pasture wood derivatives, the epiphytic flora of the Inclosures is relatively impoverished. Partly because of the lack of variety in tree form and thus the narrower range of physical niches, bryophytes are limited to comparatively few, common species. Few trees are able to support the prolific growths of common polypody so frequent in the pasture woods. Rose & James (1974) found that their 'climax' and 'post-climax' communities of old-forest lichens were, predictably, effectively absent from the plantations, although rich assemblages of pioneer species could occur in open, well-illuminated woods of younger trees close to sources of colonization in the pasture woods. The most notable example was Brockishill Inclosure (SU298113) where they recorded eighty-three species. The rarer, old-forest species occur with uncanny frequency where fragments of pre-inclosure woodland survive. For example, in Sloden Inclosure, *Chaenotheca aeruginosa* and *Lobaria pulmonaria* occur on oaks and two other rarities, *Becidia rubella* and *Collema subfurvum* on the base-rich bark of ashes, which it will be recalled, have been recorded from Sloden since the 16th century. Even the oldest plantations are relatively impoverished. South Bentley, cleared and replanted in 1700, had sixty species, but a high proportion occurred mainly at the Inclosure edge where they had evidently recolonized from the adjoining Anses Wood: one Inclosure oak here carried *Parmelia taylorensis*, which together with nearby oaks in Anses Wood forms the only British site east of Exmoor. Beech Bed Inclosure (planted 1775), much of it superficially similar to

Pondhead Inclosure, 1904. There was then an abundance of brambles and other shrubs in the rides. The notice says 'Sugaring is not permitted in this enclosure': few entomologists would bother now (Photo Robert Coles collection)

SCENE IN POND HEAD INCLOSURE

pasture woodland, has a poor ancient woodland lichen flora, which, indeed, confirms the historical evidence that it was mainly planted.

Invertebrates

Although the plantations lack the rich dead wood fauna of the unenclosed woodlands, the Inclosures were formerly rich in butterflies, moths and probably other nectar-feeding and scrub-dwelling insects. Between about 1870 and 1960, the Forest was renowned among butterfly and moth collectors and it generated a remarkably rich and voluminous entomological literature, albeit largely anecdotal. Both the literature and the recollections of those who collected here confirm that its wealth resided essentially in the little-grazed Inclosures.

'As I walked slowly along, butterflies alarmed by my approach arose in immense numbers to take refuge in the trees above. They were so thick that I could hardly see ahead and indeed resembled a fall of brown leaves. As soon as the sun came out again they descended from the trees and resumed feeding on the bramble blossoms.'

So S. G. Castle Russell (1952) described Ramnor Inclosure on his first visit to the Forest in July 1892. Then, and in the early decades of this century, he says that the Inclosure rides were trimmed infrequently and were:

'lined with bramble, each side getting its full share of sunshine in the morning, afternoon and evening. At the cross rides on which the sun shone from sunrise to sunset the bramble blossoms were crowded with insects of all kinds.'

In a remarkably detailed account derived from recollections and (importantly) notes made between 1892 and 1950, he described most of the southern Inclosures reachable in a day by rail, but he does not mention a single locality on the open Forest.

From the late 19th century until the 1930s, the Inclosures and their Lepidoptera sustained not only the annual invasions of amateur collectors, but those of local professionals, semi-professionals and dealers, among them a number of Forest keepers. So far as is known, the only species they actually managed to exterminate was the New Forest burnet moth (*Zygaena viciae*) (Tremewan, 1966). W. H. Hudson, who stayed at Boldre, detested the collectors:

'Lyndhurst is objectionable to me not only because it is a vulgur suburb . . . but also because it is the spot on which London vomits out its annual crowd of collectors' – Hudson, 1903.

It is clear from the entomological literature that there were always periods of abundance and times of scarcity, and that few Inclosures were consistently good collecting grounds. However, the inclosures remained a magnet to collectors until the 1950s. By 1960 it was generally agreed that numbers of most insects had declined. Harper (1963), after a summer in the Forest, attributed this to conifer afforestation, ponies, the mowing of rides and cutting of rideside scrub, which seems to have started in the early 1950s, perhaps before, and a series of wet summers. Other entomologists in the 1960s were in broad agreement (e.g., Symes, 1963). Rear Admiral A. D. Torlesse tells me that bramble clearance started in the early 1950s, well before many ponies penetrated the Inclosures.

The entry of stock into the Inclosures after 1969 administered the *coup de grâce*. With the removal of nectar sources and food plants, butterflies and moths declined alarmingly. Unfortunately, these declines were not quantified, but the universal opinion of entomologists is that the Forest in the mid-1980s is grossly impoverished of woodland butterflies and that the Inclosures are now poor places in which to seek moths. An NCC survey in 1985 confirmed the extreme paucity of butterflies of all species, and confirmed the general absence of nectar sources and most food plants other than trees and tall shrubs.

Of thirty-seven species of butterfly recorded in the Forest, all but one (the black-veined white (*Aporia crataegi*), extinct by 1883) were abundant or at least locally common from the 1870s to the 1940s. By 1960, wood whites (*Leptidea sinapis*), purple emperors (*Apatura iris*), and large tortoiseshells (*Nymphalis polychloris*), were extinct. Of thirty-three species remaining in 1970, a further three, probably five, have now joined them (Duke of Burgundy fritillaries (*Hamearis lucina*), high brown fritillaries (*Argynnis adippe*), small pearl-bordered fritillaries (*Boloria selene*) and green-veined whites (*Pieris napi*)). Most other species now occur in only very small numbers, often very locally. It is sad that such beautiful and once common woodland insects as white admirals (*Ladoga camilla*) and silver-washed fritillaries (*Argynnis paphia*) are now reduced almost to rarity. Even the common grass-feeding butterflies are now as few in the inclosures as they are on the unenclosed Forest. Significantly, purple hairstreaks (*Quercusia quercus*), whose larvae feed on oak and which do not appear to be nectar feeders, remain common.

Other grass- and shrub-dwelling insects have been affected. As in the pasture woods, the shrub-dwelling crickets are now rare, although the oak bush cricket remains common enough. I recollect the long grass of the rides alive with meadow, common green and woodland grasshoppers in the 1950s and 1960s, but the three species persist now only in low numbers. The Lepidoptera and Orthoptera must stand proxy for other groups of insects about which we lack information.

One large and characteristic insect of the Inclosures, the wood

Wood ant's nest

ant (*Formica rufa*), may have benefited from heavy grazing. The ants build enormous nest mounds of organic debris, situated so that they benefit from direct sunlight. Most are at ride edges and would thus be adversely affected by dense rideside scrub. The insects also forage extensively in trees to which they develop well-marked routes which would be impeded by tall vegetation. However, it is not known if the density of nests has increased with grazing. The insects are common, mainly in association with conifers, and one wonders also if they have benefited from the conifer afforestation which has adversely affected other species. Ant mounds are scarce in the broadleaved pasture woods.

Breeding Bird Communities

One would anticipate that the bird communities of the broadleaved plantations would be impoverished compared with the pasture woods, because holes and crevices are fewer, and the shrub layer is less well developed. However, the only quantitative data is from studies by June Irvine of plots in an even-aged 1811 oak plantation, Broomy Inclosure, in 1973–4, and an 1811 beech–oak plantation, Park Grounds Inclosure, in 1975–6 (Irvine, 1977; and unpublished). The species composition of both bird communities was remarkably similar to those of the pasture woods, but the total number of territories was significantly smaller. Nearly half of the

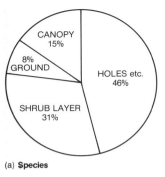

(a) **Species**

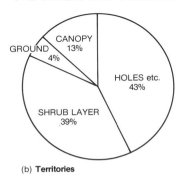

(b) **Territories**

Fig. 28.
*Bird species and
Territories associated
with Different Elements
in Broomy Inclosure,
1973–4*

species present were hole- or crevice-nesters, and 43% of the total number of territories were held by them (Fig. 28; cf. Figs. 22 and 23). There were no dead trees in either plot, but the trees were old enough to have developed a minimal number of holes and crevices, and in Broomy most trees supported vigorous old ivy which probably substituted for holes and crevices and provided sites for shrub-layer nesters. As in the pasture woods the most numerous species were blue tits, wrens, robins and chaffinches, but in Broomy, goldcrests and tree-creepers were numerically sub-dominant instead of blackbirds, great tits and coal tits, probably because of the abundant nest sites for these species provided by the ivy. Both plantations supported densities of wood warblers similar to those of the pasture woods: these mature plantations admirably fulfil the species' requirements for an open woodland floor and mature broadleaved canopy with suitable song posts.

In the 1950s and early 1960s the Inclosures provided a bird habitat which was, and is, otherwise largely missing from the Forest. There were then extensive areas of natural Scots pine regeneration derived from mother trees left after clear-felling in the 1940s and 1950s, mixed with invasive oak, birch, blackthorn and bramble. These areas provided perfect habitat for such scrub birds as whitethroats (*Sylvia communis*), garden warblers, willow warblers, blackcaps, lesser whitethroats (*Sylvia curruca*) and nightingales (*Luscinia megarhynchos*). In the more open parts, the bird community included red-backed shrikes (*Lanius collurio*), tree pipits and nightjars (*Caprimulgus europaeus*). In the 1970s and 1980s, this transient habitat and its bird community have largely gone from the Inclosures with the growth of the trees and the closure of the canopy, though some of the commoner species persist in the few areas of dense thicket stage plantation. Nightingales in particular are now rare in the Inclosures, and the shrikes have gone entirely from the Forest (chapter 14). Since the 1960s the fashion seems to have been to suppress the scrub in replanted areas by weeding – where the ponies are not already doing the job. Such broadleaved scrub as persists in the Inclosures has been heavily suppressed by pony-browsing.

With the maturing of the 19th-century conifer plantations and their successors, a distinctively Boreal bird community has developed, characterized by crossbills (*Loxia curvirostra*), siskins (*Carduelis spinus*), redpolls (*Acanthis flammea*), coal tits and goldcrests, besides firecrests (*Regulus ignicapillus*), which have a more southerly continental distribution. Only a few of the oldest stands support all six species. Chaffinches and wood pigeons are consistently present and in the oldest stands where the trees are large, widely-spaced, and have fissured bark, and in which dead limbs and trees occur, the community includes low densities of other species such as blue and great tits, robins, wrens, tree-creepers, woodpeckers, starlings and, often, hawfinches which seem to like the spreading branches of mature Douglas fir for nesting.

Only the crossbills are dependent on pine seed. In the Forest I have watched them feeding from Scots pine, Corsican pine and larch cones. None of the other species are able to extract seed from cones more robust than larch. Siskins and redpolls feed extensively on birch and alder seed and in the breeding season both are strongly associated with conifer or mixed stands in which there is some larch or abundant naturally-regenerated birch. Firecrests, goldcrests and coal tits are mainly insect-feeders and occur most commonly where conifer is mixed with broadleaved trees.

Crossbills were recorded breeding in the Forest in the 19th century and have probably bred regularly since 1910*, the population being supplemented by the periodic westward irruptions from the Boreal forests of northern Europe in years when the pine crop fails there. Large numbers bred after an irruption in 1961, but, despite subsequent influxes, the population has remained small in the 1970s and 1980s. Siskins and redpolls have probably bred periodically since the 19th century but only regularly since the 1950s and only commonly since the late 1970s. In the 1980s suitable pine stands are alive with calling and singing siskins in the spring. Redpoll colonies are more localized. Breeding firecrests were first found in Britain by Mike Adams in 1961 in a 19th-century Douglas fir stand in the New Forest. They have since been found widely in conifer, and mixed conifers and broadleaves, but whether they have increased, or whether we have simply become more accomplished at finding them is uncertain.

Conifers, mainly Scots pine, are important in the Forest in providing nest sites for carrion crows (*Corvus corone*) and birds of prey. In my studies of these species since 1961 (chapter 15), I found that more than 70% of crow nests, more than 50% of the buzzard's (*Buteo buteo*), all the hobby's (*Falco subbuteo*) and kestrel's (*Falco tinnunculus*) and all but two of the sparrowhawk's (*Accipiter nisus*)

*Wise, 1863; Kelsall & Munn, 1905; Witherby *et al.*, 1943.

nests, were in conifers. In pre-Inclosure days the distribution and perhaps density of at least some of these species must have been very different from that of the 1980s.

Concluding Comments

The recent biological impoverishment of the Inclosures has not been confined to their flora and invertebrates, nor have the effects been wholly confined within their boundary banks and fences. Roe deer (which feed mainly on climbers and low shrubs) declined by 58% between 1970 and 1984 (chapter 8) and though it is difficult to confirm, I strongly suspect that this was due to the removal of their preferred foods by pony-browsing, besides which roe are not tolerant of other large herbivores. Small mammals have also declined drastically and this in turn has adversely affected their predators (chapter 15).

Largely as a result of the demonstrable decline in butterflies and their food plants, and the changes in the buzzard population resulting from small-mammal declines, by 1980 the Forestry Commission acknowledged the ecological effect of pony- and cattle-grazing in the Inclosures and in 1983, a policy of ejecting stock and repairing fences commenced. At the time of writing, in late 1985, most Inclosures remain heavily grazed: keeping the animals out is not easy because gates, locked or not, can always be opened or left open. It will require great persistence to clear the Inclosures of stock, but the ecological benefits would be considerable.

Two questions remain in my mind. First, will the plants and animals which were formerly abundant revive their fortunes? Second, where were they before the Inclosures were made, mostly in the 19th century? There can be no certain answer to either question. The enrichment of the Inclosures may have derived from sources around the Forest as much as within it. Alternatively, in the pre-Inclosure conditions, when the Forest was part of a greater area of common land, grazing pressure may have been lighter than subsequently. In either case, the capacity of the Inclosures to recover may depend on the proximity of plant seed sources and butterfly populations around the Forest – and these, too, may be impoverished compared with earlier times.

CHAPTER 12 Heath, Mire and Grassland

Beyond the margins of the pasture woods, ericaceous heath is spatially dominant especially on the terraces, but it is patterned with acid grassland, bracken and gorse. Along terrace slopes there are arcuate lines of seepage step mires, wet heaths and flushes. The drainage networks are marked by ribbons and patches of grassland, often interspersed with scrub and wood, or by lozenges of valley mires and their peripheral wet heaths. Lawns extend among the woodlands, and the interface of wood and heath is often marked by an ecotone of grassland, bracken, scrub and trees – either invasive birch and young oak, or the old and often decrepit relicts of once more extensive woodland. Everywhere in the Forest there is the evidence of woodland invasion and withdrawal.

Fig. 29 distinguishes eleven plant communities which, with variants and intermediate gradations, make up the mosaic of heath, mire and grassland. The classification is mine and is subjective. It is confined to plant communities which are clearly

Plant community dominants	Soils	Area
Dry Heath Heather, bell heather, cross-leaved heath, dwarf gorse; common gorse frequent and occurring as dense brakes on disturbed areas	Permeable humus-iron podsols in sands in gravels	8121 ha
Humid Heath Heather, cross-leaved heath, purple moor grass	Slowly permeable ferric or humic-gley podsols in gravels, clays and loams	
Tussock Heath Purple moor grass tussocks; cross-leaved heath, petty whin consistently present in tussocks; intervening low, cropped purple moor grass – cross-leaved heath	Seasonally water-logged in hollows and on slight gradients	
Wet Heath Cross-leaved heath, purple moor grass, deer grass, *Sphagnum compactum, S. tenellum, Cladonia impaxa*	Seasonally water-logged surface water ferric or humic gleys and gley-podsols with peaty surface horizon	2894 ha

Seepage Step Mire
Cotton grass, deer grass, white-beaked sedge, purple moor grass, *Sphagnum tenellum, S. papillosum*, cross-leaved heath, bog asphodel

Permanently water-logged peat on impermeable or very slowly permeable clayey head below hillside seepage

Valley Mire
Central sallow or alder carr; complex lateral arrangements of purple moor grass – bog myrtle or reed; purple moor grass – Sphagnum – sedges; and Sphagnum lawn; grading at mire edges to wet heath

Permanently water-logged peat over impermeable or slowly permeable valley infill

Grass Heath
Bristle bent, bell heather, dwarf gorse, common gorse, tormentil, heath bedstraw

Argillic brown earth, mainly in brickearths and gravels

Acid Grassland
Bristle bent, purple moor grass, bracken; thickets (brakes) of common gorse, tormentil, heath bedstraw

Mainly gleyic, argillic brown, locally podsolic soils, in wide range of parent material

3993 ha

Improved Acid Grassland
Fertilized and limed bristle bent – purple moor grass from which bracken eliminated: brown bent, red fescue; rich associated assemblage of creeping perennials and rosette-forming herbs

Gleyic, argillic earths in loams and clays

Neutral Grassland
Brown bent, velvet bent, red fescue, perennial rye-grass, white clover; many rosette-forming herbs. Grades to wet fenny grassland where drainage impeded at surface

Gleyic argillic brown earths mainly in stream-side alluvium or clayey material in association with woodland, settlement edges and pond-sides

353 ha

Reseeded Areas
Brown bent, daisy, cat's ears; ribwort plantain etc. and rich assemblage of prostrate herbs

Mainly permeable soils derived from brown earths by cultivation

528 ha

Fig. 29.
Heathland, Grassland and Mire Plant Communities in the New Forest

identifiable in the field, but does not conflict with detailed classifications derived from statistical analysis of randomly selected quadrats by Fisher (1975a) and Atkinson (1984). This chapter describes the main plant communities, and chapter 13 discusses the extent to which the mantle of vegetation has been modified by grazing, fire, drainage, the cutting of bracken, turf and peat, mineral working and other activity.

Heathland

Heathland, in which heather (*Calluna*) is a dominant plant, clothes most of the open Forest (Fig. 4). It occurs consistently on the gravel terraces and over much of the intervening eroded valleys and hollows, though there are few large tracts unbroken by other vegetation. The leached soils are nutrient-deficient and acid, with a pH range in the bleached horizon of 3.4–4.5. The precise composition of the community depends mainly on soil moisture regime. On permeable sands, in which a humus-iron podsol has usually developed, bell heather and dwarf gorse are constant associates of the heather, and where the vegetation has been spared repeated burning, lichens of the *Cladonia* genus are numerous and luxuriant.

Most of the heaths, however, are formed on slowly permeable gley-podsols in which illuviation has resulted in a high subsoil clay content. These moisture retentive soils support a 'humid' heath of heather, cross-leaved heath and purple moor grass, and the lichen *Cladonia impexa*. On the highest, northern terraces, the humid heaths include some of the species characteristic of wet heaths, notably deer grass (*Trichophorum cespitosum*) and the moss *Sphagnum compactum*. Here, winter waterlogging is common and there are sometimes sheets of standing water on the level terrace surfaces in winter. Soils increase in permeability with the southward decline in terrace elevation, and, thus, in the degree to which they are invaded by dry heath plants such as bracken, bell heather, dwarf and common gorse.

Humid heath occurs only very locally on the extensive low southern terraces, where it is replaced by dry heath, grass heath and acid grassland, on loamy, relatively permeable brickearths (Fisher, 1975b). The north–south variation in terrace vegetation appears to be related to differences in the composition of the plateau gravels and brickearths, but perhaps equally to the differing time scales of soil development (especially illuviation) between the oldest (highest) and youngest (lowest) deposits. Gimingham (1972) includes a heather–cross-leaved heath humid heath community in his classification of heath communities, and the importance of the heather–cross-leaved heath–purple moor grass community in the New Forest emerged from statistical analyses of the heathland vegetation by Williams and Lambert (1961), Drapier (1966) and Fisher (1975a). However, it does not require numeracy to recognize humid heath as a common and characteristic element of the Forest vegetation.

Humid heaths are characteristic of the more elevated parts of stream catchments. Wet heath and tussock heath develop in the receiving areas of catchments, on gentle gradients lateral to streams or valley mires; in low depressions in undulating heathland; and on hill-sides downslope of groundwater seepages where permeable and impermeable strata meet. In all these circumstances they receive abundant ground and surface water. The wet heath community diverges from that of humid heath in the much poorer representation of heather and the consistent occurrence of deer grass, heath rush (*Juncus squarrosus*), common and long-leaved sundews (*Drosera intermedia*, *D. rotundifolia*), heath spotted orchid (*Dactylorhiza maculata*), *Cladonia impexa*, and the mosses *Sphagnum compactum*, *S. tenellum*, *Cornicularia aculeata*, *Campylopus brevipilus* and *C. introflexus*. The richness of the community depends partly on the amount of bare peat surface and thus on how recently fire has occurred; and partly on the occurrence of wetter hollows in the peat. Long-leaved sundew and mosses colonize the bare peat, and this habitat also supports a number of local plants such as the club moss *Lycopodiella inundata*, and brown-beaked sedge (*Rhynchospora fusca*). Common sundew is more characteristic of the wet hollows.

The dominant feature of tussock heath is the dense cover of mature purple moor grass tussocks. Tussock formation occurs where seasonally there is a steady movement of surface water, usually on relatively enriched soils. The most extensive tracts of tussock heath occur on the lower slopes of wide hollows between the low southern terraces, where they are often inundated for long periods in winter. They are rare, small and isolated on the more impoverished parent material in the north and west of the Forest. Cross-leaved heath grows abundantly in the tussocks, with small and variable amounts of heather. Petty whin (*Genista anglica*) is consistently present and creeping willow (*Salix repens*) and sneezewort (*Achillea ptarmica*) occur frequently. Between the tussocks there is a low sward of purple moor grass, cross-leaved heath, heath-grass (*Danthonia decumbens*), carnation sedge (*Carex panicea*), devil's-bit scabious (*Succisa pratensis*), heath spotted orchids (*Dactylorhiza maculata*), and in runnels, marsh pennywort (*Hydrocotyle vulgaris*) and marsh St John's wort (*Hypericum elodes*). Such an assemblage is indicative of relatively enriched, flushed conditions, but wet heath species, notably long-leaved sundew, *Sphagnum compactum* and *S. tenellum* also occur.

The tussock heath community has affinities with both humid heath and neutral grassland. Indeed, in places it grades downslope into the latter, and it usually grades upslope into the former. One nationally rare and declining plant, the marsh gentian (*Gentiana pneumonanthe*), is largely confined in the New Forest to tussock heath. In a survey of known and potential localities in 1984, my wife and I counted 1580 plants and estimated that the total population was probably in excess of 2000. More than 90% were in tussock heath, mainly in the Beaulieu River catchment. The remainder grew in wet heath at valley mire margins, with a few plants in humid heath. Most plants grew from the purple moor grass tussocks,

rather than from the intervening sward. Gentians are unpalatable
and if bitten off are discarded, but they probably depend on heavy
grazing to suppress competition from the potentially overwhelming
purple moor grass.

Mires

Various hypotheses have been developed to explain the origins of
valley mires. Mire initiation has been linked with forest clearance
and increased surface water run-off (e.g., Newbould, 1960); the
development of impermeable iron-pans in soils which have become
podsolized after forest clearance (e.g., Rose, 1953); beaver dams
(Sjors, 1976; Coles & Orme, 1982); and the impeding of drainage
by soliflucted clay plugging a watercourse (Hudson, 1957). Some
or all of these phenomena doubtless contributed to mire inception,
but I see no reason to modify my original view (Tubbs, 1968) that
the ultimate causes of mire development are the combination of a
poor hydraulic gradient and the presence of impermeable fill in
valley bottoms. In such circumstances, mire formation seems
inevitable: it needs only a nudge from climate (increased rainfall),
man (woodland clearance) or morphological accident (dams) to
initiate peat accumulation. The water-retentive property of the
peat will then ensure continued growth. *Sphagna*, in particular,
greatly assist the process: they have remarkable water-holding
capacity and grow from tip to capitulum, the lower parts of the
plant dying but decaying little in the waterlogged environment.
Thus, the combination of *Sphagnum* and year-round waterlogging
leads inevitably to upward peat growth which can only be reversed
by dramatic climatic change or artificial drainage.

Valley mires are most extensive in the south of the Forest, where
the valleys are wide and shallow and valley bottom gradients are
slight. In the north of the Forest, where the valleys are narrower
and more deeply incised into the higher terraces, and stream
gradients are steeper, valley mire development is more local,
though seepage step mires are better developed. Wherever hydraulic gradients remain adequate, accumulations of humose,
iron-rich alluvium have given rise to stream-side lawns instead of
mire.

An important characteristic of valley mires is that they receive
the products of leaching from their catchments. Nutrients are
most concentrated along the axis of flow, which may be neutral or
slightly alkaline in reaction, and increase in concentration downstream. They are least concentrated at the mire margins, which
may be very acid. Thus, there are declining nutrient gradients
both lateral to the axis and axially towards the headwaters. The
degree of enrichment depends on the base status of the parent

material from which soil water derives. Thus, the central flows of Denny Bog (SU347053), Matley Bog (SU335073) and Holmsley Bog (SU240002), which receive water from the Headon Beds or Barton Clays, are about neutral in reaction. Those of Harvest Slade Bottom (SU216070), Backley Bottom (SU223085) and Buckherd Bottom (SU214083), fed from sands and gravels, are decidedly acid.

The earliest description of the vegetation of New Forest valley mires was that of Rankin (1911). The first systematic survey of English lowland mires, including the New Forest, was carried out by Rose (1953), who synthesized mire structure in a cross-sectional diagram which remains difficult to improve upon (Fig. 30). Since then there have been at least five studies of New Forest valley mires which have classified the plant communities*, a survey of twenty-two selected mires by the Nature Conservancy Council in 1983 (unpublished); and a detailed study of the ecology of Cranesmoor mire (SU1902) (Newbould, 1960). The results vary, at least partly, because the diversity and local variability of the vegetation gives varied responses to the statistical treatment of quadrat data, but allowing for this, they do not essentially conflict with Francis Rose's concept, nor indeed, with the earlier ideas of Rankin (1911).

In Francis Rose's representative mire (Fig. 30), the water flow

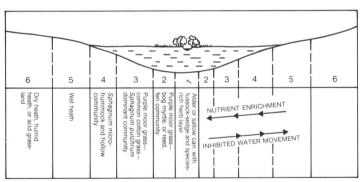

Mainly after Rose, 1953.

Fig. 30.
Diagram of a New Forest Valley Mire

is most rapid and concentrated, and the base status is highest, along the axis. Flow rates and base status decline laterally. Where the axial flow is neutral or alkaline, there is a linear carr maintained by continuous flushing of nutrients. The canopy is dominated by alder, often with sallow (*Salix cinerea*) and birch (*Betula pendula*) and a shrub layer of holly and alder buckthorn. Tussock sedge (*Carex paniculata*) forms magnificent tussocks within and at the carr margin. The stools of the alders are clothed in mosses, lady

*Newbould, 1960; Newbould and Gorham, 1956; Mussett, 1964; Wheeler, 1980; Atkinson, 1984.

Shatterford Bottom – a valley mire draining an acid heathland catchment, and hence with a poorly-developed vegetation zonation

fern, male fern and hard fern (besides the rarer species – see chapter 9), and the intervening wet peat supports a rich fen-woodland flora including such species as marsh bedstraw (*Galium palustre*), water mint (*Mentha aquatica*), yellow loosestrife (*Lysimachia vulgaris*), purple loosestrife (*Lythrum salicaria*), gipsywort (*Lycopus europaeus*), flote grass (*Glyceria fluitans*), remote sedge (*Carex remota*), creeping buttercup (*Ranunculus repens*), and lesser spearwort (*R. flammula*). Where the axial water flow is acid, the heavily flushed, species-rich carr vegetation may be replaced by sallow car or open mire communities: alder carr in the lower reaches of a mire usually grades to sallow carr in the headwaters. The latter may be comparatively poor in species, dominated by purple moor grass, and carpets of *Sphagnum palustre*, *S. recurvum* and *S. squarrosum*.

Flanking the carr is a transitional zone, intermediate between fen and mire, and particularly rich in species. This is often marked by purple moor grass tussocks from which abundant bog myrtle (*Myrica gale*) grows, or by reed (*Phragmites australis*), but it includes mats composed of such plants as marsh St John's wort, marsh cinquefoil (*Potentilla palustris*), sharp-flowered rush (*Juncus acutiflorus*), bog rush (*Schoenus nigricans*), bogbean (*Menyanthes trifoliata*), spike rush (*Eleocharis multicaulis*) and bog pimpernel (*Anagallis tenella*). The zone is penetrated by many acid bog plants, such as *Sphagnum contortum* and *S. subsecundum* and gradually gives way to an acid mire community of purple moor grass, cotton grass (*Eriophorum angustifolium*) and *Sphagnum* lawn (*S. pulchrum*, *S. papillosum*, *S. magellarium*) through which there is a low, diffuse flow of nutrient-poor water. This intergrades with or grades into an outermost *Sphagnum* zone in which such species as cross-leaved heath, bog asphodel (*Narthecium ossifragum*), sundews, white-beaked sedge (*Rhynchospora alba*), and cotton grass, are abundant. The *Sphagnum* lawn often exhibits a complex of hummocks and hollows, the former densely carpeted with *Sphagna*, the latter rich in higher plants. The structural diversity of the mires is further enhanced by the occurrence of numerous pools, many derived from war-time bomb craters, many deliberately excavated, some derived from ancient peat diggings, some apparently natural.

The idealized zonation is distinguishable in many mires, but in most, it is modified by such factors as the bifurcation of the axis of flow; differences in flow rate and water dispersion through the mire arising from topographic constraints on mire shape; and variations in the chemistry and volume of water reaching the mires. In Cranesmoor, for example, there are two peripheral lines of flushed vegetation dominated by purple moor grass–bog myrtle and bog rush (but no carr), with a *Sphagnum*-rich community in the shielded area between them (Newbould, 1960). The valley mires exhibit a range of structural variation which defies brief summary.

Mire vegetation also occurs on peat accumulated immediately downslope of hill-side seepages. Fig. 31 places these seepage step

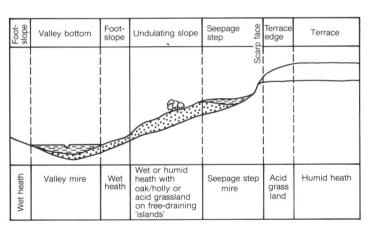

Fig. 31.
Terrace Slope Plant Communities and Morphology

mires in their topographic context. The origin and development of the seepage steps is described in chapter 2. In the cross-section, humid heath on the terrace surface grades to dry heath or acid grassland at the terrace edge, where surface run-off improves. Below that is the scarp face of the seepage step, and at its foot, the mire, which has developed on slight hollows in impermeable slumped material. Further downslope, a mosaic of wet or humid

heath, and acid grassland, sometimes with oak–holly woods, reflects irregularities in surface drainage and subsoil permeability
in the head deposits. This grades to the wet heath and mire of the
valley bottom. Such a profile is characteristic of the valleys pene-
trating the middle and higher terraces, and its incipient development can be seen in the lower terraces of the southern Forest,
where there may be no more than a wet flush line marked by wet
heath plants. In the valley heads, where the seepage step has
migrated the least distance from the valley axis, seepage step mires
may grade directly to the valley mire below, becoming isolated on
the valley side with progress down-valley.

The vegetation of most seepage step mires is close in composition
to the outer *Sphagnum* zone of valley mires. Most mires comprise
Sphagnum lawn (notably (*S. tenellum*), with deer grass, cotton
grass, bog asphodel and white-beaked sedge, on semi-liquid peat,
alternating with purple moor grass clumps. Where the groundwater
emerges from enriched strata, notably the Headon Beds, purple
moor grass is often abundant and there can occur such species as
marsh St John's wort, early marsh orchid (*Dactylorhiza incarnata*),
pale butterwort (*Pinguicula lusitanica*), and bog orchid (*Hammar-
bya paludosa*). One such seepage step mire has the only known
New Forest population of common butterwort (*Pinguicula vulgaris*),
essentially a northern species.

The structural diversity of the mires is reflected in the numbers
of plant species recorded. In Fig. 32 the number of species of
mosses and higher plants recorded for the twenty-three mires surveyed by the Nature Conservancy Council in 1982 is expressed as
a range and a mean. Species diversity increased with structural
complexity, and/or, with increasing pH in the axial water flow and

*Whitemoor Bog – a
valley mire with well-
developed alder carr and
lateral zonation*

	Sphagna	Bryophytes	Higher plants	Total species	pH range
Range	3–12	8–50	17–88	32–138	3.7–7.6
Mean	7.5	29	52.5	85	
Average	8.7	28	48	76	

Derived from unpublished NCC survey, 1982.

Fig. 32.
*Plant Species Recorded
in 23 Valley Mires*

thus in the representation of both acid mire and alkaline fen elements. The richest mires were Holmsley Bog (which also had the highest pH and the widest range in pH readings), Church Moor, Denny Bog, Shatterford Bottom, Row Hill Bog, Whitemoor Bog and Wilverley Bog, all with more than 100 species. The mire communities include a large number of species which are now rare or uncommon, especially in southern England, because of habitat destruction. They include one *Red Data Book* species, slender cotton grass (*Eriophorum gracile*), which is closely associated with old peat diggings in more enriched parts of a few mires; a second extreme rarity, the semi-aquatic pillwort fern (*Pilularia globulifera*); and at least seven species that are now very rare in southern England – bog sedge (*Carex limosa*); great sundew (*Drosera anglica*); bog orchid; pale butterwort; marsh fern; bladderwort (*Utricularia intermedia*); and small bladderwort (*U. minor*). What is more significant than the rarity of individual species, however, is that the whole inter-related sequence of plant communities which make up the valley mires, comprises a rare and precious habitat.

Grasslands and Grass Heaths

Tracts of acid grassland occur widely in the matrix of heather-dominant heath. In its most widespread form, this community comprises a field layer of bristle bent and purple moor grass which unless heavily shaded by bracken or gorse, forms a dense mat in which the only other species consistently present are heath grass, tormentil (*Potentilla erecta*), heath bedstraw (*Galium saxatile*), heath speedwell (*Veronica officinalis*), heath milkwort (*Polygala serpyllifolia*) – a species which occurs in the whole range of heathland plant communities – heath dog violet (*Viola canina*), lousewort (*Pedicularis sylvatica*), heath spotted orchid and petty whin. Bracken is widespread and common gorse (*Ulex europaeus*) occurs commonly in thickets, or 'brakes'. This vegetation is associated with the occurrence of acidic brown earths poor in phosphate and potash and acutely deficient in lime, but also occurs on soils in various stages of podsolization which are yet more impoverished in the upper horizons. The upper 10 cm of profile usually give a pH reading of 4.5–5.5, though it is sometimes lower. Towards the

Stream-side lawn, Ober Water

upper limits bristle bent–purple moor grass grades to brown bent (*Agrostis capillaris*), sheep's fescue (*Festuca ovina*) and red fescue (*F. rubra*), with sweet vernal grass (*Anthoxanthum odoratum*) on damper sites. The diversity of associated plants, mainly prostrate or rosette-forming species resistant to grazing, increases, though it is ultimately limited by the amount of litter generated by the bracken, and by the amount of shade cast by the fronds. The richest of the acid grasslands are those where the bracken has been suppressed by swiping and the base status slightly elevated by liming.

During 1969–71, the bracket was mown on forty-six widely-scattered areas totalling 266 ha (c. 6 ha/site). Another four sites (5 ha) were mown in 1984 and 1985. Thirty-four of the 1969–71 sites received single applications of chalk (c. 12 tonnes/ha) or lime (c. 5–14 tonnes/ha), temporarily elevating pH to as much as 6.0, though it has since fallen to 5.4–5.7. Together with heavy trampling and grazing, this has since kept the sites relatively bracken-free. The main effects on the vegetation were to greatly increase the density and enrich the species composition of the sward; and to encourage fescues, brown bent, perennial rye-grass (*Lolium perenne*) and meadow grasses (*Poa* spp.) at the expense of the more calcifuge bristle bent, purple moor grass, heath grass and sweet vernal grass. The limited lime applications were probably directly responsible for the changes in the dominant grasses, but relief from bracken competition was probably important in encouraging many other herbs.

The limed areas today support a rich acid grassland flora, with twenty to twenty-six species per 2 × 2 m quadrat (1984) and a total recorded flora of about fifty species. Grasses occupy less than half the cover. The remainder comprises rosette-forming species, mainly daisies (*Bellis perennis*), hawkbits (*Leontodon*) species, cat's ears (*Hypochaeris radicata*), ribwort plantain (*Plantago lanceolata*), mouse-ear hawkweed (*Hieracium pilosella*), dandelions (*Taraxacum officinale*), yarrow (*Achillea millefolium*), and ragwort (*Senecio jacobaea*); and a profusion of small perennial and annual herbs with low growth forms such as tormentil, heath bedstraw, heath milkwort, lousewort, common mouse-ear (*Cerastium fontanum*), self-heal (*Prunella vulgaris*), procumbent pearlwort (*Sagina procumbens*), birdsfoot-trefoil (*Lotus corniculatus*), slender trefoil (*Trifolium micranthum*), lesser trefoil (*T. dubium*), eyebright (*Euphrasia* spp.), squirrel-tail fescue (*Vulpia bromoides*), parsley-piert (*Aphanes arvensis*), black medick (*Medicago lupulina*), field wood rush (*Luzula campestris*), and a number of small sedges including carnation sedge, pill sedge (*Carex pilulifera*), oval sedge (*C. ovalis*) and common yellow sedge (*C. demissa*). All these small, low-growing plants are placed at an advantage by heavy, close grazing and trampling, which creates small gaps in the sward which they may colonize. Species of taller habit persist only as dwarf forms, but there is one notable exception.

Latchmore Brook – flash flooding helps maintain the nutrient status of stream-side lawns

One plant confined in Britain to the New Forest, the wild

gladiolus (*Gladiolus illyricus*), occurs on the more enriched, better-drained acid grassland soils, always beneath a canopy of bracken fronds. Most of the fifty to sixty localities from which it has been recorded here are at or near woodland edges, or are places from which woodland has been lost since the 18th century. Probably it is best regarded here at the edge of its range as a plant of the wood–heath ecotone, though it has a wider habitat tolerance in continental Europe. Dense bracken is little grazed during the growing and flowering season of the plant, and is, moreover, unattractive to stock because its litter has shaded out the other herbage. It seems that only in such places can the gladiolus escape grazing, for it is unquestionably palatable.

Acid grasslands are extensive on the southern terraces but become progressively less widespread on the terrace succession northwards. On the highest terraces they sharply demarcate small pockets of brown earth in the heathland matrix. They are a recurrent feature of valley slopes and hollows, where their persistence may be partly attributable to flushing. Their status seems precarious. There is strong evidence that many sites are woodland relicts of comparatively recent origin, and on many the soils are evidently deteriorating. Scattered holly, hawthorn, oak and yew, often fire-damaged or degenerate, are common, marking former woods which can sometimes be traced on the 18th- and 19th-century maps. In many places, relicts of a woodland ground flora persist. Species such as bluebells, wood sorrel and wood anemones linger where formerly there probably was oakwood; and on more acid sites, bilberry and common cow wheat persist, the former often abundantly, where once there were holly holms or beech-woods. Soils often exhibit iron movement and many are definitely podsolic. On many terrace sites at least, heath species are apparently invading. However, reversion to woodland is equally possible. Much of the post-1850 woodland expansion took place on acid grassland, and there are abundant localized examples of sites where holly, birch and oak are colonizing in the protection of a gorse brake which has long escaped burning and which has remained dense enough to provide protection against browsing animals. Equally, there are many sites where invading trees remain suppressed by browsing.

On the southern terraces, and locally elsewhere, the bristle bent–purple moor grass association is widely replaced by grass–heath. It occurs mainly on acid brown earths in permeable, loamy brick-earth and would appear to be at the arid, acid, end of the spectrum of acid grassland communities. Heath species, notably bell heather, are common, but purple moor grass is largely missing, and bracken has often failed to colonize. The sward is dominated by bristle bent, and small perennials such as tormentil, heath bedstraw and lousewort, are frequent. Gorse brakes are common. One area supports the only green-winged orchid (*Orchis morio*) population known to me on the unenclosed Forest. The plants are small, in this comparatively hostile environment, for a species more characteristic of neutral or alkaline meadows.

Natural grasslands on relatively enriched soils are confined in the Forest to woodland glades, clearings, rides and margins; stream sides; settlement edges; the periphery of certain ponds and elsewhere where stock congregate; and to roadside verges. Though their soils seldom achieve neutrality (indeed pH is sometimes quite low) it is convenient to distinguish them as 'neutral' grasslands. Their notional area (353 ha) is only about 2% of the unenclosed Forest (although the small size and irregularity of innumerable small lawns makes accurate measurement impractical), but they represent the richest grazing. The stream-side lawns in particular have traditionally been regarded by the commoners as critically important areas because of their relatively high yields and the early bite they provide in spring.

The base status of the woodland lawns has been maintained by centuries of leaf fall, and large amounts of organic debris being washed on to them from the interior of the woods during heavy rain. The most extensive woodland lawn is the 150 ha plain of Balmer Lawn (SU3003). Though most of this expanse would seem beyond the influence of the surrounding woods, it receives their drainage, and in winter is awash with organic material and enriched drainage water derived from their interior. The alluvial stream-side lawns are similarly nutrient-flushed, and benefit from periodic flooding by stream water enriched with the products of leaching

Bolton's Bench, Lyndhurst, a settlement edge lawn, probably of great antiquity

Settlement edge lawn,
Fritham

from the catchments. Stream-side lawns are relatively rich in exchangeable bases, though pH can be surprisingly low. The lawns
around settlements and isolated ponds clearly have a different
origin. The former arose from the concentration of stock close to
the villages and holdings from which they were turned out. Today
there is not the constant passage of milch cows and followers to and
from the holdings, but the lawns, once established by constant
dunging, perhaps centuries ago, have continued to attract large
numbers of animals, the dung of which maintains a supply of
nutrients. Similarly, the pond-side lawns evidently owe their origin
to intensive dunging by stock going to drink, or shading beside the
pond. Many of these ponds (good examples are Longcross Pond
(SU247153), Green Pond (SU226135) and Broomy Pond (SU
211107)), all on the higher terraces and dependent on a water table
perched on illuviated clay) were probably dug specifically as
watering places, though Sumner (1931) speculated that they had
natural origins. The strips of grass along almost every Forest road
are equally clearly artefacts and probably most were deliberately
constructed and seeded as road shoulders. In any event, they incorporate much alien material, some of it calcareous.

The flora of the lawns, like that of the acid grasslands, is dominated by species which are adapted to or demand heavy grazing.
Species diversity is lowest on those lawns where grass productivity
is highest because of concentrated dunging or extreme flushing.

Here, vigorous grass growth excludes competititors despite the heavy grazing. Thus, many settlement-edge lawns and most of those at pond-sides, tend to be species-poor with a high percentage cover of brown bent and fescues, and a low cover and species diversity of other herbs. Similarly, stream-side lawns often have a high percentage cover and diversity of grasses, mainly brown bent, red fescue, velvet bent (*Agrostis canina*), Yorkshire fog (*Holcus lanatus*), sweet vernal grass, and perennial rye-grass. White clover (*Trifolium repens*) is common and several rosette-forming species (plantains, hawkbits, cat's ears, yarrow, etc.) occur, but the vigorous grass growth limits diversity. Species diversity is also low on the smaller woodland lawns where the proximity of tree shade tends to exclude open grassland species and the sward is composed mainly of brown bent with small amounts of woodland plants such as wood sorrel, yellow pimpernel, creeping soft grass and tufted hair grass.

Diversity increases where the balance between grazing and grass production is tipped against the latter, and the grasses are sufficiently suppressed and damaged to permit the entry into the sward of the array of rosette-forming, low-growing or prostrate plants characteristic of the more species-rich acid grasslands. Other species, which demand more base-enriched or flushed conditions, also occur. Even so, the percentage cover of grasses – mainly brown bent, sheep's fescue, red fescue, sweet vernal grass, annual poa (*Poa annua*) and compressed poa (*P. compressa*) – is usually higher

Long Slade Bottom, cropped and reseeded in the 1940s

than on the richest acid grassland sites and other herbs are proportionately less abundant. The total grassland flora, however, is considerably larger at seventy to ninety species, depending on whether semi-aquatics which occur on the wetter sites are included.

On the drier lawns and on roadside verges, surface disturbance by trampling, and summer desiccation and grass die-back, are important in providing niches for small annuals, such as parsley piert, wall speedwell (*Veronica arvensis*), all-seed (*Radiola linoides*), sticky mouse-ear (*Cerastium glomeratum*), yellow centaury (*Cicendia filiformis*) and common centaury (*Centaurium erythraea*), many of which are generally rather uncommon because such conditions of intensive grazing and trampling on common land are now rare in southern England. These grasslands have several populations of the fern, moonwort (*Botrychium lunaria*). They also support some distinctly calcicole species – autumn lady's-tresses (*Spiranthes spiralis*), fairy flax (*Linum catharticum*), dwarf thistle (*Cirsium acaulon*), and at one road-side, bee orchid (*Ophrys apifera*).

Many lawns associated with the woodland and stream networks are either on impermeable or slowly permeable clays which are seasonally waterlogged, or in water-collecting places, or both. Among the lawns associated with the woodlands, there are abundant groundwater seepages and slow-yielding springs which give rise to acid flushes. The sward of these seasonally wet grasslands is very different from that of the drier lawns and is dominated by heath grass, sweet vernal grass, velvet bent, and moor mat grass (*Nardus stricta*), with abundant carnation, pill, oval, common and common yellow sedges, tormentil, devil's-bit scabious, creeping willow (*Salix repens*) and meadow thistle (*Cirsium dissectum*). Bog pimpernel sometimes forms extensive carpets, and in the more persistently wet places are marsh pennywort and sharp-flowered rush. The flushes may be marked by such species as marsh St John's wort and water mint, or where the water is more acid, by *Sphagnum* lawn. In some woodland lawns on more acid parent material, purple moor grass and cross-leaved heath are important constituents of the vegetation. The species diversity of the lawns is greatly enhanced where ant hills and mounds derived from grazed purple moor grass tussocks provide sites for many species otherwise confined to drier lawns. Where these occur, species diversity is often very high: Balmer Lawn, for example, has at least sixty species, including mosses.

Stream-side lawns often exhibit great variety of microtopography. Surface drainage is often impeded by levées (artificial banks) and there are frequent depressions and ancient stream channels which tend to develop, on soils with peaty surface horizons, a sward comparable with the wet woodland lawns. Diversity increases further in muddier, wetter depressions, which are dominated by marsh foxtail (*Alopecurus geniculatua*) and small sweet grass (*Glyceria declinata*), with abundant water purslane (*Peplis portula*), water mint, marsh pennywort and other wetland plants. Floating sweet grass (*Glyceria maxima*) is common in more or less permanent water. A number of these marshy grasslands have large populations of pillwort. They are a short step away from marsh or fen but their further development is arrested by the constant grazing and trampling of stock.

Seasonally-poached, muddy grassland, notably around ponds; supports several low growing or creeping plants of damp, disturbed places which have become nationally rare or scarce with the demise of heavily grazed commons on acid or neutral soils. They include coral necklace (*Illecebrum verticillatum*), confined in Britain to south-west England; ivy-leaved bellflower (*Wahlenbergia hederacea*), which has a wider western distribution but is uncommon; small fleabane (*Pulicaria vulgaris*), penny royal (*Mentha pulegium*) and slender marsh bedstraw (*Galium debile*), for which the New Forest is now the most important British locality; and Hampshire purslane (*Ludwigia palustris*), a semi-aquatic of muddy pools and their edges which is confined in Britain to the Forest. Much commoner occupants of the habitat include water purslane and marsh cudweed (*Gnaphalium uliginosum*). Most of the group flower rather late in the season and subsequent poaching and waterlogging appears to reduce competititon and aid germination before the ground dries again the following year.

Over-deepened drain, Denny Lawn. It denies the grassland the nutrients left from flash flooding

The Reseeded Areas

Since 1941, about 530 ha of the Forest have been reclaimed and reseeded. The first such attempts to 'improve' the grazing, at Ober Heath (SU285040), Longcross Plain (SU241150) and Long Bottom (SU185140) in 1941, consisted of ploughing, followed by light dressings of lime and fertilizer, and a broadcast seeds mixture partly consisting of barn sweepings. No fencing was attempted, and predictably 'improvement' was ephemeral. However, between 1944 and 1952, 350 ha in fifteen places, mainly acid grassland on well-drained sites, was fenced, reclaimed, and with two exceptions, grew arable crops – mainly cereals, potatoes, turnips, rape and flax – for three to four years before being put down to grass and the fences eventually removed. Two areas (Wootton (SZ248985) and Black Knowl (SU288035)) proved too wet to cultivate (they had probably been humid heath) and were seeded direct. Interestingly, to assist drainage, the final ploughing was done in ridge-and-furrow so that today in the New Forest there are two perfect mid-20th-century examples of the accentuated narrow rig ploughing marks more characteristic of early 19th-century reclamation of wet land (Browning, 1951).

About the same time parts of the war-time airfields at Stoney Cross (SU245125), Holmsley (SZ217090) and Hatchet Moor (SU350010) were reclaimed and reseeded. Three more reseeded lawns were added by the Verderers in the late 1950s at Fritham Plain (SU220130), King's Garden (SU210093) and Thorney Hill (SU210030), and the reseeded strips were established round the new Verderers' Inclosures (chapter 6). These reseeded areas established in the 1940s and 1950s persist as rectilinear, close-bitten lawns in the irregular mosaic of natural vegetation. They have changed remarkably in species composition since they were established. The seeds mixtures used in the Pastoral Development Scheme in 1944–52 mainly comprised commercial varieties of perennial rye-grass in various combinations with cock's-foot (*Dactylis glomerata*), Timothy (*Phleum pratense*), crested dog's-tail (*Cynosurus cristatus*), meadow fescue (*Festuca pratensis*), red fescue and usually some strain of clover (Browning, 1951). The wartime airfields were given prodigious quantities of fertilizer and lime, and were reseeded mainly with perennial rye-grass and small amounts of white clover (Brooke, 1961). Pickering (1968) studied the composition of reseeded areas of different ages and found that the rate at which new species invaded increased with time: the richest site, with thirty species (Black Knowl (SU290035)) was also the oldest. The leys could then still be detected, but by the 1980s all but their last faint traces had vanished. As a measure of declining nutrient status, pH fell from 5.9–6.8 in 1959 to 5.0–5.3 in 1979 on the 1944–52 reseeded areas (Ministry of Agriculture). The late

1950s reseeded areas similarly show little of the species with which they were sown.

Now, in the mid 1980s, common bent forms 30–50% of the cover of these grasslands. The rosette plants common in all the Forest grasslands, such as daisies, hawkbits, yarrow, ribwort plantain and dandelions, occupy 20–30% of the sward and the balance mainly comprises small, low growing species among which white clover, trefoils, self-heal, procumbent pearlwort, field woodrush, squirrel-tail fescue and early hair grass are the most constant and abundant. On the more acid sites, heath bedstraw, tormentil and bird's-foot trefoil are common. Damper sites tend to have a low percentage of grasses and a proportionately higher percentage of rosette plants and low-growing herbs, including many annuals and small sedges.

Despite their relative youth, the reseeded areas possess a rich flora which closely resembles that of the richer natural grasslands: diversity is lower if measured as species per unit area, but similar in terms of the total number recorded. Moreover, it includes populations of a number of uncommon plants mainly of neutral grasslands including all-seed, yellow centaury, chaffweed (*Anagallis minima*), autumn lady's-tresses, field gentian (*Gentianella campestris*), and moonwort. In 1985, my wife and I estimated that two of the reseeded grasslands alone supported about 400,000 field gentian plants – a truly remarkable sight, perhaps one of the largest English populations. One common chalk grassland species, fairy flax, is also common on some of the more base-enriched reseeded areas. Thus, they have developed a remarkably rich and interesting flora which includes both calcifuge and calcicole elements. Though their base status has declined (despite some fertilizer and lime applications in the 1960s), they appear remarkably stable and there are few indications of reversion to the acid grassland with bracken and gorse from which they were derived. Bristle bent and purple moor grass scarcely occur, and bracken or gorse invasion has occurred only on parts of some of the late 1950s reclamations. The former vegetation appears to be excluded by the large concentrations of stock on the reseeded areas, which maintains base status through dunging, thus excluding the acid grasses, and suppresses bracken and gorse by trampling and grazing. The rigid boundaries of reseeded areas now forty years old are remarkably intact.

CHAPTER 13

Heathland Exploitation

The Effects of Grazing

The composition of the heath, mire and grassland plant communities is as profoundly affected by herbivores as that of the pasture woods. Fig. 17 shows that in the later 1970s, most of the annual production of vegetation within reach of large herbivores was removed in the growing season, but studies also showed that different plant communities were exploited at different intensities and at different times of year. So, the extent to which the animals have modified the vegetation varies between plant communities. The most graze-adapted communities are those of the less acid grasslands, which are of limited extent and on which stock concentrate in large numbers. The least modified (and also the most uniform) are the drier heathlands.

The direct effects of grazing on plant communities depends on the density of grazing animals. Various studies have shown that light grazing of open range can stimulate productivity and increase species diversity,* but heavy grazing depresses production and

Ponies grazing purple moor grass in Holmsley Bog – grazing of valley mires enhances plant diversity

*e.g., Willard and McKell, 1978; McNaughton, 1979; Gessaman & MacMahon, 1984

tends to eliminate or suppress more palatable species unless they are adapted to heavy grazing (like grasses which respond by tillering). Beyond a certain threshold density, the grasses, too, become suppressed, partly because they are physically damaged by trampling, a situation which can be exploited by small plants with low growth forms which help them to escape defoliation and which cannot compete in a more closed community. This is the situation in the New Forest of the 1970s and 1980s. The lawns and re-seeded areas are particularly heavily grazed, and there is evidence to show that their productivity is being depressed (NCC, 1984). Though direct evidence is lacking, it would be surprising if reduced production were confined to grasslands. In any event, the large herbivores must be a causal mechanism in an inevitable long-term decline in base status and productivity. A large amount of the energy in the system is tied up in the animals and they are continuously sold off the Forest (commonable stock) or killed for meat (deer). The removal of trees, turf and bracken cutting and probably heath burning must all have contributed to the same process down the centuries.

The large herbivores also re-distribute nutrients within the system. On a macro-scale, the residue of nutrients taken up in food is re-deposited in dung and urine, which is most concentrated where most animals assemble. The persistence of the lawns is, in some measure, attributable to this, and its effects are particularly clear around settlements and drinking places. On a micro-scale, the tendency of ponies not to graze where they defecate produces local and often subtle variations in vegetation.

The effects of grazing on ericaceous heath in the Forest are clearest when comparison is made with ungrazed heaths on similar soils elsewhere in the Hampshire and Thames Basins. There are two major differences. Firstly, dwarf gorse is less common in the New Forest than in ungrazed heathland. It is preferentially grazed by ponies, and I suggest that its relatively low frequency in the Forest heaths is a result of this. Secondly, except on the most porous soils, purple moor grass achieves a high percentage cover on ungrazed heaths and abundant leaves and flower heads rise above the level of the heather. In the Forest, where most purple moor grass production is removed by animals, this layer is largely missing. On humid heaths, suppression of purple moor grass after fire is important in permitting ericaceous species to rapidly re-assume dominance. On ungrazed heathland, fire can result in purple moor grass dominance. In the Thames Basin and Weald this is often accompanied by birch invasion, which ultimately completes the transformation of the habitat.

To a casual observer, the Forest mires are not strongly influenced by grazing, although ponies can be seen foraging in all but the most inaccessible places. However, comparisons of grazed with ungrazed or lightly-grazed plots by M. J. Clarke in 1984, clearly showed the effects of grazing. The mean number of species in ungrazed or little grazed plots was 11.2 and in grazed plots 19.0, a 71% increase with increased grazing intensity. Species-richness declined with increased purple moor grass cover. Grazing checks the tendency of tussock-forming purple moor grass to overwhelm the complex mire communities and permits the non-tussock and especially the smaller species, to flourish. Heather and cross-leaved heath are checked with the purple moor grass from whose tussocks the plants grow. All other higher plants benefit from reduced purple moor grass cover, both in percentage cover and number of species.

Michael Clarke's measurements confirm my own unquantified observations, which suggest that in the absence of grazing purple moor grass eventually obscures much of the vegetation zonation lateral to the mire axis. In extreme cases almost monospecific stands of dense, tall tussocks are formed, whose dead straw chokes the mire each winter and spring, and among which only fragmentary relicts of more diverse communities persist. I suspect that many New Forest mires would become increasingly diverse if grazing were more intensive. Besides the removal of purple moor grass by stock, poaching by animals' hooves has an important role to play in providing habitats for the less robust flowering plants.

Similarly, the flora of the Forest grasslands is highly distinctive, and with the exception of the bristle bent/purple moor grass community, is strongly adapted to heavy grazing. The grasslands are collectively and sometimes individually species-rich, which is not wholly in accord with the general view of heavily-grazed grassland. Their flora is greatly enhanced by the profusion of small annuals which colonize bare places resulting from trampling (on dry sites) and poaching (on wet sites), and which comprise a floristic element largely missing from less heavily-grazed grassland on similar soils.

Five main elements are discernible: grasses, which tolerate defoliation; rosette-forming plants, low-growing perennials and small (often tiny) annuals, all of which can, in varying degrees, escape defoliation; and somewhat taller, but unpalatable plants, both annuals and perennials. Many of the rosette plants and small, creeping species are unpalatable as well, and are thus doubly afforded protection – penny royal is a notable example. The gentians, centaurys, orchids (though not their leaves), moonwort and to some extent sneezewort, are among the taller unpalatable plants. The flowering stems of most rosette plants are often nipped off, but the animals are not avid for them and they are so abundant that large numbers of flowers survive. One species – common ragwort – is unpalatable when alive and toxic when wilted.

Not only is the species composition of Forest grasslands adapted to grazing, but the size of individual plants (including grasses) is much reduced and more prostrate than in less grazed places, and only a small proportion succeed in flowering. Thus, a newcomer is confronted with the necessity of identifying many species by the vegetative characteristics of often dwarfed forms. Interestingly, mat grass, and heath rush, usually indicative of heavy grazing in upland Britain, are not widely abundant in the Forest, though the former is sub-dominant in some damper lawns. It may be suppressed by ponies, for lawns are often littered with mat grass tufts which have been discarded as unpalatable.

The closest parallel to the Forest grasslands would seem to be some grazed stream-side lawns in acid upland areas of south-west Britain. Comparison with enclosed but agriculturally unimproved meadows in and around the Forest is difficult, since these, too, are mostly heavily grazed. However, the richest and lightest grazed, which is also a Hampshire & Isle of Wight Naturalists' Trust reserve, includes what amounts to a stream-side lawn, wet flushes and dry acid grassland, and shows what might happen to Forest grassland if grazing pressure declined dramatically. The small annuals, many of the rosette plants, heath grass and the small sedges, are scarcely represented, but there are dense stands of tall rushes (*Juncus articulatus, J. bufonius, J. effusus*) and sneezewort, and abundant pig nut, water dropworts (*Oenanthe crocata, O. fistulosa, O. pimpinelloides*) and other palatable plants, besides at least ten abundant grass species. The vegetation is lush compared with the familiar Forest lawns. Only on the highest and driest parts does the flora begin to take on some of the characteristics of Forest grasslands.

Cattle grazing tussock heath.

Since about 1960 large areas of heathland have become much modified in physical structure and species composition, and most lawns have expanded through increased grazing pressure. Many lawns yield evidence of earlier similar phases. Three mechanisms are involved: defoliation through grazing, with a loss, often total, of photosynthetic capacity; the physical damage to plant material caused by trampling; and the deposition of dung and urine, with consequent smothering, scorching and local nutrient change. Trampling and defecation are potent phenomena. Ericaceous plants are highly susceptible to destruction by trampling, and they are also killed by the concentrations of nitrogen and potassium in urine. Bristle bent seems similarly susceptible, but heath grass, carnation sedge, several of the other small sedges, purple moor grass, common bent, fescues and other species common lawns, are more-or-less resistant, though they may suffer temporary scorching. Because ponies in particular tend to defecate in definite latrine areas or (like cattle) during route marches between shades and feeding grounds, their eliminatory behaviour has considerable potential for locally modifying the vegetation.

I estimate that since 1966, when I mapped the vegetation of the unenclosed Forest, c. 400 ha of dry and humid heath, mostly near lawns, re-seeded areas or elsewhere where animals congregate, have been converted to a low, suppressed sward of heather, heaths and purple moor grass, with abundant heath grass, carnation sedge and other small sedges entering the community. This grades to a purple moor grass sward below flush lines on slopes, and then to expanding lawns in valley bottoms. Over a similar time span, the ericaceous vegetation has been reduced and suppressed in most areas of tussock heath, often after fire has eliminated the mature plants, and regeneration has been limited in vigour by repeated cropping of the young shoots. Possibly these tussocky purple moor grass grasslands were once humid heath, in which abundant surface water led to purple moor grass tussock formation during periods of low grazing pressure. Subsequently, grazing suppressed heather and cross-leaved heath and permitted the variety of small herbs (and the gentians) to increase by opening up the canopy.

Many woodland glades and clearings supported humid heath in the late 1960s, though this vegetation was said locally to have invaded grassland during the 1920s and 1930s when stock numbers were low (Figs. 9, 10; Tubbs, 1968). Since 1966, most of these glades have been transformed into the wet woodland lawns described in chapter 12, by concentrated grazing based on residual grassland. The transformation coincides with the suppression of invasive birch and an end to regeneration of birch and other woody species (chapter 9). An important mechanism in lawn expansion is the tendency for ponies to establish latrines at lawn margins, leading to the replacement of heath by grassland plants in a progressively extending zone. An associated phenomenon is the persistence of belts of gorse, notoriously a plant of enriched or disturbed soils on heathland, at the edges of the reseeded areas.

Latrines are distributed within as well as at the margins of grasslands. Edwards & Hollis (1982) found that the faeces of ponies, cattle and deer, were concentrated in well defined areas on the lawns, clearly visible on aerial photographs as darker areas in a matrix of lighter grey. The latrines were stable in area over the three years of the study and were marked by a comparatively tall sward with abundant creeping and spear thistles (*Cirsium arvense*, *C. vulgare*) and common ragwort. Ponies tended to graze in non-latrine areas but cattle, which usually defecate at random (Marsh & Gampling, 1970) were not similarly inhibited. Cattle, and apparently deer, were thus attracted to the longer grass which they found easier to graze, rather than the close cropped sward on the remainder of the lawn. Hence they contributed further to the manuring of the latrines. Notably, on most lawns, the margins were non-latrine areas, ponies deliberately leaving the lawn to dung or urinate on the adjacent heath or acid grassland.

A characteristic feature of New Forest lawns on low-lying ground is the occurrence of numerous low mounds. Some are certainly the domed hills raised by the yellow meadow ant (*Lasius flavus*), but dense aggregations of anthills are confined to a relatively few drier lawns, some of which are impressive 'antscapes': sadly, the best of them at Fletchers Thorns (SU278044) was partly destroyed during the formation of the grazing strip around a Verderers' Inclosure, in 1959. The 'moundscapes' so common in the Forest lawns prove to have a wholly different origin.

In some places, mounds occur at very high densities. Over most of Balmer Lawn (150 ha) there are 80–110 mounds/10 m^2, each 10–20 cm high, flat-topped and up to about 100 cm long and 50 cm wide. Anthills are more domed and circular, though some mounds have been adopted by ants and may be intermediate in shape. Comparable densities occur elsewhere but not over so large an area. Densities of 40–80 mounds/10 m^2, however, are more usual. I estimate that about 40% of the woodland and stream-side lawns are thus covered. The mounds are always elongated along the axis of surface water flow, suggesting that they had extended axially by the accumulation of particles deposited by slow-flowing water against their upstream side. Long ago I concluded that these remarkable moundscapes must be derived from the intensive grazing of purple moor grass tussocks and Peter Edwards (in press) has now confirmed this in a study centred on the lawns along the Ober Water (SU255038). There, he found that mounds occurred on cropped grassland at similar densities to purple moor grass tussocks in the longer vegetation of little-grazed latrine areas. Excavation showed that purple moor grass remains could still be found in many mounds. All stages in the conversion of purple moor grass tussocks to low, consolidated mounds dominated by common bent, fescues and other small herbs, could be seen. In a survey of lawns in 1982–3, I similarly found that mounds in all stages of this metamorphosis were characteristic of lawn margins which adjoined zones of tussock heath, as for example along much of the Dockens Water and Beaulieu River. Bog myrtle, which is seldom browsed, evidently benefits from the suppression of purple moor grass and heaths, and occurs abundantly in the mounds: it is, indeed, the characteristic occupant of a zone at the junction of lawn and wet, often tussocky heath.

Thus, the moundscapes derive from hard grazing of purple moor grass-dominant tussocks. The extent to which dunging aids lawn expansion in this context is unclear. The implication is that many lawns, especially those at stream-sides, formerly resembled tussock heath. The transformation to lawn has in part taken place within the span of my own experience and is continuing. However, it must also date from earlier periods of high grazing pressure and in places conversion to lawn has clearly been aided or initiated by drainage, which encouraged animal access. The lawns with the highest density of mounds – Balmer Lawn (SU305035), Alum Green (SU278074) and Warwick Slade (SU272066) – were drained between 1846 and 1852 (Pasmore, 1977). These, and many other lawns, though thought of as anciently stable, are evidently of recent origin although there are no means of knowing if the tussock heath which occupied them had itself invaded former lawns.

Fire and Drainage

'Management' of the heaths, mires and grasslands in the sense of deliberately manipulating plant communities and water regime, dates from the mid 19th century and has mainly taken the form of heath burning and drainage, as well as the various reclamations of natural vegetation to 'improved' grassland described earlier. In the 1970s and 1980s cutting has partially replaced burning and there have been limited attempts to eradicate bracken. All these activities were legitimized by the *New Forest Act 1949* (chapter 6). Heath fires lit by the local inhabitants with the intention of 'making pasturage more plentiful' (Gilpin, 1791) occurred in the 18th century and probably before, despite the efforts of the crown to prevent them. Controlled burning by the crown dates from about 1870.

In the mid 19th century, B generation trees and shrubs invaded the lawns, and heaths and pine spread widely from the seed sources in the enclosures. This was a contentious issue between crown and commoners in the debate preceeding the 1877 Act, and the Verderers' records show that it has periodically been so since. The

Carting bracken cut on the Forest, early 20th century (Photo Phillip Allison collection)

crown began burning mainly to forestall incendiary fires, but there was seldom enough done to satisfy the Verderers, and it was sometimes claimed that invasive pines were deliberately avoided. Inevitably, what was seen as a shortfall in official burning provoked unofficial fires, especially in the 1920s and 1930s, when they appear to have been important in checking the spread of C-generation trees. In the absence of modern fire appliances they were often devastating. Sumner (1931) described 'blackjacks', the charred stems and stumps of holly and gorse, as being widely collected and sold for firewood. A sporting licensee, C. C. Dallas (1927) complained about the destruction of the covert:

The commoners demand this burning to improve the feed for their cattle and ponies, and I believe the Crown fear that unless their wishes are complied with, there will be a risk of fires in the plantations . . . Not only is the Forest excessively burnt by the Crown servants but many incendiary fires take place which, during the dry weather of spring can be seen burning day and night.'

Since the 1949 Act the Forestry Commission have carried out an annual programme of controlled burning, mainly of ericaceous heath and gorse brakes. At first, 800–1200 ha were burnt annually, but since 1965 (when 1000 ha were burnt) the area has averaged 100 ha (Small, 1982), distributed in numerous patches rather than (as hitherto) a few large areas, in order to limit the fragmentation of plant and animal distributions.

The main purpose of burning or cutting is to limit colonization by Scots pine, birch, and other woody vegetation, and to maintain the quality of the herbage for stock, which benefits from the stimulation of purple moor grass and the fresh growth of gorse and heather which succeeds fire. The amount of purple moor grass forage produced is greater on humid and wet heaths, where it occurs most abundantly, and least in dry heath, where only a sparse scatter of shoots appear. Thus, for forage, it is better to burn or cut the former than the latter. In general, this is consistent with nature conservation, because mature dry heath, especially where it includes gorse brakes, is richest in bird, reptile and invertebrate life. Dry heath is also of much more limited extent than humid and wet heath. Hence, the NCC has consistently argued for a longer rotation on its limited area and the concentration of most of the annual programme on humid and wet heath. In practice, the rotation has varied widely from place to place because the programme is planned (inevitably by a committee of Forest Commission, Verderers, commoners and the NCC) mainly in response to commoners' demands and firebreak needs. Few areas are burnt at less than eight-year intervals, most go much longer, and some heath has not been burnt since the 1950s, though this includes the swards heavily suppressed by grazing. It has proved difficult, however, to check the tendency to constantly deplete the resource of mature dry heath, which is always seen as 'needing' burning.

Burning is legally confined to the period 1 October–31 March, and the practice in the New Forest is to confine cutting to this period as well. Most burning is carried out in March. Provided the fire has not destroyed the peaty soil, which seldom happens at this time, purple moor grass regeneration is rapid, the burnt sites often showing as conspicuous light green patches in April. Regeneration from roots, first of heather, then cross-leaved heath, gorse and other species follows. On wet and humid heath it may be 3–4 years before the Ericaceae regain co-dominance with purple moor grass, depending partly on the degree to which the latter is suppressed by grazing. There is a tendency for heather to remain suppressed for several years, during which cross-leaved heath becomes dominant and the percentage cover of purple moor grass declines. Heather exclusion may be further prolonged by another fire. Old heather bushes regenerate least successfully from rootstock, and the success of recolonization from seed may depend partly on the density of other vegetation, in turn part dependent on grazing intensity. Cross-leaved heath appears less inhibited in both respects and is moreover comparatively little grazed. In contrast, on dry heath, burning usually results in bare peat surfaces in which heather and heaths regenerate more slowly, first from roots and later from seed. Purple moor grass is often completely absent from the driest sites, but bristle bent sometimes invades and achieves local dominance for a time after fire. The drier sites also tend to be invaded by bracken, which locally remains dominant for many years.

Though many effects appear short-term, burning tends to simplify dry and humid heath communities, and in particular to destroy the lichen component which may need more time to re-establish than the interval between fires. This does not occur with cutting. In some cases, on seasonally waterlogged humid heath on the higher terraces, fire has resulted in some nearly monospecific stands of purple moor grass which after fifteen years or more, have been scarcely penetrated by heath species, though deer grass and some other wet heath species occur on bare peat. Indeed, on wet heath, burning often diversifies the community by permitting the colonization of deer grass, sundews and other species which require bare, wet peat. The precise sequence of events after fire is influenced by so many variables, among them the age of the stand, the temperature of the fire, and the density of grazing animals, that predictions are often hard to make.

One medium-term effect of burning has become increasingly clear. Since the 1950s it has combined with grazing to suppress the gorse brakes which are so characteristic a feature of the acid grass-lands and dry heaths. They are a rich wildlife habitat and provide both food and shelter for stock. Hence they deserve special manage-ment attention. However, the regenerating shoots are avidly con-sumed by ponies and in extreme cases, this results in the death of the bushes. It universally retards regeneration. Many gorse brakes have been reduced to scattered, topiarized, bushes. Other brakes have been eliminated. In an age-structure study of heathland vegetation in 1972–3, I found that 94.4 ha had thus failed since March 1967 (Tubbs, 1974) and large areas have gone since. At the other extreme, large tracts of old, straggling gorse with low photo-synthetic potential, persist unburnt, mainly on acid grassland. These have limited functions as forage, stable, or wildlife habitat. The management problem is that fire will inevitably lead to their destruction for bushes of such age have poor powers of regeneration and cannot survive browsing of the first new shoots (Tubbs, 1974).

In a general sense, burning maintains the heathland in a fire-plagioclimax. Its long-term effect will be to diminish nutrient re-sources which are partly lost in smoke (which contains much of the nitrogen and some of the other nutrients) and partly in the removal of ash in surface water run-off to streams and valley mires (Giming-ham, 1972). Such effects may be reduced by cutting the vegetation, though losses will be incurred by the removal of heather bales which are sold as sub-base material for drives, and until recently, public highways.

The structural pattern of the heathlands changes continually through fire. The effects of drainage are more localized and more lasting. The earliest drainage schemes, intended, like burning, to 'improve' the Forest for stock, were carried out between 1848 and 1852, and a further twenty-seven schemes were carried out in 1923, 1924 and 1930 (Pasmore, 1977). Since the 1950s, there has been an annual programme of drainage, mainly maintenance work. The 19th-century schemes were mainly confined to the lawns around and among the woods in the centre of the Forest, roughly between Brockenhurst and Lyndhurst, including Balmer Lawn, Pignal Hill Lawn, Weare's Lawn, Sporelake Lawn, Alum Green and Warwick Slade. All these schemes left a legacy of moundscape lawns derived from wet purple moor grass tussock heath, though in most places there are areas of lawn which were always clearly drier, presumably pre-dated drainage and probably formed the focus for the individual schemes.

I have traced most of the 1923–30 drains in the field and it seems that at least five schemes comprised maintenance of drains first cut during 1846–52. Of the remainder, at least nine schemes involved fundamental damage to all or part of the same number of valley mires. Deep, canalized channels were cut along the axes of the mires and the spoil heaped on top of the peat beside them. In most cases some lateral drains were cut. In no case did this savage treatment of fragile habitats which had probably taken 2000 years or more to develop, completely succeed in destroying them, but it ruptured their hydrological regime and lateral vegetation zonation and must have indirectly destroyed many of the plants and invertebrates which comprised the mire communities. Easily the most disastrous cases were those of the mires flanking the Avon Water, which were the most extensive to be drained, even then known to be biologically among the richest, and which today still bear the scars of maltreatment. In the 1980s, there has again been pressure for the drainage of Holmsley Bog, close to the source of the Avon Water. Even in the 1920s, drainage intentions there provoked protests from naturalists, though in vain. It is a measure of changed perceptions that fifty years later, the proposals have been successfully resisted.

The remaining thirteen schemes dating from 1923–30 essentially involved the clearing out, deepening and in some cases straightening of streams beside which there appear already to have been lawns, though in most cases localized moundscapes suggest that they were extended by reducing the water table and thus the vigour of the purple moor grass, in stream-side tussock heath. A few schemes, some of which are now difficult to trace, appear to have been further attempts to drain woodland clearings.

The expressed intention of the recent annual programmes of drainage has been to prevent existing lawns from becoming progressively inundated by standing water and hence returning to something akin to the vegetation from which they appear, at least partially, to have been derived. The difficulty lies in the numerous claims by commoners that areas were once lawn which manifestly have been mire for a thousand years or more, or which, equally, have long been wet heath on extremely acid soils.

Moreover, demands for lawn 'restoration' can sometimes only be satisfied by cutting a drain through a down-slope mire. Hence, drainage has emerged as the most contentious issue between the commoners and conservation organizations. During 1965–85, ninety-six drainage projects of varying magnitude were carried out by the Forestry Commission as part of the duty imposed by the *New Forest Act 1949* (chapter 6). Of these, thirty-five were within eighteen mires, eight of which suffered significant ecological damage; five were on wet heath and had little effect other than to create a mess; and fifty-six were on lawns. Four of the schemes involving valley mires were ecologically disastrous: in 1966, a cutting was dredged through the head section of Matley Bog alder carr (SU328061); in 1971–2 axial drains were cut in Dibden Bottom (SU393062) and Bagshot Moor (SZ369999); and in 1968 and 1970 Denny Bog, among the largest of the Forest mires, was partly drained. This last scheme, like others, was justified on the grounds that the mire was spreading across adjoining lawns, but the scale of the drainage was wholly out of proportion to the problem, and though nominally intended to skirt the mire, the main drain grossly modified its hydrology and plant zonation. The axial flushed zone in the upper mire, which was aligned down its south margin, was destroyed by the new drain which ran down the same side, and both here and in the lower mire, the acid outer zones were also lost. Populations of many scarce plants, including great sundew, pale butterwort, slender cotton grass and pillwort, were destroyed. Compared with its earlier glory, the mire remains structurally impoverished today.

The Legacies of Exploitation

Documentary and field evidence show that the unenclosed Forest was formerly a more used and exploited place than now. Until well into this century, the commoners cut turf from the heaths, and each autumn cut the bracken for bedding and litter. Gorse was collected for fodder and in faggots for the ovens and kilns. The gravel terraces bear the superficial scars of innumerable small gravel workings. Marl was dug until late in the 19th century, though perhaps for cob building construction rather than for dressing the land, and clay was dug for local brickworks. Ill-defined cart tracks linked all these activities with villages and holdings, or village with village, and have left their marks on the Forest of today, often as parallel hollow-ways where they cross shoulders of hillside or converge on a single point. In this century, military use, mainly during two wars, has left the relics of airfields, camps, batteries, ranges and the gravel pits which provided material for their construction. Over 2000 ha in the north of the Forest were appropriated as a bombing range between 1939 and 1946 (Pasmore, 1977), and there was extensive disturbance there to the surfaces of the high terraces. Casting back into the centuries, there is the abundant evidence of ancient field systems, pounds, paddocks and bee gardens. Though not simultaneously occupied, they underline the extent to which the forest was formerly exploited.

The scale of exploitation in the 19th century is reflected in the accounts of Forest keepers. In 1854, George Cooper, keeper of Boldrewood and Castlemalwood Walks, sold 497 yards (380 cu m) of gravel, 600 faggots and 20 yards (15 cu m) of sand, besides issuing 'tickets' for the cutting of 455,000 turves. The following year he sold 1264 yards (967 cu m) of gravel, 7400 faggots, 2 cart loads of rushes and 100 'black thornes', and licensed the cutting of 597,000 turves. We do not know for how long exploitation on this scale had occurred and it had doubtless escalated in the 19th century with the local share of national population growth, but probably all the commodities sold by George Cooper in the 1850s had been exploited for centuries.

The scale on which turf was cut inevitably begs the question of its effects on the heaths. We can derive some order of scale for turf-cutting in the 19th century from keepers' accounts and diaries. In Boldrewood and Castlemalwood Walks, an average of 515,000 turves were cut annually from 1853–6, and in Eyeworth and Bramblehill Walks, an average of 232,714 were cut annually from

Mr Wyatt of Furze Hill demonstrating how turf was cut (Photo Phillip Allison)

1864–70. These Walks represent roughly 20% of the Forest, giving an estimated annual average total of 3,755,000 turves. Assuming a turf to be 30 × 30 cm (roughly one square foot), 35 ha of heath would be cut annually. In 1892, the new Agisters made a return to the Verderers giving an estimate of 1,250,000 turves cut annually (Pasmore, 1977) which would mean cutting 11.6 ha of heath each year. If the customary practice of 'cutting one and leaving two' was followed (and we know from complaints that this was not always so), three times the area would be needed annually. Most heath with suitable peaty surface humus must have been cut at some time, though from the Agisters' returns, there were then favoured areas to which the cutter returned repeatedly, and this must always have been so.

In effect, turf-cutting repeatedly truncated the soil profile and (aided perhaps by summer fires) prevented the accumulation of more than a very shallow surface organic layer. The result (apart from destroying the recent soil pollen record) is to perpetuate the acid-tolerant heathland plant community, and in particular to check purple moor grass on less permeable soils, leaving bare surfaces for colonization by mosses, sundews, deer grass and other plants besides the recolonizing heather and cross-leaved heath. In Holland, turf-cutting is now used as a means of restoring heathland by the removal of the litter layer left by the grassland and woodland which have succeeded it (e.g., Werger et al., 1985).

Peat cutting in the mires was discussed in chapter 4. That it occurred is indisputable, but unlike turf-cutting it seems undocumented. It has, however, left clearer physical traces in regular depressions and rectilinear pools rich in aquatic plants and insects which occur frequently in the mires.

That the cutting of bracken and faggots (like turf-cutting) was a constant check on tree colonization is confirmed by the vehemence with which the Commissioners of 1789 condemned the practices, and the 19th-century documents are punctuated with comparable complaints by the crown. However, autumn bracken cutting, by preventing the progressive accumulation of litter, also enabled the grassland field layer to flourish, the mature bracken fronds at the same time reducing summer dessication. With the decline of bracken-cutting since the 1930s, the field layer has widely been impoverished or eliminated by smothering, and the total forage resource for stock on acid grassland consequently much reduced.

Comparison of aerial photographs of 1947, 1977 and 1983, however, yield little certain evidence that bracken has spread widely from the old-established stands, and indeed, with the exception of local invasion of heather after fire, bracken distribution seems remarkably stable. There is some indication that many wild gladiolus colonies have declined recently, and it may be that litter accumulation within bracken stands is having an adverse effect on this, as

Bracken cutting on the Forest c.1905 (Photo Arthur Kemish, Edward Jewell collection)

well as other plants (notably lesser butterfly orchids) which appear to benefit from a degree of bracken shade. The post-1970 bracken eradication schemes do nothing to assist such species, nor would they seem to help the stock. The sward is continuously hard-grazed in summer, a time of ample forage, and yields nothing in autumn when it is more needed. The grass and forbs beneath the bracken, however, are comparatively little exploited until late summer, though cattle tend to lie up in the bracken and fallow deer leave their fawns there. Thus, it forms a forage reserve which is being largely lost with the virtual demise of autumn bracken-cutting.

Marl pits, clay pits, gravel pits, road-side and railway borrow pits and bomb craters (and there were many left by war-time visitors to nearby Southampton, besides those on the range), have left a legacy of ponds which range from near-alkaline (some marl and clay pits) to the very acid (some gravel pits). In the 1960s, Arthur Cadman, the Deputy Surveyor, added a series of pools intended simply to enhance the wetland habitats on the Forest. One, happily, bears his name. There are now at least 329 ponds in the Forest, most of them derived from human activity since the 18th century. The more enriched pools support a rich aquatic flora, including rarities such as Hampshire purslane, pillwort and water violet (*Hottonia palustris*); many have interesting poached-ground

The bracken stack at Penn Farm, Bramshaw, c.1905 (Photo Arthur Kemish, Edward Jewell collection)

floras at their margins; and a large proportion are important amphibian breeding sites.

Time has clothed the ancient enclosure banks and ditches, the former trackways, the mineral workings and the relics of 20th-century war, with a mantle of natural vegetation approximating to that of their surroundings. However, telling signs of the disturbance survive in the present vegetation. The effect of much ground disturbance was to leave steep, free-draining slopes, and hence many features are marked by dry heath in a matrix of humid heath or acid grassland. In summer, many banks and the sides of hollow ways are crimson with bell heather, contrasting with the rose-pink of the cross-leaved heath flowers in the surrounding heathland. Similarly, old enclosures often support grass-heath or acid grassland, often with gorse brakes, in contrast to the surrounding heathland, the enclosure bank forming so abrupt a boundary between the communities that it is difficult not to conclude that farming has enriched the soils within the enclosure. Perhaps the most significant legacy of ground disturbance, however, lies in the distribution of common gorse.

In 1974 there were 1557.8 ha of gorse brakes in the Forest, of which 490.4 ha (32%) occurred in heather-dominant heath and 1067.4 ha on acid grassland (Tubbs, 1974). Most of the former and about half of the latter were, and are, associated with old gravel workings, military disturbances, tracks, hollow ways, banks, barrows (most of which were disturbed by 18th- and 19th-century treasure hunters and antiquaries) and other artefacts of human activity. Such features are probably mainly of post-17th century origin, but many enclosure banks are of earlier origin (Jones & Tubbs, 1963; Tubbs & Jones, 1964). A similar relationship has been found in Ireland (Lucas, 1960), the Isle of Man (Killip, 1963), Dartmoor (Dearing, 1977), Dorset (Moore, 1962) and Brittany (Gehu-Franck, 1961, 1974), and, indeed, it is commonly remarked upon.

Gorse is intolerant of the very low nutrient levels in most heath soils, and will not usually persist in seasonally waterlogged gleys. Free-draining, acid brown earths suit it well. Its persistent occurrence on disturbed ground has been explained by the elevation of nutrient levels on the upper horizons by the inversion of podsol profiles, and by the initial advantage it possesses in its ability to fix gaseous nitrogen through root nodules, thus permitting it to gain a secure hold in soils deprived of nitrogen by the absence of vegetation (Gehu-Franck, 1961, 1974). Once established, the gorse brakes persist tenaciously, assisted by periodic fire following which the bushes coppice vigorously unless they are very old or, and, very heavily browsed. The gorse brakes may prove to ameliorate the soils: there are examples of soil profiles beneath dense gorse in the New Forest which appear to be regenerating podsols. Where they remain unburnt, they also shelter colonizing birch, holly and oak, and may thus form part of the succession back to woodland, a succession perhaps aided by their capacity to regenerate degraded soils.

The Heathland Fauna

In this chapter I revert to the term used in chapter 1 to describe the mosaic of ericaceous vegetation, grassland, scrub and mire which collectively characterize impoverished, base-poor rocks in lowland England – that is, lowland heath. The definition is useful, because few birds, mammals or insects are confined to any one of the component plant communities, and indeed, most occur in open habitats elsewhere. Within the lowland heaths, most occur at boundaries between plant communities or require combinations of them.

For the vertebrates of the New Forest lowland heaths there is a comparative wealth of information derived from national and local population surveys and ecological studies. Our knowledge of invertebrates is more sketchy. There is enough information to come to some very general conclusions about the composition and ecology of the fauna, and for grasshoppers, crickets, dragonflies, butterflies and some moths we have a somewhat better understanding of distribution and ecology. The first comprehensive sampling of invertebrates from any of the heathland habitats, however, did not take place until 1983 when Dr D. A. Sheppard (NCC) sampled a number of valley mires. There is abundant scope for research, notably into the relationships between species composition and ecology, and herbivore grazing and fire.

From a palaeo-ecological point of view it is interesting that a relatively large number of animals are, or appear to be, adapted to heath, grassland, mire or scrub habitats, all of which, in the fashionable scenario, are supposed to have succeeded a primary woodland cover. I have expressed doubts about the validity of the continuous Atlantic forest in chapter 4 and I am led back to them here.

Heathland Vertebrates

In Britain, only two species of vertebrates are confined to the lowland heaths – the Dartford warbler and smooth snake. Two other species – the sand lizard (*Lacerta agilis*) and natterjack toad (*Bufo calamita*) – also only occur on coastal dunes on the north-west and east coasts. On the lowland heaths, all four species are closely associated with mature dry heath, though natterjacks also require near-neutral pools for breeding (Beebee & Griffin, 1977). All are at the north-western limit of their geographical range in Britain, and it is interesting that all occur in a wider variety of dwarf shrub, scrub and open habitats in more southerly and easterly parts of

Europe. The New Forest supports nationally important populations of Dartford warblers and smooth snakes and a small population of sand lizards. Natterjacks are now absent from the Forest.

Most vertebrates characteristic of the lowland heaths also occur in other habitats. They include avian and mammalian predators which range widely over woodland, farmland and coastal country as well as heathland (chapter 15). Many are common to other steppe-like vegetation and to scrub or scrub–woodland ecotones. In the New Forest, open-steppe species include red-legged partridges (*Alectoris rufa*), skylarks (*Alauda arvensis*), woodlarks (*Lullula arborea*), meadow pipits (*Anthus pratensis*), wheatears (*Oenanthe oenanthe*) and common lizards (*Lacerta vivipara*). Ecotone species include cuckoos, nightjars, tree pipits, grasshopper warblers, whitethroats, whinchats (*Saxicola rubetra*), stonechats (*S. torquata*), yellowhammers (*Emberiza citrinella*), linnets (*Acanthis cannabina*), slow-worms (*Anguis fragilis*), grass snakes (*Natrix natrix*) and adders (*Vipera berus*). This group included black grouse (*Lyrurus tetrix*) and red-backed shrikes until their extinction in the Forest in the 1930s and 1980s respectively (Tubbs, 1968 and 1985; Bibby, 1973). The Forest heathland shares comparatively few non-raptorial species with the deciduous woodland from which most of it probably derives, but exceptions are chaffinches, robins, willow warblers, blue tits, wrens and perhaps some of the reptiles. The diversity of the heathland vertebrate community depends mainly on the extent to which the matrix of ericaceous dwarf-shrub vegetation is diversified by gorse brakes, other scrub, invasive trees, bracken and acid grassland. The bird community of continuous tracts of heather is poor in diversity and density, particularly in winter, when the heaths often seem empty. It is not always similarly impoverished of reptiles: all six native species are known to achieve high densities in mature dry heath diversified only by patches of sand and bare soil.

In spring the Forest wetlands are enlivened with the sounds of displaying waders; some streamsides and mire edges are dotted conspicuously with pairs and groups of shelduck (*Tadorna tadorna*), mostly non-breeders; and pairs and small groups of mallard (*Anas platyrhynchos*) are everywhere. A few pairs of teal (*Anas crecca*) – probably no more than ten to fifteen in total – breed around some of the southern mires. There is a constant passage of waders and shelduck between the Forest and the coast. Redshank (*Tringa totanus*), in particular, journey daily to the coastal mudflats to feed, often until well into May, perhaps reflecting only a slow increase in available invertebrate food biomass in the mires early in the breeding season.

The populations of lapwing (*Vanellus vanellus*), redshank, curlew (*Numenius arquata*) and snipe (*Gallinago gallinago*) are relatively large and important (Fig. 33). All four species have suffered nation-

Species	Breeding populations
Lapwing	Locally dense breeding aggregations, e.g. 41–49 pairs in 196 ha, Hatchet Moor, 1971–74 (Jackson and Jackson 1975). Widely distributed elsewhere, e.g. 47 pairs in 3100 ha 1981. Estimated population 1981 250–450 pairs
Redshank	60 breeding pairs, 1961 and 14 pairs found 1962 in area not searched 1961; 20–30 pairs 1963 after severe winter; 42 pairs 1966; 105–140 pairs 1981
Curlew	Estimated 55 pairs 1960 (44 pairs in 75% of heathland/mire area); c. 58 pairs 1966 (29 pairs in 50% of heath/mire); notable increase from late 1960s; estimated total 120 pairs 1981–1984
Snipe	Breeding numbers small before 1970s. Increase evident c. 1975–1981; estimated 120–200 pairs, 1981, sustained to at least 1985
Ringed Plover	Forest colonized 1978 onwards; 7–12 pairs 1981–1985

(C. R. Tubbs and J. M. Tubbs, unpublished surveys)

Fig. 33.
*Numbers of Wading
Birds Breeding in the
New Forest*

al declines of breeding habitat: redshank especially have declined with the agricultural improvement of meadowland nesting ground. In the Forest, all four species depend heavily on the valley mires and on wet, neutral grassland around pools and streams, for feeding sites, and if they nest on the heath (as do most curlew and many lapwing) they mostly take their young to the wet ground.

Nothing, however, is known about their food species in the Forest, although all are mainly feeders on ground-dwelling invertebrates. Grazing animals must be important in keeping these feeding sites open and accessible: dense purple moor grass would be as inhospitable a feeding ground as the dense cord-grass (*Spartina anglica*) marshes of the coast, and it may be significant that waders are few on other, ungrazed, lowland heaths. Grazing is probably also an important factor in the colonization of parts of the Forest since 1978 by ringed plover (*Charadrius hiaticula*) (Fig. 33), which breed on war-time airfields, gravel pits, and other places which combine close-bitten turf, bare stony ground and concrete relicts.

The Forest wetlands provide an abundance of potential habitats for amphibians. Fig. 34 summarizes the succession of newt surveys of Forest ponds carried out since 1960, mainly by Arnold Cooke and Deryk Frazer.* Newts also occur in some streams and ditches,

*Creed, 1964; Cooke & Frazer, 1976; Frazer, 1978

	Number of ponds
Newts found in one or more surveys	76
No newts detected in any survey	38
Great crested newt *Triturus cristatus* present	7
Smooth newt *Triturus vulgaris* present	32
Palmate newt *Triturus helveticus* present	67

Fig. 34
Summary of New Forest Newt Surveys

Surveys were carried out in 1960, 1961, 1974, 1975, 1983 and 1984 (Creed, 1964; Cooke and Frazer, 1976; Frazer, 1978; Frazer, unpublished).

but the Forest watercourses are mostly too fast-flowing to make good breeding sites, while the axial flows of valley mires have insufficient open water. During the surveys, newts were seldom found in small ponds with a surface area less than 100 m², or in ponds where there was little aquatic vegetation. Of the three species, smooth newts (*Triturus vulgaris*) rarely occurred in acid ponds (up to pH 6) and tended to favour water with relatively high calcium and potassium concentrations. Palmate newts (*T. helveticus*), however, preferred metal-deficient pools especially those poor in potassium, and with a pH value down to 3.9. The rarest of the newts, the great crested (*T. cristatus*), required similar chemical conditions to smooth newts, but was confined to a few ponds with deep water and a high proportion of water surface free of vegetation. Cooke & Frazer (1976) suggested that these relationships arose because the different species are adapted to respond to the distinctive smells of algae characteristic of metal-rich and metal-deficient water. They pointed to the work of Savage (1971), which suggests that spawning in anurans is instigated by algal metabolites in the breeding pond.

Beebee (1983) studied the amphibia of a heath-farmland transect in the western Weald, and found that the smooth newt, great crested newt, common toad (*Bufo bufo*), natterjack toad and common frog (*Rana temporaria*), all required near-neutral breeding ponds, the greatest tolerance being shown by the common frog, which occurred in a wide range of pH from 5.8–7.9. There is some indication that the species will accept an even wider range of conditions in the New Forest where Cooke & Frazer (1976) found it within the range pH 4.2–8.2. In the Weald, as in the New Forest, only the palmate newt penetrated the most acid heathland ponds. The ponds richest in amphibia were those at the heath-farmland ponds. Though quantitative data are lacking, my strong impression is that in the Forest the richest pools reflect this pattern. Here, besides the native amphibia, at least one small population of the introduced European

The red-backed shrike – once epitomizing the New Forest heathlands in summer . . . now extinct (Photo F. V. Blackburn, Nature Photographers)

tree frog (*Hyla arborea*) persists. Common frog and common toad colonies occur mainly in these localities or within the farmland areas: few heathland ponds have them, even though many seem suitable, and they are absent from pools in the valley mires.

For nine species of vertebrates, the lowland heaths are especially important because a large proportion of the British population occurs on them. In order of increasing dependence on the heathland they are: hobby, stonechat, nightjar, woodlark, red-backed shrike, natterjack toad, sand lizard, smooth snake and Dartford warbler. Two of these are now extinct in the New Forest.

The natterjack toad was once widely distributed on lowland heathland and on coastal dunes at least as far north as the Solway (Taylor, 1948; Beebee, 1976). In heathland districts it requires near neutral (pH down to 6.0) pools for breeding, combined with mature dry heath in sandy soils which facilitate burrowing (Beebee & Griffin, 1977). During this century and especially since the 1930s, heathland populations have steadily declined, until in the 1980s only one colony survives, bolstered by habitat management and the rearing and release of toadlets. The dune populations have fared somewhat better, but have nonetheless declined through habitat destruction and degradation. Trevor Beebee attributed the heathland decline to habitat destruction through development, agricultural reclamation, afforestation, tree invasion, acidification of some breeding pools, collection for the pet trade, and the widespread use of pesticides (Beebee, 1976, 1977). Few colonies were ever known from the heathlands of the Hampshire Basin and only two from the New Forest, both of which seem to have gone by 1950

(Beebee, 1976). If the species did occur in the Forest, it seems unlikely that it would have been confined to two (widely-separated) sites, although the predominance in the Forest of seasonally waterlogged humid heath rather than the sandy dry heaths which the species requires, would have limited its potential distribution. However, it is difficult to account for its loss to the Forest, for none of the factors identified by Beebee (1976) seem relevant here, where the habitat has changed much less than elsewhere.

The second species now extinct is the red-backed shrike. In the early 1950s, when I first explored the Forest, shrikes were still numerous, and I thought of them as the epitome of the summer heathlands. Yearly, pairs appeared in the same places in the gorse brakes and scrubby valleys and bottoms. Subsequently, I helped chronicle their decline and extinction. Because they are part of my early recollections of the Forest I cannot contemplate their passing without sadness. The first shrike census was in 1957, when seventy pairs were found, but some large tracts of Forest were incompletely surveyed. During the national census of 1960 we found sixty-one pairs in the New Forest. The decline between 1957 and 1960 was steeper than the figures alone suggest, for in 1960 they had gone from several tracts of heathland in the south of the Forest. There had been twenty-nine territories here in 1957, suggesting a mid-1950s population of around 100 pairs. Further surveys revealed only thirty pairs in 1966 and nine pairs in 1971. The last year in which red-backed shrikes certainly bred in the Forest was 1978, though individuals appeared annually for a further three years. In 1982, for the first time, there were none. The decline mirrors the national trend. Surveys in 1960 and 1971 gave 253 and eighty-one pairs respectively (Bibby, 1973). In the mid-1980s the last pairs hang on in East Anglia.

The national and local status of the remaining seven species is summarized in Fig. 35. Only the Forest's sand lizard population is insignificant in national terms. The sand lizard occurs widely on other southern heathlands, but there is no evidence that it was ever widespread in the New Forest. Like the natterjack it requires mature dry heath on sandy soils, which is limited in distribution in the Forest. However, it formerly occurred in a number of areas, but was probably extinct, or nearly so, by the 1970s and was successfully reintroduced to one area in 1978. The causes of its apparent decline are unclear, but both collecting and too-extensive burning of its habitat have been suggested as causal factors.

Of the nine species, only the hobby has not declined. At least two (red-backed shrike and nightjar) belong to a group of insectivorous migratory birds whose range in Britain has contracted to the south and east this century and which are also declining elsewhere in north-west Europe. The wryneck (*Jynx torquilla*), extinct

Species	Population in Britain	Population on lowland heaths	Population in New Forest
Hobby	Parslow (1973) estimated 85–100 pairs, Sharrock (1976) c. 100 pairs. Subsequent work (unpublished) suggests >300 pairs.	Probably <30% of national total (Tubbs, 1985).	20–25 pairs or c. 7–8%, 1962–1984.
Stonechat	Probably c. 5000 pairs at peaks; population fluctuates mainly with severity of winters (Tubbs, 1985).	c. 1000 pairs at peaks (Tubbs, 1985).	c. 430 pairs, 1961; c. 60 pairs, 1963 after two severe winters; 324 pairs, 1966; 350 pairs, 1974, probably rising to 1961 level by 1977; decline to c. 320 pairs 1978; 290 pairs 1979 after hard winters, increasing subsequently and declining sharply after 1984–5 winter (Tubbs, 1968, 1976 and unpublished).
Nightjar	1784 singing ♂, national survey, 1981 (Gribble, 1983).	c. 50% in 1981 (Gribble, 1983).	Poorly covered in 1981 survey: 56 singing ♂ in partial survey in 1979, probably c. 30% of total (J. Pain, unpublished).
Woodlark	Possible max. 440 pairs, 1981 (Tubbs, 1985). Since declined, perhaps by 50%.	c. 90%	46 pairs in c. 50% of suitable habitat, 1981, i.e. estimated 90–100 pairs or c. 20% of British population.
Sand Lizard	c. 7–8000 animals 1976, declined since (NCC, 1983).	All but c. 200 in 1976 (NCC 1983).	Less than 100, partly deriving from re-introductions.
Smooth Snake	Probably c. 2000 (NCC, 1983).	100%	Probably in range 100–500.
Dartford Warbler	1960, 1961, c. 460 pairs; 1963, 11 pairs; 1974, 565 pairs; 1984, 423 pairs (Tubbs, 1963, 1967; Bibby and Tubbs, 1975; Robbins and Bibby, 1985).	100%	c. 350 pairs, 1961; 60 pairs, 1962, 6 pairs, 1963 after successive severe winters; 250 pairs 1974; reduced to c. 120 pairs 1978 and c. 70 pairs 1979 after two hard winters; subsequent increase to 203 pairs 1984 and rather more 1985 despite severe weather 1984–5 winter (Tubbs, 1963, 1967, 1968; Bibby & Tubbs, 1975; Robbins & Bibby, 1985.

Fig. 35.
Populations of Seven Vertebrates Partly or wholly dependent on the English lowland heaths.

as a breeding species in England, also belongs to this group and was once sufficiently common in the New Forest to be known locally as the rinding bird, because it arrived in April when the bark-strippers were at work (Kelsall & Munn, 1905). It had probably gone from the Forest by 1940.

Though habitat destruction may have contributed to these declines, the ultimate cause may be linked with changing climate (cooler, wetter springs) and declining food supply, or with more subtle factors of which we remain unaware. Habitat loss, however, is certainly the most important factor for the natterjack and the remaining species. It is clear from the literature, for example, that the Dartford warbler formerly occurred over a wider area than now, and has declined with the loss of its heathland habitat. On the assumption that the lost heaths would have supported similar densities to those which survive, there would have been 1600 pairs in 1800, and 1000 in 1930 (Tubbs, 1985). These are minimal figures because we know that large areas of heath support higher densities than small areas (Bibby & Tubbs, 1975), and there were once more of the former. The decline of the sand lizard, smooth snake and natterjack, and indeed, of other reptiles and amphibia, have been extensively documented.* In every case it is clear that present populations are small fractions of those of earlier times.

Except for the hobby, the birds have tended to retreat to heathland in southern England as their range has contracted and their populations have diminished. None of the birds are characteristic of uniform ericaceous heathland: even the Dartford warbler derives most of its food from gorse brakes (Bibby, 1979a). All are ecotone species which occur where the heath is diversified by gorse, invading trees, bracken or wet valleys, situations in which their invertebrate food appears especially abundant when compared with other open lowland habitats, all of which in any case have suffered even higher loss rates than heathland. The lowland heaths may simply be the most viable remaining habitat for insectivorous species which have declined through climatic change, habitat destruction or both. The reptiles and the natterjack are clearly more closely adapted to mature dry heath, and I speculate that this arises from a balance between their thermo-regulatory needs, which would not be satisfied in denser cover, and the protection from predators afforded by deep heather.

Stonechats, woodlarks and Dartford warblers are made more vulnerable by their susceptibility to severe winters, which can greatly reduce populations and cause local extinctions. Dartford warblers and stonechats, in particular, were reduced to very low levels by the 1962–3 winter. Dartfords were lost to the Thames Basin and Wealden heaths for more than a decade and were nearly extinguished in the New Forest. The much larger populations of the huge tracts of heath which formerly covered much of the southern counties would have been better buffered against depletion by severe weather than the smaller, more fragmented populations of today. Habitat loss has probably compounded vulnerability to severe winters to leave the Dartford warbler and woodlark in a tenuous position in England. Stonechats will presumably persist

*Prestt *et al.*, 1974; Spellerberg, 1975; Spellerberg & Phelps, 1977; Corbett & Tamarind, 1979; Beebee, 1976; and the NCC, 1983.

on the heathy fringe of the milder parts of the west coast of Britain, whatever happens to the remaining lowland heaths.

From a management point of view in the New Forest, the heathland vertebrates include two disparate elements. First, Dartford warblers, the reptiles and, if it were to be reintroduced, the natterjack, all require mature heather, in the case of the Dartford diversified by gorse – most nests are in heather but most feeding takes place in gorse (Bibby, 1979a, 1979b) – and in that of the other animals, on dry, sandy soils. The former habitat is also shared by many other heathland birds, including stonechats. This mature heath element of the vegetation is a limited resource. In 1973 there were only 490.4 ha of optimum Dartford warbler habitat and another 873.2 ha of mature heather, only a small proportion of which will have been optimal for the reptiles (Tubbs, 1974). Preliminary calculations from a survey carried out in 1984 suggest some improvement, but the area of mature heath habitat remains less than 8% of the total area of heather-dominant vegetation. As remarked in chapter 13, there is constant pressure to burn off this element of the vegetation at a greater rate than it is replaced by the maturing of younger age classes. Besides limiting habitat, burning kills individual animals, either directly in the flames, or, in the case of the reptiles, indirectly, by exposing them to predators (notably crows, kestrels and buzzards) when they emerge from their refuges below the soil surface.

Grazing has widely checked gorse regeneration after fire and is now limiting heather regeneration over large areas of Forest (chapter 13). Locally, trampling by cattle is also damaging prime mature heath, to the extent that Dartford warblers at least have been lost to several sites in the 1980s. Thus, for some rare species, burning and grazing potentially set limits to the size which the population can achieve in the New Forest.

On the other hand, a few species, notably woodlarks, wheatears and probably skylarks, are favoured by intensive grazing and burning. Superficially, the hard-cropped Forest grasslands might seem to satisfy this requirement, but trampling, combined with the total absence of cover for nesting, largely excludes woodlarks and skylarks from them, while the few wheatears which breed in the Forest (up to thirty pairs) are confined to localities where there are suitable nest holes, often at the edges of cropped grassland. Most woodlarks occur on well grazed or recently burnt heathland and it is possible that the population in the New Forest is limited by the comparatively small area which is now burnt annually.

Heathland Invertebrates

Heathland, in the sense of heather-dominant vegetation, is both nutrient impoverished and structurally simple. It is not therefore surprising that its invertebrate fauna is low both in species diversity and in biomass compared with more base-enriched and structurally varied habitats. It nonetheless supports a relatively large number of species which appear to be specialized to heathland. There have been no studies of the total fauna of the Forest heaths but the ecologically comparable heaths of Dorset have been studied by Nigel Webb and other biologists from Furzebrook Research Station, Wareham*and Colin Bibby sampled various heathland habitats in Dorset to determine the food available to the Dartford warbler (Bibby, 1979). The results are consistent with general observation in the New Forest and confirm that the fauna mainly comprises the larvae and adults of beetles (Coleoptera), spiders (Araneae), bristle tails (Collembola), three-pronged bristle tails (Thysanura), plant bugs (Hemiptera) and two-winged flies (Diptera). There are low densities of woodlice (Isopoda), grasshoppers and crickets (Orthoptera), butterfly and moth caterpillars (Lepidoptera), ants (Formicidae) and some other groups. Overall densities of animals were low, and although Webb & Hopkins (1984) recorded a large number of species (272 species of Coleoptera, 158 species of spider), this was mainly because the fragmented heaths of Dorset are highly susceptible to the intrusion of animals from surrounding habitats. Most individual animals comprising the heather fauna are herbivores, like the heather beetle (*Lochmaea saturalis*) and common plant bugs such as *Kleidocerys truncatulus*, *Scoloposthetus decoratus*, *Macrodeme micropterum*, *Orthotylus ericetorum* and *Ulopa reticulata*.

The invertebrate biomass of gorse may be several times that of heather, which accounts for the preference of Dartford warblers for feeding in the former. Most of the biomass comprises spiders, beetles and butterfly and moth larvae. Weevils are abundant, notably *Apion ulcis*, which lays its eggs in young gorse pods, where metamorphosis takes place, the adults emerging in the summer when they are cast into the air as pods burst. The weevils *Strophosomus curvipes*, *Sitonia regensteinensis* and *S. striatellus*, the gorse shield bug *Piczodorus lituratus*, various small plant bugs and a number of flower-dwelling micro-moth larvae, make up much of the browsing force.

The biomass of predators, mainly spiders, would seem to be higher in the gorse than in heather. Invertebrate samples from Homsley Bog in the New Forest, suggest that predators, again mainly spiders, may be easily the most abundant invertebrates in the valley mires. The samples contained 7423 specimens of over 300 species from seventeen orders, and 39% of individuals were spiders. A high proportion of other animals were also predatory (e.g., carabid beetles and dragonfly larvae). Thus, it seems that the theoretical community structure, in which a large biomass of resident herbivores provide food for predators (and they for other

*Webb & Hopkins, 1984; Hopkins & Webb, 1984; Webb *et al.*, 1984.

predators), breaks down for the mires. Instead, the paucity of herbivores may reflect the ecologically severe nature of the mires. Those herbivores which do occur are specially adapted to survive there, predators hypothetically therefore relying on mobile generalists which attempt to colonize the mire, or on prey which stray onto or are blown onto the mire surface from the surrounding heathland and woods (D. A. Sheppard, unpublished).

Nigel Webb and his colleagues found that the smaller and more isolated the heather area, and the more structurally diverse the adjoining habitats, the greater the faunal diversity of the heath. The heathland fauna was being diluted by animals straying in from other habitats and the richer they were, the greater the dilution. Woodland adjoining a heath was a source of more species than pasture. At the same time the smaller and more isolated the heath, the more vulnerable to local extinction its specifically-heathland animals became. Extrapolating to the New Forest, one would anticipate that despite the extent of heather-dominant communities, the internal diversity of the assemblage of heathland habitats, combined with the proximity of extensive woodland and hedgerow-rich farmland, would give rise to great species diversity combined with high diversity of heather specialists. An added invertebrate habitat in the New Forest is the profusion of dung: though such animals as dung beetles and dung flies are abundant, neither their species diversity nor densities appear ever to have been measured and compared with the ungrazed heaths elsewhere. Likewise, for few species is there any information about the effects of grazing and controlled burning. There are potentially many new lines of research.

The heaths, grasslands, mires and other wetlands of the Forest support a comparatively large number of invertebrates which appear to be specialized to these habitats. We have most information about orders containing many large and conspicuous species, notably butterflies and moths, grasshoppers and crickets, and dragonflies, but in considering them it must be recalled that the density of individuals is generally low compared with that of the many much smaller animals which inhabit the heathland.

Of the 1234 butterfly and moth species recorded from the New Forest more than two-thirds require trees and shrubs as larval food plants, and thus inhabit woodland, wood edges and scrub. A large (but uncalculated) number penetrate the heathland by inhabiting the alder carrs in the valley mires and wet valleys, and the invasive birch, thorn, bramble, sallow and other shrubs. However, at least thirty species of macro-moths, and an unknown but seemingly larger number of micro-moths, are heathland animals in the sense that their larvae feed exclusively on heather, cross-leaved heath, bell heather, gorse or other major components of the heathland, acid grassland and mire vegetation. Many more species include such species as heather and gorse among a wider range of non-heathland food plants. Macro-moths whose larvae depend on *Calluna* or *Erica* include the grey scalloped bar (*Dyscia fagaria*), true lovers' knot (*Lycophotia porphyrea*), neglected rustic (*Xestia castanea*), heath rustic (*X. agathina*), and the day-flying common heath (*Ematurga atomaria*), clouded buff (*Diacrisia sannio*), beautiful yellow underwing (*Anarta myrtilli*) and shoulder-striped clover (*Heliothis maritima*). The large, conspicuous day-flying fox moth (*Macrothylacia rubi*) and emperor moth (*Pavonia pavonia*) are common in the Forest and are among a group for which heather is the commonest food plant but which also occur in bilberry and a variety of low shrubs, or on gorse and other members of the pea-flower family, notably petty whin and birdsfoot trefoil, both of which are characteristic elements of the Forest vegetation albeit suppressed by grazing. A further group appears to be characteristic of heathland grasses, notably the antler moth (*Cerapteryx graminis*), anomalous (*Stilbia anomala*) and marbled white spot (*Lithocodia pygarga*).

Of the ten butterfly species common on the Forest heathlands, the larvae of seven are grass-feeders and occur in other open habitats, though they include such characteristic heath species as the grayling (*Hipparchia semele*) and small heath (*Coenonympha pamphilus*); one, the small copper (*Lycaena phlaeas*), feeds on docks and sorrels and is widespread on acid grassland; and another, the green hairstreak (*Callophrys rubi*) is characteristic of the gorse brakes which provide the main larval food. Only the silver-studded blue butterfly is a heather specialist, though the larvae are said also to feed on gorse and other peaflowers.

I use the term 'common' in a relative sense in relation to the heathland butterflies. All except the silver-studded blue occur at very low densities and I believe populations are severely depressed by heavy grazing pressure which removes the larval food plant and, with trampling, must inevitably kill many insects in their larval stages, besides suppressing nectar sources for the adults. I speculate that the increase in bracken density and litter since the demise of autumn cutting has also helped impoverish the butterfly (and moth?) fauna by eliminating food plants. Only the silver-studded blue remains abundant. It is the most characteristic of heathland butterflies and its numbers over the still-extensive tracts of little-grazed or trampled heather can be prodigious in July and August.

Of the twenty species of Orthoptera currently known to occur in the Forest, eleven occur in heathland, grassland and mire habitats. In the Forest the characteristic species of dry heath is the mottled grasshopper (*Myrmeleotettix maculatus*). This species is replaced on humid and tussock heath by the meadow grasshopper, and on acid grassland also by the common green grasshopper, though the three can occur together and sometimes also overlap with the common field grasshopper (*Chorthippus bruunreus*) which occurs locally on the most arid sites including war-time runways and similar places. A second species confined to heather, the heath grasshopper (*C. vagans*), occurs on the dry, sandy heaths of the Bagshot Beds on the south-west of the Forest, which is the eastern-most point in a confined British distribution extending from there to the heaths around Poole Harbour in Dorset. The common ground hopper (*Tetrix undulata*) occurs widely on heathland but numbers increase with the aridity of the habitat.

On the lower valley slopes and in hollows, where the humid and wet heath has remained long unburnt and the purple moor grass is tussock-forming and associated with cross-leaved heath, the bog bush cricket (*Metrioptera brachyptera*) is abundant. The species is closely associated with purple moor grass–cross-leaved heath tus-socks but penetrates both valley mires and relatively dry heathland where there is a sufficiently luxuriant cover of purple moor grass, cross-leaved heath, heather, or bog myrtle. Though so common in the Forest, it is confined nationally to suitable heathland and its distribution is centred on the heathland districts of south-east England. A second characteristic New Forest mire species, the large marsh grasshopper (*Stethophyma grossum*), tends to select the more open mire surfaces dominated by *Sphagnum* lawn, bog asphodel, white-beaked sedge and cotton grass, and saturated year-round. The species occurs in all the valley mires in which I have searched and in most of the wetter, *Sphagnum*-rich seepage step mires, however small they may be. Nationally, however, this, the largest and most spectacular of the grasshoppers, is now confined to the mires of the New Forest and Dorset, and to an introduced colony on Thursley Common in Surrey, though it also occurs on some raised mires in western Ireland.

Two other crickets occur in the mires, the short-winged cone-head (*Conocephalus dorsalis*) and long-winged cone-head (*C. discolor*). Both are generally said to be associated with rough, marshy pasture, mainly on the coast. The long-winged cone-head was until recently considered a rarity, known in Britain only from the south coast from Dorset eastwards and in few localities there. The short-winged had a wider distribution in southern and eastern England. Brown & Searle (1974) in a survey of the New Forest Orthoptera, recorded the short-winged only in Wilverley and Matley Bogs, and were unable to find the long-winged. Ragge (1975), in describing the Forest Orthoptera, mentions neither species. In the late 1970s, however, it became apparent that both species were spreading both on the coast and inland, and occupying a range of meadow, rough pasture, marsh and mire habitats, among them the tussocky purple moor grass–cross-leaved heath vegetation of the New Forest, besides clumps of tall rushes in the mires and in choked drains. Both species are now widespread in the Forest. Conjecturally, the population explotion – for it was no less – may have been initiated by the series of long, hot summers in the south of England which began in 1975. The wet summer of 1985, however, does not seem to have checked either populations or continued expansion.

If purple moor grass–cross-leaved heath is especially significant to the heathland Orthoptera, its grazed derivatives, the wet hummock-grassland, and notably the comparatively vast area of Balmer Lawn, support the only populations of the lesser marsh grasshopper (*Chorthippus albomarginatus*) in the Forest, though they occur on Balmer Lawn at only very low densities in the face of intensive grazing. The densities of common grasshoppers on Forest lawns, re-seeded areas and improved acid grasslands are generally very low (and indeed, the insects are usually absent from reseeded areas), which is hardly surprising considering the close-cropping and trampling which the sward sustains. The effects of intensive grazing and trampling are best appreciated by comparing the Forest lawns with, say, fragments of ungrazed grassland on the nearby downs. The latter support staggeringly high densities of grasshoppers, compared with those on Forest grassland. The bush crickets and grasshoppers mostly lay their eggs in the soil surface or in the basal parts of grasses and the combination of close-cropping and trampling must limit the survival of eggs and early instars.

The Forest, with its abundant wetlands set in the heathland matrix, supports breeding populations of twenty-nine of the thirty-nine species of dragonflies known to breed in Britain. The larval stages of all species are aquatic and contrary to most ecological generalizations, most species occur in acid or neutral waters. Dragonflies require unshaded waters in reasonably open situations although the adults of some species occupy hunting territories in woodland or scrub. In the New Forest the abundance of ponds, pools, wet flushes, seepages and mires, and the networks of small streams which drain the heathland catchments, comprise an assemblage of dragonfly habitats unparalleled elsewhere in Britain. The shelter often afforded by the proximity of the woods is an added dimension of the Forest as dragonfly habitat.

Stability of water level, temperature and nutrient status are important to dragonfly egg and nymph survival and a degree of shelter (such as may be provided by tall gorse in otherwise exposed places) is important to adult insects. In addition, as with the amphibians, the very acid heathland pools are relatively poor in species, and the richest are those which are relatively enriched, notably at the heath-woodland and heath-farmland interface. The best and largest can support up to eighteen species. The number of stream breeding species is small – seven at most – and shaded reaches are frequented only by the demoiselle *Calopteryx virgo* and the seemingly ubiquitous golden-ringed dragonfly *Cordulegaster boltonii*. Noelle and Tony Welstead, who produced a remarkable publication on New Forest dragonflies, described the valley mires as the prime breeding sites (Welstead & Welstead, 1984), though I would extend the definition to include the whole assemblage of mires, flushes, seepages and pools which occur in the valleys. These habitats possess the maximum stability of temperature, water level and chemistry. Twenty-one breeding species have been recorded from them in recent years, including numerous populations of southern coenagrion (*Coenagrion mercuriale*), scarce blue-tailed damselfly (*I. pumilio*), small red damselfly (*Ceriagrion tenellum*) and downy emerald (*Cordulia aenea*), all of which have very restricted national distribution centred mainly on the lowland heath districts. The southern coenagrion in particular, is a very rare insect confined in Britain to mire systems in the New Forest, Purbeck in Dorset, and a number of localities in west Wales.

I think that dragonflies and damselflies may well be strongly influenced by grazing animals. On the other hand, grazing and trampling checks the tendency towards purple moor grass domination of the mires, flushes and seepages, and hence maintains the open, watery, peaty habitats required by species such as scarce blue-tailed damselfly and southern coenagrian: indeed this has been suggested for its Pembrokeshire localities. On the other hand, stock graze bare the stream banks and thus impoverish the habitat for riverine species, which in particular need riparian vegetation on which to emerge for their final metamorphosis into adult insects. One notable rarity, the club-tailed dragonfly (*Gomphus vulgatissimus*), once abundant on the Ober Water, declined there after the 1950s and in the mid-1980s appears to be locally extinct following clearance of scrub, which allowed stock access to the banks. The formerly luxuriant streamside vegetation has been completely denuded by grazing. The species was not certainly known from any other Forest locality.

Adaption to open habitats is widely evident in other groups. M. V. Brian's work on ant community structure, foraging behaviour and ecology, for example, makes it plain that most ant species are adapted to open or seral habitats and construct nests in a fashion which will employ direct sunlight in raising the internal temperature (Brian, 1977). The nest mounds of the yellow meadow ant are conspicuous examples of this and will not survive tree shade. The heaths and acid grasslands of the Forest support 25 or more of the forty-two species recorded in Britain, whilst in much of the woodlands only one species, the wood ant (*Formica rufa*) occurs commonly. Indeed, the British distribution of several species is concentrated on the lowland heath districts of the Hampshire and Thames Basins and Weald. Several species penetrate the valley mires. One, the black bog ant (*Formica transkaucasica*), known only from five Forest mires and others in Purbeck, appears totally adapted to the mire environment, constructing small mounds of vegetation on purple moor grass tussocks and foraging in *Sphagnum* lawn and other mire communities saturated year-round with water.

Many heathland animals specialize in preying upon, or developing symbiotic relationships with ants. Green woodpeckers, several species of spiders and many predatory beetles prey on ants, in some cases exclusively. Several bees, wasps and flies specialize in parasitizing them. Caterpillars of many blue (Lycaenid) butterflies, including the silver-studded blue, produce volatile secretions which attract ants, the caterpillars hypothetically deriving protection against predators from the ants. Many beetle species spend much or all of their life cycle within ants' nests and are wholly dependent on them. Other insects are commensal with ants. It is extremely difficult to conceive how such relationships could have evolved without long-term stability of open habitats and in particular the heathy or grassy places of which both the ants and the other insects are today characteristic.

I draw two main threads from this superficial scan of the invertebrate ecology of the Forest heaths, grasslands and mires. Similar threads emerge from my scan of the heathland vertebrates. First, the biomass and species diversity of invertebrates is low in ericaceous heath, but it increases as the habitat diversifies. Nonetheless, many species are adapted to heath, acid grassland and mire, and many more occur in open habitats generally. Many have developed life histories intimately associated with their open habitat or with other local residents such as ants. Are such adaptations of no greater antiquity than the past few millennia, or does the concept of the continuous primary Atlantic forest require revision?

My second thread is the conservation importance of the Forest. Those groups for which it can, at least crudely be measured, the Forest supports a high percentage of the British species specialized to the mosaic of heath, grassland, mire and scrub which comprise the lowland heathlands, a mosaic which remains most complete in the New Forest. Much of this diversity depends on the grazing of commonable stock: yet, perversely, grazing pressure may now be such as to depress the populations and diversity of some invertebrate groups.

Predator and Prey CHAPTER **15**

Earlier chapters focused primarily on the interactions between the physical environment, vegetation and land use of the Forest, and on the related composition of some animal communities. A consistent thread in the narrative is that the effects of pastoral usage pervade the ecosystem. Here, I focus mainly on the implications of pastoral usage for predators and their prey.

Thus far, I have deferred mentioning the small herbivorous mammals. They are a critical link between the vegetation which they consume and which comprises their above-ground habitat, and those predators which consume them. They, and consequently their predators, are profoundly affected by the grazing and browsing of the larger herbivores. The numbers of small rodents are also influenced by another factor – the variable annual production of acorns, beech mast and other tree and shrub seeds, which are important foods for hoarding against the privations of winter and early spring. A good seed crop can balance the depressant effect of large herbivores on their populations. It also directly influences the population levels of some of the crow family, which also hoard seed for later retrieval.

A major physical limitation of the environment is the acidity of most Forest soils, which limits the distribution and density of earthworms (and, incidentally, excludes snails), and thus limits the abundance of avian and mammalian predators which specialize in this food source. Bird-feeding predators are, perhaps, the least likely to be influenced by either low small mammal densities or poor soils. This possibility I explore briefly here.

Rodents, Lagomorphs and Insectivores

Attempting to study small mammals in the New Forest is frustrating because one catches so few. I discovered this in the early 1960s and others have done so since. Mice, voles and shrews are mainly absent from open habitats, though wood mice (*Apodemus sylvaticus*) sometimes occur in gorse brakes, and field voles (*Microtus agrestis*) are occasionally recorded. These animals may be transients. Spellerberg and Phelps (1977) record the common experience: a transect of Longworth live-traps across dry heath, wet heath and young conifer, caught only two wood mice in 348 trap-nights during 7–9 July 1974 and only six wood mice during 26–28 October 1974 (0.75 and 1.72 mice/100 trap-nights respectively).

The deciduous woodlands are richer in small mammals but numbers are low compared with ungrazed woods in southern England. Catches of mice, locally including yellow-necked mice (*Apodemus flavicollis*), seldom exceed 15/100 trap-nights and are usually much lower. Bank voles (*Clethrionomys glareolus*) have a patchy distribution and are now absent from most woodland in the Forest. Dormice (*Muscardinus avellanarius*), which are essentially arboreal in woods with a dense shrub layer, are absent. Both common shrews (*Sorex araneus*) and pygmy shrews (*S. minutus*) are comparatively scarce, though there are no quantitative data from which to determine numbers: shrews are insectivores and thus caught only incidentally in Longworth traps baited for rodents. Moles, also insectivores and worm eaters, occur patchily in the more enriched woodland and grassland soils.

In 1982–3, Stephen Hill compared rodent numbers in four grazed plots in the Forest, embracing deciduous woodland, grassland and heath, with two ungrazed plots in woodland and heath adjoining the Forest. In addition, some trapping was carried out in two 5 ha deer-fenced wooded pens at Denny Lodge, one ungrazed and the other grazed by fallow deer but not stock. During November–December 1983, at the end of the breeding season, the grazed woodland areas yielded 3.7–12 wood mice and 0–0.68 bank voles per 100 trap nights, compared with 7.8 mice and 14.3 voles per 100 trap nights in the ungrazed Royden Woods, which adjoin the Forest and have a profuse shrub layer with abundant bramble. Mice and voles were effectively absent from grazed heathland and grassland but at Pound Bottom, an ungrazed heath adjoining the Forest, there was a resident population of wood mice and also some harvest mice (*Micromys minutus*). In the ungrazed Denny pen there was a small population of bank voles (5.42/ha) but they were absent from the pen grazed by deer. Wood mice were present at low density in both pens (2.43/ha). Densities are often difficult to calculate from trapping results, but they appear to range between 0–10 wood mice/ha in grazed Forest woodland, while catches of bank voles are too few to make calculations. In many places there are scarcely any mice, and from most places, bank voles are absent. What is clear is that densities, especially of bank voles, are very much lower in the grazed Forest woods than in ungrazed southern woodland. In H. M. Southern's classic study of tawny owls and their prey in Wytham Woods, during 1948–68, wood mice achieved a maximum density of roughly 14/ha and bank voles 40/ha, though densities of the former were more often around 8/ha and the latter around 15–18/ha (Southern, 1970).

There is every reason to suppose that numbers of small mammals are low in the Forest because of competitition from large herbivores for food and shelter. Bank voles require dense cover, especially of brambles and other low shrubs and forage extensively in the taller shrub layer (Southern & Lowe, 1968). Wood mice show no similarly clear preferences but are most numerous in low cover. In the open, both voles and mice are likely to be highly susceptible to owl predation. Similarly, shrews prefer a low ground cover and seldom forage in completely exposed situations. In the Forest woods, both ground cover and shrub layer have long been suppressed by stock and deer, and indeed, are generally absent. Moreover, I suspect that trampling severely limits the development of the burrows and surface or sub-surface runs of the small rodents. The field vole, an animal of rough, ungrazed or lightly-grazed grassland, preferably with a deep litter layer in which to burrow, is at a severe disadvantage in the Forest. It is no wonder that it is effectively absent from the heavily-grazed Forest grasslands, from which almost all the above-ground production is removed by stock during the growing season; nor is it a wonder that both grasslands and heaths are inhospitable to other small mammals for similar reasons. The thin litter layer, the trampling of stock, and the extent of seasonally waterlogged soils, must also help depress their numbers.

Since the mid-1960s, the Forest has deteriorated further as a habitat for small mammals because of increased grazing pressure arising from continually increasing pony numbers and the gridding and fencing of the perambulation in 1965 (Fig. 20). With the intensive grazing of the Inclosures after 1969 (chapter 11), the main reservoir of small mammal habitat largely disappeared. Most was grazed out by about 1973, though more persists today in the Inclosures than in the unenclosed woods. Wood mice have probably been less affected than bank voles, which are now scarce where once they were common. In the 1950s and early 1960s they were sufficiently numerous to be thought a pest because of their bark-stripping and shoot-eating activities in young plantations, a topic studied in the Inclosures near Lyndhurst by the late Oliver Hook. I recall them as common in unbrashed plantations as late as the mid-1960s.

Rabbits (*Oryctolagus cuniculus*), whose incisor arrangements are adapted to crop the vegetation even more closely than ponies, ought potentially to be the animals least affected by competition from larger herbivores. However, rabbits are not abundant in the Forest. Before myxomatosis they were common, and large warrens were relatively numerous. After myxomatosis numbers remained very depressed until well into the 1960s and it was only after 1964 that they began to rise noticeably. Subsequently, rabbits became widespread and increased steadily, though depressed periodically by outbreaks of myxomatosis. In the mid-1980s, however, breeding groups remain small and scattered and most frequently occur in dense gorse or such other cover as has survived. None of the old warrens have been reoccupied by more than a tithe of their former populations. Besides the depressant effects of recurrent epidemics of myxomatosis, there is possibly an interaction between stock and rabbits which eludes me: the local population ecology of the latter remains unexplored. Besides their relatively low populations, rabbits in the New Forest tend to be more strictly nocturnal than elsewhere, perhaps because of the disturbance from unimpeded public access. This is important in limiting their availability to diurnal raptors.

Brown hares (*Lepus capensis*) occur only at very low density in the Forest. Hares are structurally somewhat less well adapted than rabbits to exploit very short vegetation, and like the smaller mammals may suffer from competitition with the larger herbivores. Interestingly in this context, it is often said by those who hunt the New Forest Beagles that hares are found less frequently than in the 1960s, though the numbers killed have always been too small to provide certain comparison.

The Autumn Seed Harvest

An important part of the annual production of plant tissue – the seeds of trees and shrubs – is literally beyond the reach of the large herbivores until it falls, often in great profusion: then it is temporarily in such abundance as to obviate competition between large and small herbivores. Hence, this major source of food is not strongly influenced by stock and deer grazing.

Small rodents, grey squirrels (*Sciurus carolinensis*), jays (*Garrulus glandarius*), magpies (*Pica pica*) and carrion crows all depend to some degree on the provident autumn harvest of acorns, beech mast and berries. All seven species cache seed and retrieve it in winter and spring. A large seed crop ensures good winter survival. It probably helps the survival of young jays in the following year because the adults sometimes feed their young on seed hoarded the previous autumn (Coomes, 1979).

From 1968 onwards, my wife and I estimated the annual relative abundance of wood mice, bank voles and grey squirrels and the size of the autumn seed crop. The Forestry Commission provided records of squirrels, carrion crows, jays and magpies killed annually as pests between 1970 and 1982, and although numbers are partly related to shooting or trapping effort, fluctuations also reflect changes in absolute numbers of the four species (Tubbs & Tubbs, 1985).

Even without systematic long-term trapping, it was usually easy to determine the relative numbers of the mammals. Squirrels are conspicuous, and the presence of wood mice and bank voles is plainly revealed by their burrows, evidence of feeding, and sightings of animals. Fig. 36 shows that the abundance of the three

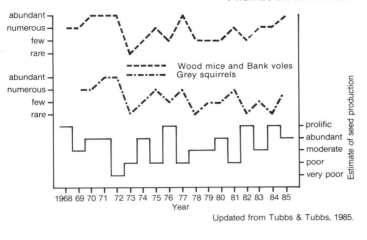

Fig. 36.
The Abundance of Rodents in Relation to Seed Production of Trees and Shrubs, 1968–85

Updated from Tubbs & Tubbs, 1985.

species varies in response to the amounts of acorns, beech mast, holly, hawthorn and other berries and fruit produced the previous autumn. In each year most species of tree and shrub, except rowans, produced seed in similar relative abundance: rowan trees are invariably laden with berries but the number of trees is small. From autumn 1981 until 1984 our records were confirmed by Stephen Hill's small mammal trapping. A poor seed year in 1981 resulted in very low animal populations in spring 1982 and they remained low until the autumn, when there was a prolific seed crop. Winter survival seems to have been good, but numbers were depressed in 1983 probably by the cold, wet spring. The seed crop in 1983 was mediocre, and numbers of rodents early in 1984 were very low indeed. Then, in 1984 there was an enormous autumn harvest and in 1985, when I write, rodents are more abundant than I can recall since 1977, which followed a similar seed crop. Though the populations of mice and voles may be depressed compared with the 1960s, a massive seed crop is temporarily capable of off-setting the dampening effect of stock grazing.

For grey squirrels, the relationship between population levels and seed production is confirmed by the annual kills (Fig. 37) though there are anomalies which arise from changes in control policies. Before 1975, squirrels were killed year-round, but especially in the autumn and early winter when they were most numerous. Thus, before 1975, peaks in the graph tend to occur during a good mast year rather than in the year following. The large numbers killed in the early 1970s can be attributed partly to the payment of head-money but it also coincided with a run of good seed years. The overall decline in numbers killed probably reflects a decline in control effort rather than a decline in squirrels.

The numbers of crows shot in the Forest between 1970 and 1981

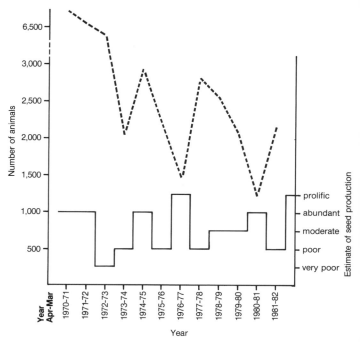

Fig. 37.
*Numbers of Grey
Squirrels Killed on the
Crown Lands and
Estimates of Seed
Abundance*

show trends which are similarly related to seed production (Fig. 38). From 1973, numbers of jays and magpies shot annually were proportional to the relative abundance of tree and shrub seed produced the previous autumn and there was a similar relationship for carrion crows after 1975. In Fig. 38 the relationship is less evident for the early 1970s because there was a gross reduction in shooting effort in 1972 and 1973. Shooting mainly occurred in spring and early summer, apparently with the intention of reducing predation of other birds' eggs and young, and the number shot is thus likely to reflect winter survival which in turn is assisted by the hoarded acorns, chestnuts and other large seeds.

Predators and Their Prey

Rodents, insectivores and rabbits are important in the diet of many predators including stoats (*Mustela erminea*), weasels (*M. nivalis*), foxes (*Vulpes vulpes*), most owls and many diurnal birds of prey, notably kestrels and buzzards. In the Forest, kestrels and buzzards take many birds, the latter tending to specialize in jays and carrion crows during the breeding season (Tubbs, 1974; Tubbs & Tubbs, 1985). The presence and success of the predators is likely to be influenced by 'background' levels of the prey species and also by the incidence of good seed years.

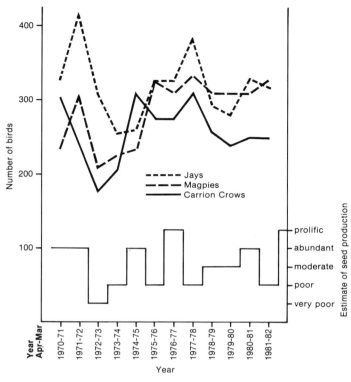

Fig. 38.
*Numbers of Magpies,
Jays and Carrion Crows
Killed on the Crown
Lands and Estimates of
Seed Production*

In the Forest, stoats and weasels seldom occur away from farmland. Weasels are small mammal specialists and it is understandable that they are rare in the Forest. Similarly, the absence of stoats reflects the comparatively low numbers of rabbits, on which they extensively feed, but they are also bird eaters and their absence may be attributed partly to the low densities of birds on the open heathlands and to the poor representation of accessible shrublayer species in the woods. A survey of the fox population in 1974 gave a density of 0.75 adults/km², which is lower than that recorded on farmland or in urban areas elsewhere (Insley, 1977). What do foxes feed upon which stoats and weasels cannot exploit, that they should persist even at low densities?

The Forest is poorly endowed with owls. Only the tawny owl (*Strix aluco*) is common. In a study of Forest tawny owls during 1982–5 Graham Hirons found that owl densities were only about half that in comparable habitat elsewhere, but that territory sizes were similar (18–23 ha). In most deciduous woods, wood mice and bank voles each comprise roughly 30% of prey items in owl pellets, whilst field voles make a further important contribution to the diet. In the Forest 42% of identifiable prey items in pellets during 1982 and 1983 were small rodents, but they were mostly mice, with very few voles. Moles, which can contribute significantly to the owl's summer diet (Southern, 1969) were not recorded from pellets in the Forest, but, interestingly, there was a high frequency of dung beetles (Hirons, 1984 & unpublished). Speculatively, the ease with which mice can be captured on the bare woodland floor of the Forest woods enables the owls to exploit the low density of animals and in this case they probably take a high proportion of the mouse population. Territories, though at relatively low density, are perhaps located on pockets of higher mouse density. Nonetheless, productivity of Forest tawny owls seems poor. Even in the 'good' small rodent year of 1983, Graham Hirons found that fewer owls reared broods in the forest (25%) than in an adjoining area of ungrazed woodland (65%). In 'poor' small rodent years, such as 1982, which followed a failed seed crop and severe winter, there are few breeding attempts, though such a phenomenon is far from confined to the New Forest (e.g. Southern, 1970). There is insufficient information to determine whether brood sizes in the Forest are consistently smaller than in woodlands with consistently larger rodent populations.

I recall that in the 1950s pairs of barn owls (*Tyto alba*) bred in several localities in the Forest, mainly near smallholdings and settlements, but these breeding sites became disused one by one from about 1965 and were all empty by the early 1970s, conjecturally as grazing pressure mounted. Breeding barn owls now occur only within the largest farmland enclaves and beyond the Forest margins. To a hunter of small mammals in open habitats, the Forest must now be wholly inhospitable. Similarly, little owls (*Athene noctua*), which also hunt small mammals in open places, seldom penetrate beyond the farmland margins. Earthworms, which are an important secondary food, are also few and locally distributed in the Forest.

Among the commoner diurnal birds of prey, the kestrel is the most dependent on small mammals. Predictably, the density of breeding pairs in the Forest is very low compared with estimates for other areas of Britain (Brown, 1976), or indeed, with farmland adjoining the Forest. Moreover it has declined since the 1960s. In a study area of 292 km^2, including most of the crown lands and much of the farmland within the perambulation, I found that the kestrel population fluctuated between sixteen and twenty-four pairs during 1961–81. During 1961–71 densities varied between one pair/12.17 km^2 and one pair/13.27 km^2; during 1971–81 they fell to between one pair/16.22 km^2 and one pair/18.25 km^2. The decline is likely to reflect the reduction in small mammal densities resulting from increased numbers of stock and their penetration into the Inclosures, where kestrels once commonly hunted in clearings. In most years, more than 50% of known nests were within o.8 km of farmland, where most observed hunting took place. Brood sizes of two to three young were usual in the Forest, which is low compared with the average of 3.65 for southern England derived from British Trust for Ornithology nest record cards (Brown, 1976).

In the absence of voles, Forest kestrels kill many birds and lizards. Few birds over-winter in the heathlands, most reappearing in April and May, when lizards are important in the diet, several birds sometimes congregating where they are abundant. Subsequently, the pressing demands of breeding prompts a switch to avian and mammalian prey. In 190 kestrel pellets collected from roosts and perches in 1982 and 1983, field voles, evidently taken on farmland, comprised 40.6% of the prey by weight, birds 30.7%, common shrews 12% and, interestingly, harvest mice 5.4% (Hirons, 1984). Studies elsewhere* have consistently yielded very much higher percentages of voles. Congregations of birds over heathland rich in lizards, grasshoppers and bog bush crickets, continue to occur periodically throughout the breeding season, and are sometimes a recurrent feature of the late summer after the broods have fledged.

My exploration of predator–prey relationships began with buzzards in 1961. The buzzard study continues in a contracted form in the mid-1980s. The density of buzzards in the Forest is low compared with other areas of Britain where the species is well established. Average clutch size (1.97) and size of fledged broods (1.2/breeding attempt; 1.5/successful attempt) is small compared with most other populations. There have been many non-breeding pairs and nest failures in most years. In Britain most populations depend heavily on small rodents and rabbits. In the absence of an adequate prey-base of these animals, Forest buzzards rely exten- sively on jackdaws, jays, carrion crows, wood pigeons, thrushes, woodpeckers and other medium-sized birds during the incubation and fledgling periods. The buzzard is not morphologically best- adapted to catching birds, and I concluded in the 1960s that the poor breeding performance of the population arose from a failure to make good a deficit of mammalian prey, because birds are harder for a buzzard to catch than small mammals (Tubbs, 1972, 1974). Since 1973, the already shaky position of the Forest buzzards has taken a turn for the worse. Four measures of the annual state of the population during 1961–85 are shown in Fig. 25. Until 1973, the number of territories occupied annually varied within narrow limits (32–36) and breeding performance was relatively constant. In 1973, however, only two pairs fledged young. Most probably did not attempt to breed. Between 1974 and 1981, the population declined by 42% from thirty-three to nineteen pairs, and then levelled off at nineteen to twenty-two pairs. The number of breed-

*Brown, 1976; Yalden & Warburton, 1979.

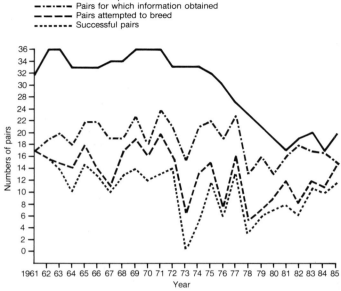

Fig. 39.
Breeding Success of the
Buzzard Population,
1962–85

Updated from Tubbs & Tubbs, 1985.

ing attempts varied widely between years, though less so after 1981. As the population declined there was a reduction in visible territorial activity as surviving pairs became more widely spaced, and an increasing tendency to range long distances, often to farmland, in search of prey. Few pairs wintered on the Forest, where previously many had done so.

For a long time the importance of birds, and, increasingly rabbits, in the breeding season diet of Forest buzzards obscured what I believe to be the explanation for the 1973 crash and subsequent decline. The penny dropped in 1980, by which time it was evident that since 1973 'good' small rodent years were also 'good' buzzard years, and that the former followed an abundant autumn seed

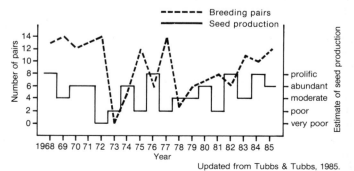

Fig. 40.
Numbers of Successful
Breeding Pairs of
Buzzards and Estimates
of Seed Abundance

Updated from Tubbs & Tubbs, 1985.

crop. The relationships are shown in Figs. 36 and 40. Data on the prey taken by buzzards in the Forest is confined to the period from late April until after the broods fledge, and relies heavily on pellets and prey remains recovered at or near nests. At this time, birds and a miscellany of items including snakes, lizards, frogs, small rabbits, mice, voles and squirrels are taken. There are no data, however, for the diet during February–April when territories are re-established and nest building begins. I suggest that rodents are especially important to buzzards at this critical time, when wood-land birds are few (except for mistle thrushes and the crows), reptiles have not emerged from hibernation, and there are few or no small rabbits.

Before 1973, it seems that population levels of small rodents were sufficiently high in the Inclosures even after a poor seed year, to form the basis of early spring food supply. Only when general population levels were reduced by habitat changes in the Inclosures (26% of the study area) brought about by stock penetration, did fluctuations become critical to buzzards. Bank voles were probably more significant in this respect than wood mice, for they are less nocturnal and they probably suffered more from the removal of their above ground habitat (Tubbs & Tubbs, 1985).

The sudden crash in breeding success in 1973 followed an exceptionally bad seed year nationally. In the Forest, wood mice, bank voles and grey squirrels were rare. However, 1972 was pre-ceded by a run of good seed years which probably buffered the small rodents, and hence the buzzards, against the growing impact of stock in the Inclosures, an effect which was abruptly removed in 1972. Since 1972, buzzards may be responding to spring num-bers of crows and squirrels as well as small mammals, and, indeed, it is possible that with a decline in small rodents, these species may have assumed proportionately greater importance in the late winter and early spring diet. Their numbers are considerable. Parr (1985) found densities of two pairs of carrion crows per km^2 in parts of the Forest in 1982, following a poor seed autumn. Taking non-breed-ing groups into account I calculate that there were probably 2000 or more crows on the Forest that spring. Densities of jays and mag-pies are also high in both woodland and farmland areas. Thus, the crows alone comprise a large biomass of potential prey which may be significantly enhanced after an autumn of abundant acorns, mast and other seed.

The decline and stabilization of the buzzard population at a lower level between 1972 and 1985 has a parallel in the myxomato-sis episode. Then, too, there was a massive decline in productivity, with erratic breeding performance, followed by stabilization and adjustment to a new prey spectrum. From local anecdotes and a fragmentary written record, including my own early observations, I believe the pre-myxomatosis population of the Forest was around forty pairs, and the average brood size was between two and three young. The 1980s may be a period of stabilization similar to that following myxomatosis and represented during my study by the 1960s: but, equally, apparent stabilization may merely be an effect of an increased incidence of good seed years since 1980 (Fig. 40).

Earthworm Eaters

Besides the pervasive influence of grazing, the Forest's acid soils are an important, ecologically-limiting factor. Earthworms seldom tolerate soils of below pH 5.0 and seldom achieve high densities much below neutrality; nor do earthworms tolerate waterlogged soils. Hence, their distribution in the Forest is fragmentary and their densities low. They are absent from heathland, most acid grassland and most conifer woodland, but there is generally evidence of worm activity in free draining lawns, improved grassland and oak woodland. Packham (1983) found that densities in quadrats in Forest oakwood (18.4/m^2, SD = 15.91) were extremely low compared with oak–hazel–ash woodland on richer soils adjoining the Itchen valley in south Hampshire (115.0/m^2, SD = 28.39). The isolated enclave of meadow at Eyeworth Lodge in the Forest yielded a mean of 149.6 worms/m^2 (SD = 26.61) compared with 192.0/m^2 (SD = 95.7) in Itchen valley meadows. Densities in Forest lawns are certainly lower than in the enclosed and fertilized meadow at Eyeworth. Higher densities of worms in the Forest woods and heathlands are closely mirrored by the distribution of moles (*Talpa europaea*), which occur locally in the richer oakwoods and lawns. The overall paucity of earthworms may at least partly explain the low numbers of shrews and the virtual absence of hedgehogs (*Erinaceus europaeus*) away from farmland, though earthworms are only one important component of the hedgehog's diet (Yalden, 1976) and the abundance of beetles associated with dung and dead wood ought, superficially, to be an attraction. Earthworm scarcity probably also contributes to excluding the little owl from the Forest. It helps to account for the near absence of rookeries from the Forest. Like hedgehogs and little owls, rooks are essentially farmland birds. There are only eight rather small rookeries within the Forest, of which five are on the largest farmland enclaves and three are in small enclaves close to the Forest edge. Foraging in the Forest is usually confined to some reseeded areas and improved acid grasslands, but an abundance of defoliating caterpillars in the oakwoods, as in 1980, 1982 and 1983, will attract large flocks of both rooks and jackdaws.

　　The influence of localized distribution and low densities of worms in the Forest has been best investigated for the badger (*Meles meles*), which is an earthworm specialist, though it will take a wide range of other foods. Since 1976, the Forestry Commission

Badger Protection Group has monitored 147–154 setts on the crown lands, of which 42–62 (30–40%) were unused in any one year, while others were occupied for only part of the year. Between 1976 and 1984, the estimated annual population varied between 235 and 262 adult animals (Forestry Commission, 1984). In 1982 the Forestry Commission carried out a thorough search for badger setts and found 322 setts (0.85/km^2), which by extrapolation would give 5–600 animals (1.8–2.0/km^2). However, probably most of the 'extra' setts found in the Commission survey were periodically occupied outliers of known main setts, and the density of badgers is probably nearer one adult or less per km^2. An average of 61% of occupied setts watched in the evening by Badger Group members between 1976 and 1984 held litters, but there was a bias towards watching successful setts and the proportion of 'main' setts producing young in the population as a whole is probably about 50%, perhaps smaller. This is low compared with elsewhere (Neal, 1977). Average litter size, at 2.3–2.7, however, is similar to that recorded by Neal (1977) for south-west England.

During 1981–3 Chris Packham compared the population ecology of badgers in a 16 km^2 area in the north of the New Forest, centred on the oakwoods of the Latchmore Brook valley and including the meadows of Eyeworth Lodge, with 14 km^2 of farmland and woods straddling the Itchen valley in Hampshire. In both areas badgers fed mainly on earthworms, but earthworm densities in the Forest study area were very low and their distribution patchy compared with corresponding habitats in the Itchen valley. Only at Eyeworth Lodge were densities high and here badgers from several social groups (clans) congregated to forage. Five measures of the two populations are given in Fig. 41. Density and productivity are significantly lower in the Forest than in the Itchen. All clans in the Itchen produced cubs but less than 50% did so in the Forest. The diet in the Forest was the more varied and besides the earthworms ubiquitous in badger diets, included larger amounts of fungi, acorns, crab apples, berries and invertebrates. Range behaviour in

	New Forest	Itchen Valley
main setts/km²	0.375 (n=6)	0.7 (n=10)
outlying setts/km²	1.69 (n=27)	0.857 (n=12)
adults/clan	3.2	4.0
cubs/clan	1.0	3.3
mean litter size	2.3	3.3

From Packham, 1983.

Fig. 41.
Five measures of the badger populations in study areas in the New Forest and Itchen Valley, Hampshire (from Packham, 1983).

the two populations differed markedly. In the Itchen, each clan maintained a relatively small, exclusive range, the boundaries of which were marked with latrine pits and within which there were only a small number of setts outlying the main one. In the impoverished conditions of the Forest, ranges were larger, boundary marking only occurred where animals from three clans exploited the one area of high earthworm density (Eyeworth fields), and there were many more outlying, periodically-used, setts. It seems that at the lower Forest densities the ranges were generally too large to defend and mark adequately.

Bird Eaters

Predators specializing in birds should be the best buffered against the environmental limitations of intensive grazing and poor soils. Two bird eaters, sparrowhawks and hobbys, breed in the Forest, and merlins (*Falco columbarius*), hen harriers (*Circus cyaneus*), peregrines (*Falco peregrinus*) and great grey shrikes (*Lanius excubitor*) occur in winter. As it happens, probably only the sparrowhawks and shrikes are heavily dependent on bird food found within the Forest.

Merlins, hen harriers and peregrines hunt beyond the limits of the Forest as well as within it, and, indeed, the Forest may be more important in providing secure roosts than as a hunting ground, for the densities of potential prey species are low compared with farmland or coastal habitats nearby. Certainly, there is at least one communal merlin roost and several communal hen harrier roosts in the Forest which draw birds from beyond it. Hunting hen harriers seen in the Forest by day are usually males, which are most often bird eaters, whereas more than half those roosting in the Forest are females, which are most often vole eaters. Only the great grey shrikes winter wholly within the Forest: ten to twelve occupy winter ranges on the heathlands and these have been re-occupied each winter since at least the early 1960s. Although no quantitative data have been collected, my observations strongly suggest that they feed mainly on pipits, wrens, Dartford warblers, robins and finches roosting in the gorse brakes, though at the beginning and end of the winter they take many beetles, bumble bees and other large insects.

During the 1960s, when sparrowhawks in most of south and eastern England were at a low ebb through contamination by agricultural pesticides accumulated through their prey, a successful breeding population persisted in the New Forest. During 1961–6 about forty territories were occupied in the Forest woods, of which about half were searched annually for nests. The percentage searched in which breeding attempts were made rose 70–100% and the percentage of breeding attempts which succeeded 40–90%

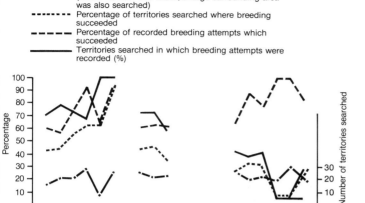

- — - — - Number of previously-known territories searched
  (where no nest was found, a large surrounding area
  was also searched)
- - - - - - Percentage of territories searched where breeding
  succeeded
- - - - - Percentage of recorded breeding attempts which
  succeeded
——— Territories searched in which breeding attempts were
  recorded (%)

Fig. 42.
*Breeding Information on
Sparrowhawks in the
New Forest*

in that time, perhaps reflecting an early and rapid recovery from the pesticide era. However, surveys in 1968–70 and again in 1975–80 revealed an alarming decline in numbers of active nests, though a high percentage of those found were successful (Fig. 42). We saw fewer birds displaying in the spring (always a sure way of locating pairs) during and after the late 1960s than before.

The decline is contrary to the national recovery of the sparrowhawk and it may be associated with the simultaneous maturing of the conifer plantations favoured by sparrowhawks for nesting, and the intensive thinning and clear-felling which started in the mid 1960s. A possible alternative or contributory explanation is that increased grazing pressure has eliminated the shrub layer, and especially the bramble, from the Inclosures, and hence destroyed the nesting habitat of blackbirds and song thrushes, on which sparrowhawks tend to depend heavily during the fledgling period.

If sparrowhawks have declined, the hobby population has remained remarkably constant since at least 1960. In a 465 km² area including but extending beyond the Forest, hobbys have nested regularly in twenty-five localities (1 pair/19.4 km²) since 1960, though the maximum number located in any one year was only nineteen. I found most nest sites in the early 1960s and my wife and I refound most of them after 1974. In the interval, few nests have moved more than 0.5 km.

Stephen Parr compared the density, habitat, productivity and diet of hobbys in the Forest with a well wooded Wessex chalk stream valley with both arable and dairy farming and with a tract of chalk downland mainly under cereals, though diversified by small stream valleys along which there were many villages and ribbons of pasture. Density was highest in the Forest, where there were fourteen pairs in 290 km^2 (20.7 km^2/pair, similar to my earlier calculation), compared with 36 km^2/pair in the valley and 64 km^2/pair on the downs. However, there were no significant differences in brood size (2.0/pair in the Forest), nor were there dramatic differences in the prey taken. During incubation, the males, which provision the females as well as themselves, tended to hunt close to the nest in the Forest, and took many woodland passerines. Later, in all three areas, they specialized in swallows, house martins and sometimes swifts, taken from a wide area. By breeding late they took advantage of the availability of large numbers of juveniles of all three species (Parr, 1985).

Stephen Parr's data confirmed earlier observations in the Forest. For much of the breeding season hobbys prey on swallows and swifts, as often as not caught over farmland or settlements. Hence, they do not wholly depend on the prey resources of the Forest itself. However, the valley mires sheltered bottoms and woodland clearings are favoured sources of large flying insects, notably dragonflies, day-flying moths (especially fox and emperor moths), beetles, bees and in late summer, ants in nuptial flights, and it is possible that the comparative abundance of invertebrates is important in enhancing hobby density. Especially early in the season, and again on warm, sunny days when the young have fledged, the birds spend hours at a time hawking with effortless grace over the heaths and mires. What is anomalous is that they should do so when a better return on energy expanded would seem to be available from other prey resources.

CHAPTER 16

The Way Ahead

The history of the Forest for at least nine centuries, has been dominated by the conflicting aspirations of the crown – first in deer conservation and the construction of a landed estate for political and economic motives, later in the exploitation, growth and harvesting of timber – and of the commoners in using the Forest to support their livestock and provide other natural produce. Gains by the crown could only be at the expense of the commoners, and exercise of traditional and natural rights by the commoners limited the resources available to the crown for deer grazing and timber production. The conflict persists in modern times in an ineradicable local suspicion of the Forestry Commission, though it has in part been replaced by a conflict between the commoners, who since the 1877 Act have persistently sought the 'improvement' of the Forest for their animals and those who perceive such 'improvements' as damaging to the Forest's natural habitats, which they wish to protect. Further problems arise from intensive grazing, which has in many respects impoverished the Forest of plants and animals; and, paradoxically, from economic circumstances which threaten the survival of the commoners.

These problems are compounded by pressures exerted externally. Of all the wild places in Britain, perhaps in Europe, the New

The A31: upgrading to dual carriageway was at the expense of the Forest

267

Forest is the most vulnerable to the vicissitudes of modern social and economic demand. East and west of it lie urban and industrial conurbations which have been deliberately encouraged to grow by long-standing government planning policies. At its eastern edge, between the perambulation and Southampton Water, lies the Esso oil refinery of Fawley and associated petrochemical industries. The combination of M27 and M3 motorways have placed the Forest within one and a half hours of ten million people. Not surprisingly, it is confronted constantly by demands for new and wider roads, for pipelines and other public utilities, for the release of farmland and village enclaves and Forest margins for housing, for more recreational facilities and for oil exploration. Multiplying numbers of charity walks, charity rides, orienteering events and similar occasions, each of them individually laudable, the explosive take-off in dog ownership, and the wear and tear of picnickers' feet, impose a far from insignificant burden on the Forest environment.

In this final chapter, I summarize my perception of the Forest as an ecological system, and review the internal management difficulties, and the demands and pressures which are generated from outside. It is inevitable that I should conclude with some ideas for the way ahead.

The Forest Ecosystem

The vegetation of the unenclosed Forest can be perceived as nature's response to human activity. The open habitats are mainly secondary to the clearance of the primary woodland for farming and rangeland. Such clearance triggered or accelerated the leaching of nutrients down the soil profile and the surface transportation of soil, much of it relatively fertile loess, into the valley bottoms. By increasing run-off, woodland clearance probably also initiated the formation of many valley mires (chapter 4). The heaths and grasslands left in the wake of these traumas have been maintained and extended since by grazing, burning and the cutting of timber, faggots, bracken, peat and turf by human communities which persisted at the edge of the wilderness. All these activities can only contribute to the continuing nutrient impoverishment of the system because all are exploitative and none put anything back into the system. Collectively they have also prevented woodland recolonization, which theoretically would help to restore soil fertility by the constant return of nutrients to the soil surface in leaf fall. A general fall in base status over a long period may help to explain the loss of many trees, shrubs and other plants which generally grow on relatively rich soils. Many activities, like peat digging, have had only local effects. Grazing, however, has affected the structure of all the Forest's plant communities.

In the royal forest, traditional land uses emerge into written

liaria) and the oak leaf roller moth (*Tortrix viridana*), resulted in widespread defoliation of the oakwoods; during 1979–81 extensive tracts of heather were completely stripped of leaf by a population explosion of heather beetles; and over the whole decade grass production was poor and by midsummer the grasslands were desiccated and brown. In 1985, the first comparatively wet summer for eleven years, the grasslands remained green, and production kept much further ahead of offtake than in previous years. It is perhaps unfortunate that the studies of the large herbivores and their food took place during the dry decade during which grassland productivity may have been depressed and the effects of grazing heightened. The dry summers must certainly have encouraged the numerous small annuals at the expense of grasses.

Oak defoliation by caterpillars, late June 1979

Internal Conflict and Symbiosis

Until the early 1970s, the dominant threats to the Forest lay in the Forestry Commission's silvicultural aspirations. Those storm clouds have now dissipated, at least for the moment, and more subtle and difficult problems have come into focus. Though grazing at the levels reached in the 1970s and early 1980s, together with the effect of the dry summers, had a generally, but not wholly, impoverishing effect, the same period paradoxically saw increasing fears for the future of the commoners and for the continued grazing of the Forest by their stock. The situation was described in chapter

7. Pony numbers peaked in 1978 and have since declined with depressed market prices. Perhaps the major problem confronting the commoners as a community, however, is illustrated by a report in the *New Forest Post* for 14 June 1985, of the sale of 2 acres of grazing land adjoining the Forest for the astronomical sum of £12,750 and of 3 acres for £16,000. It is true that these were record prices but they starkly demonstrate the problems of a small commoner trying to assemble land to serve as a base for the exercise of common rights. It is not possible to recoup that sort of capital outlay.

The commoner can do little about market or land prices. But there is something to hit out at and that is the 'failure' of the Forestry Commission to 'maintain' or 'improve' the Forest for stock as it is implied the Commission should do by section 11 of the *New Forest Act 1949*. Demands for more heath burning, scrub and bracken clearance, birch and pine felling, and wetland drainage, have mounted since the 1960s. The Forest, it is said, has 'deteriorated', echoing claims made periodically ever since the 1877 Act. It seems to me that they reflect the underlying frustrations of a community stressed by more intractable social and economic problems, for there really is little evidence of 'deterioration', which is said to reside mainly in the loss of grasslands and especially stream-side lawns. This certainly happened with the spread of scrub in the 1930s and 1940s, but all the evidence points to subsequent lawn expansion (chapter 13). Moreover, many of the claimed 'lost' lawns are peat mires of ancient origin. Many more, of course, were lost when the Inclosures were planted.

The conflict between commoners and conservationists (the distinction is more blurred than this implies) focuses on the fact that much of the 'maintenance' demanded involves the destruction or violation of the natural vegetation. The clearance of old blackthorn thickets, the cutting back of irregular birch groves at woodland margins, the treatment of grassland with artificial fertilizers, but above all, the straightening and widening of natural stream courses and the drainage of valley mires, wet heaths and even seepage steps have all been sought in the name of maintenance, and resisted strongly by the NCC and other conservation organizations. From the conservation point of view, the drainage schemes of 1846–52 and 1923–30 did more than enough damage to the Forest as a natural system (chapter 13).

The degree to which damage to natural habitats has occurred in recent times has depended on the relative strength of the pressures brought to bear on the Forestry Commission. In the 1960s, the conservation arguments were weakened for want of a strong public lobby. Since then they have been greatly strengthened and have tended to prevail. Thus, the Forestry Commission, as arbiter, has been swayed less by predetermined management policies than by expediency. This is not meant as a criticism. It is the inevitable consequence of the periodic conflicts between the management requirements of section 11 of the *New Forest Act 1949* and the conservation requirements of section 15 of the *New Forest Act 1964* and, latterly, of the *Wildlife and Countryside Acts*. In fact, strenuous efforts have been made in the 1980s to develop management policies as near acceptable to everyone as possible. There is more common ground between commoners and conservationists than the conflicts sometimes suggest.

External Threats and Planning Policies

In the 1960s, uncontrolled camping, caravanning and vehicular access was widely seen as the main threat to the Forest (Tubbs, 1968; New Forest Joint Steering Group, 1970). Despite the resulting controls it remains a significant problem, stimulated by nearby urban growth and the inflow of commuters to the Forest. The number of day visits to the Forest is estimated to have risen from 3.5 million in 1970 to between 7 and 9 million in 1984. Modern pressures on the Forest are visible in congested roads at weekends; in widespread erosion, not by vehicles now but by horse riders, especially from commercial riding stables; in expanding areas of wear and tear around car parks and camp sites, compounded by the felling of potentially dangerous trees – some magnificent beeches have gone in this way; in worrying of stock and deer by the abundant uncontrolled dogs; in the appalling numbers of road

The fate of pollard beech at a Forest car park: the limbs were thought dangerous

A-generation oak felled
for safety reasons near a
Forest car park

accidents involving stock – an average of 154 animals per year, mostly ponies, were killed or injured during 1980–4; and the gradual loss of the elusive quality of wilderness. Simply, it is being expected to absorb too many people, too many dogs and too many motor cars. Road improvement schemes, proposals for pipelines, pumped storage reservoirs and other public utilities, follow inevitably on the heels of urban and industrial development around the Forest. There is, in addition, evidence that sulphur pollution has impoverished the lichen flora of some parts of the Forest closest to Fawley oil refinery and Calshot power station, both on Southampton Water, even though the prevailing southwesterlies would carry the smoke-plumes away from the Forest (Morgan-Huws & Haynes, 1973).

More subtly, the bank of farmland in and around the Forest which provides the holdings to serve as bases for the exercise of common rights, is being lost to riding stables, paddocks for riding horses, indoor riding schools, golf courses, horticulture and other uses. Forest cottages sell for ridiculous prices beyond the means of many local people who might turn out stock (chapter 7). Few newcomers exercise the common rights attached to their newly-acquired properties, though there has been a trickle who have done so ever since the Forest became an attractive place for the middle class to live in the later 19th century. Many former commoners have concentrated on enlarging their holdings into conventional farms and have lost interest in depasturing stock on the Forest, especially if they are near busy, unfenced roads.

Some of the pressures are being confronted squarely by the policies of the local planning authority. The South West Hampshire Structure Plan, approved by the Secretary of State in 1982, is essentially a conservation document. It places severe restraints on further development, including such facilities as riding stables, within the Forest perambulation and permits only limited growth beyond. However, the parishes down the east flank of the Forest fall within the area of the South Hampshire Structure Plan, originally approved in 1977, though its thinking derives essentially from the boom years of the 1960s, and South Hampshire has long been identified as a growth area in national planning terms. Extensive development has already occurred between the perambulation and Southampton Water at Fawley, Hythe, Marchwood and Totton, and a further expansion of Totton (a 'growth sector' in the Structure Plan) is currently taking place, with the possibility of yet more to come if the proposals in the revised Structure Plan are approved. And this despite the arguments against permitting further urban growth so close to the Forest which were advanced at the Examination-in-Public.

No public authority has expressed more concern for the problems confronting the Forest than the New Forest District Council. In the statutory local plans intended to amplify the Structure Plans, the District Council has given explicit support for the conservation of the farmland land bank in and around the Forest and on the basis of the local plan policies the Council, supported by the NCC, has won a succession of planning appeals against the Council's refusal to give planning permission for riding schools and golf courses, some of which would have involved the demise of active commoners' rented holdings. Since 1983, the District Council has taken the Structure Plan restraint policies one stage further in identifying a New Forest Heritage Area extending well beyond the perambulation to include most of the land which might potentially support the exercise of common rights now and in the future, within which strict controls over development unsympathetic to the Forest and its management will operate.

Planning policies do not resolve everything. Indeed, policies of restraint on housing in themselves encourage the upward spiral of house prices and add to the difficulties of local people on modest incomes who wish to live where they were brought up. Equally, the deflection of unwanted development often depends on the strength of the environmental lobby – the assemblage of voluntary and statutory bodies and individuals which collectively act as environmental guardians. In the New Forest the lobby has proved strong and cohesive. In 1972 it defeated the Forestry Commission's intentions for the Forest woodlands. It is a measure of subsequent change that in recent battles, the Commission has itself been part of the lobby.

The strength of the lobby was thoroughly tested by public inquiries in 1974 and 1983, into proposals for a bypass for Lyndhurst, which can only be built at the expense of a major incursion into the Forest; and by a public inquiry in 1982 into a proposal by Shell UK Ltd to carry out exploratory drilling for hydrocarbons in the Forest. The first of the bypass proposals was made by Hampshire County Council and the second by the New Forest District Council in a contradiction of all the basic planning policies for the area. Both councils supported Shell's proposal, evidently having convinced themselves that hydrocarbon exploration and, if necessary, production, could be carried out without damage to the Forest. On all three occasions, the voluntary organizations (eighteen of them at the Shell inquiry) came together beneath the umbrella of the New Forest Association to present a collective case alongside those of the NCC, Verderers and at the second road inquiry, the Forestry Commission.

The road inquiries highlighted the problems arising from the Forest's location in relation to urban areas. Lyndhurst is at the centre of the Forest where the main east–west (A35) and north–south (A337) roads cross. Though the main east–west traffic is supposed to use the south coast trunk road (A31), much of it does not (Fig. 1). The A337 also takes traffic from the M27–M3 motorways south to Lyndhurst and thence to Lymington and the ferry to the Isle of Wight. Inevitably, Lyndhurst High Street is often noisy and congested. One solution is an 'outer' bypass across the Forest; the other is an 'inner' route close to the village, mostly over

The proposed route of the Lyndhurst by-pass would cross the picture obliquely from right to left

farmland. The first would violate the Forest: the second would violate the village.

Route of gas pipeline dating from the 1960s: restoration is at best difficult

The route proposed in 1974 would have devastated a swathe of heath and woodland east and west of Lyndhurst, including the magnificent pasture wood of Gritnam Wood. The Secretary of State for the Environment accepted the inquiry Inspector's view that such a route was unacceptable. The second inquiry was into the route to be adopted by the District Council in the Local Plan. The Inspector effectively discarded the outermost of the three routes canvassed but was equivocal about the others. At the time of writing the position remains unresolved. The inquiries were, in any event, only the first hurdle, for not only would legislation be necessary to fence a road built over the Forest but the consent of the Forestry Commission and Verderers would be necessary to build it. A Verderers' veto is subject only to the caveat that it must be not unreasonably applied, and there is nothing unreasonable about fulfilling a statutory duty to protect the New Forest, especially since a route less harmful to the Forest is available.

Shell's exploratory borehole was to be in an area of felled conifer plantation in Denny Inclosure. The objectors accepted that the site was of little intrinsic interest but held that were oil or gas found, the Forest could not absorb a production field without unacceptable ecological and aesthetic damage. The inquiry began in a policy vacuum. The Department of Energy declined to give a statement of government policy for oil and gas exploration and production; and the Secretary of State for the Environment had yet to pronounce on the draft Structure Plan which identified local hydro-

Erosion from horse-riding, Ibsley Common

carbon policies. After three weeks of probing the potential environmental hazards, the inquiry was adjourned to await the Secretary of State's decision on the Structure Plan.

In the draft Structure Plan the County Council's proposed policies had been based on the assumption that finding and exploiting oil and gas must be in the national interest and must therefore be as little constrained as possible. When the Secretary of State's modifications to the Structure Plan were published they proved to take a different view of the New Forest. They included a 'presumption' against hydrocarbon exploration in the Forest and a 'strong presumption' against the appraisal and exploitation of oil or gas found by anybody who managed to surmount the first hurdle. Inevitably, it is tempting to ponder the extent to which evidence given during the inquiry influenced these pronouncements. When the inquiry resumed the objectors argued that in order to overcome the presumption against exploration, Shell had to demonstrate that what they proposed was not potentially damaging to the Forest, and this they had failed to do. The NCC had several specific misgivings. There was likely to be a silt discharge to a nearby valley mire during site construction and probably afterwards. During well-testing (if hydrocarbons were found) there would be sulphur dioxide emissions which would damage the rich and pollution-sensitive lichen communities of neighbouring ancient woods. There were acute problems over the disposal of drilling mud, which contained toxic elements. There was no adequate contingency plan for accidents and in any case it did not appear possible to produce one which would properly safeguard the Forest. But most fundamentally, this well would be the first of many: there were, it emerged, other potentially hydrocarbon-bearing structures beneath the Forest. Were one or more of them ultimately exploited, the hazards to the Forest would multiply. It was not possible to superimpose on the Forest the well-sites, pipelines, roads, treatment plants and other potentially hydrocarbon-bearing structures without unacceptable ecological hazards and loss of natural habitats. The Forest was too important a part of the national heritage of wild places to place at risk.

The case for the objectors prevailed. The Secretary of State agreed with his Inspector that despite general policy to explore the nation's reserves of oil and gas, risks should not be taken with so unique a place as the New Forest. Taken with the Structure Plan policies, this is a significant event. Depending on your view, it signals national acceptance that conservation policies should be paramount in the Forest; or that it is a place with too many organized and influential protectors to make rejection of conservation policies politically expedient.

Towards New Concepts

There is an official willingness to recognize the New Forest as a special place. This is evident in the Minister's Mandate to the Forestry Commission in 1972; in the Commission's recognition of its National Nature Reserve quality in its 1982–91 Management Plan; in the policies of Structure Plan and Local Plans for the area; and in the succession of public inquiry results, notably that of the 1982 inquiry into hydrocarbon exploration. There remains, however, a reluctance to depart from the conventional in contemplating many of the Forest's problems. A willingness to explore radical solutions is needed to help resolve the difficulties of the commoners, on whom the future of the Forest in its present form depends, and in order to tackle the problems arising from all the urban-derived pressures and demands with which the Forest is confronted.

The notion that the Forest ought to be a National Park surfaces periodically but of itself it would seem to offer no particular way forward. The combination of planning policies and the Forest legislation now confers greater protection than is enjoyed by National Parks. There is, however, a need for the special importance of the New Forest to be more clearly acknowledged. A first step might be the widening of the Forestry Commission's role so that here, the Commission's silvicultural function became subordinate to that of conserving and enhancing the Forest as a biological and cultural system. Such a role might have to be enshrined in new legislation. Among other things such a move might erase the haunting collective folk memory of the 19th century appropriation of much of the Forest for silvicultural Inclosures, and dispose of the persistent local suspicion that the Commission's silvicultural aspirations are only temporarily dormant. In fact such a move would be less a radical change of stance than the completion of a process which has already begun: during the 1974 Lyndhurst bypass inquiry and the 1982 Shell borehole inquiry, the Commission sat on the fence but in the 1983 bypass inquiry it came down firmly on the side of the environmental lobby.

Much could flow from modification of the Commission's function. It would raise such possibilities as the return of parts of the Statutory Inclosures to the unenclosed Forest, notably perhaps the trapped pasture woods and the numerous former lawns, perhaps also much former heath and acid grassland now under conifers; and the more rapid return of conifers to broadleaved trees. A major contribution which could be made towards the biological enhancement of the Forest would be the exclusion of stock from the Inclosures which remained fenced, and this would be easier to achieve were there to be a radical new approach which included the return of some of the lost grazings to the unenclosed Forest.

The problems of the commoners are more intractable. The best hope for the future may lie in a combination of financial assistance, perhaps channelled to the Verderers in lieu of marking fees, combined with the assembly of a public bank of Forest-edge land which could be leased preferentially to commoners exercising rights. This is no flight of fancy, for its basis exists in the extensive crown freehold farmland within the Forest, in farmland purchased by Hampshire County Council as potentially exchangeable for Forest land needed for roadworks, and for that matter in land owned by the Hampshire & Isle of Wight Naturalists' Trust, who have already preferentially rented some to a practising commoner though a substantially greater return could have been obtained on the open market.

Financial assistance from central or local government or the EEC, in the form of a headage contribution to marking fees, could function not only as a means of supporting the commoners but as a mechanism for regulating the number of animals turned out. Payment to the Verderers could commence when the number of stock fell below a predetermined threshold, and increase with diminishing numbers. Differences in scales payable for cattle and ponies could be used to encourage one at the expense of the other in the event of a serious imbalance, remembering that ponies have the greater impact on the vegetation. There might also have to be an adjustment to encourage the 'small' commoner. There is nothing new about subsidizing agriculture and some such system would only be innovative in that it would also assist the survival of a rare ecosystem. There is nothing new about financially supporting the commoners, for since 1983 the Countryside Commission have run a scheme whereby they pay a premium on fillies of a certain standard running on the Forest. The main practical difficulty would lie in identifying the threshold at which to turn off the financial tap. Ponies are more critical than cattle in this respect and I suspect that much less than 2000 is too few and 3000 far too many from the standpoint of biological diversity. It is now, in 1985, nearer the former than the latter but there are as yet no such signs as woodland regeneration or bramble regrowth which might signal a lifting of grazing pressure.

Fig. 20 suggests that grazing pressure of the 1960s and 1970s was not unique in the Forest's history, although previous periods may not be directly comparable because the Forest was formerly the core of a large area of common grazings now enclosed and reclaimed. Moreover, the figure does not take account of the closure of the perambulation in 1965, an event which I believe to have been one of the most significant in the Forest's ecological history. Whether the impoverishing effects of intensive grazing are more acute now than before, however, is not the whole point. Biological impoverishment has proceeded too far in Britain to neglect the opportunity for reparation. In the Forest it is thus important to decide a stocking limit, adjustable in the light of monitoring, beyond which subsidy would cease. I believe this to be a necessary element in any package of proposals for the future of both commoners and Forest.

There would be further encouragement to continue the exercise of common rights were the number of animals killed on the roads to diminish. The problem is aggravated by the road engineer's response to increasing traffic density – to 'improve' road capacity by widening and straightening – which increases vehicle speeds and encourages yet higher traffic densities. Only radical policies which reduce speeds and traffic density will reduce animal deaths. They include such heresies as a speed limit within the Forest, the reduction of road widths, the return of some road surfaces to gravel, periodic or seasonal road closures, further width restrictions and a traffic management programme which makes a determined effort to divert heavy traffic outside the Forest. Such measures would help not only to reduce the accidents but would retrieve some of the lost tranquillity of the Forest.

This is not intended as a definitive package of proposals so much as an exhortation to discard conventional responses to the Forest's problems and to cast them in a new light, building upon the established acceptance of its importance and fragility. Nothing will resolve all conflict. No plan will resolve the differences between those who wish to increase the stocking capacity of the Forest by draining and 'improving', and those who wish to conserve its natural vegetation. No changed administration will deflect outside pressures, whether for new roads, pipelines (as I write there is a proposal for a 24-inch gas main across the Forest*), pumped storage reservoirs, electricity cables or other developments, nor will it remove the threat of sulphur dioxide pollution from industrial emissions, but it will help defeat them.

I recall that in my final submission as the NCC's advocate at the Shell borehole inquiry, I said that civilization demanded restraint. This meant that economic aspirations, and I would now add to that the unfettered demands of recreation, however compelling their claims, must sometimes and in some places yield to cultural, aesthetic and nature conservation needs. The New Forest was, and is, such a place. This seems to me to be the precept upon which to build the future of this rich and peculiar place.

*A proposal which was defeated by the unanimous opposition of the Forestry Commission, Verderers, NCC, local authority and voluntary organizations.

References

Abstract of Claims (1776). An Abstract of All the Claims on the New Forest in the County of Southampton Entered at the Lord Justice in Eyre's Court . . . 1670. Salisbury.

Adams, M. C. (1966). Firecrests breeding in Hampshire. *Brit. Birds.* 59:240–246.

Atkinson, T. (1984). The plant communities of valley mires in the New Forest, Hampshire. *J. Biogeography.* 11:289–317.

Barber, K. E. (1973). Vegetational History of the New Forest: a preliminary note. *Proc. Hants. Field Club Archaeol. Soc.* 30:5–8.

Barber, K. E. (1981). Pollen-analytical palaeoecology in Hampshire: problems and potential. *in:* Shennan, S. & Shadla-Hall, T. The Archaeology of Hampshire. *Hampshire Field Club Archaeol. Soc. Monograph Series No. 1.* 91–4.

Beebee, T. J. C. (1976). The Natterjack Toad (*Bufo calamita*) in the British Isles: a study of past and present status. *Br. J. Herpetol.* 5:515–21.

Beebee, T. J. C. (1977). Environmental change as a cause of natterjack toad (*Bufo calamita*) declines in Britain. *Biol. Conserv.* 11:87–102.

Beebee, T. J. C. (1983). Habitat selection by amphibians across an agricultural land–heathland transect in Britain. *Biol. Conserv.* 27:111–24.

Beebee, T. J. C. & Griffin, J. R. (1977). A preliminary investigation into Natterjack Toad (*Bufo calamita*) breeding site characteristics in Britain. *J. Zool. Lond.* 181:341–50

Betts, U. V. G. (1974). Roman road in Rockram Wood, Cadnam. *Hants. Field Club Archaeol. Soc. New Forest Section Report.* 13:8.

Bibby, C. (1973). The red-backed shrike: a vanishing British species. *Bird Study.* 20:103–110.

Bibby, C. J. (1979a). Foods of the Dartford warbler *Sylvia undata* on southern English heathland (Aves: Sylviidae). *J. Zool. Lond.* 188:557–76.

Bibby, C. J. (1979b). Breeding biology of the Dartford warbler *Sylvia undata* in England. *Ibis.* 121:41–52.

Bibby, C. J. & Tubbs, C. R. (1975). Status, habits and conservation of the Dartford warbler in Britain. *Brit. Birds.* 68:177–95.

Brian, M. V. (1977). Ants. Collins. London.

Brooke, M. D. (1961). A new look at marginal land reclamation. *Bulletin of the National Agricultural Advisory Services.* 11:1–2.

Brown, A. J. & Searle, C. A. (1974). The native Orthoptera of the New Forest. *Entomologist's Gazette.* 25:285–92.

Brown, L. H. (1976). British Birds of Prey. Collins. London.

Brown, R. C., Gilbertson, D. D., Green, C. P. & Keen, D. H. (1975). Stratigraphy and environmental significance of Pleistocene deposits at Stone, Hants. *Proc. Geol. Assoc.* 86:349–65.

Browning, D. R. (1951). The New Forest Pastoral Development Scheme. *Agriculture.* 58:226–33.

Bruemmer, F. (1967). The wild horses of Sable Island. *Animals.* 10:14–17.

Buchanan, C. & Partners (1966). South Hampshire Study Report on the Feasibility of Major Urban Growth. HMSO. London.

Castleden, R. (1977). Some aspects of the Hants plateau gravels. *Proc. Prehist. Soc. E. Anglia.* 4:15–41.

Catt, J. A. (1977). Loess and cover sands. *in:* Shotton, F. W. (ed.). British Quaternary Studies – Recent Advances. University Press. Oxford.

Coles, J. M. & Orme, B. J. (1982). Beaver in the Somerset Levels: some new evidence. *Somerset Levels Papers.* 8:67–73.

Cooke, A. S. & Frazer, J. F. D. (1976). Characteristics of newt breeding sites. *J. Zool. Lond.* 178:223–36.

Coombes, F. (1978). The Crows. Batsford, London.

Corbett, K. F. & Tamarind, D. L. (1979). Conservation of the sand lizard *Lacerta agilis* by habitat management. *Br. J. Herpetol.* 5:799–823.

Countryside Commission (1984). The New Forest Commoners. Countryside Commission Publication 164.

Creed, K. (1964). A study of newts in the New Forest. *Br. J. Herpetol.* 3:170–81.

Cunliffe, B. (1965). Report on the excavation of three pottery kilns in the New Forest, 1955. *Proc. Hants. Field Club Archaeol. Soc.* 23:29–45.

Dallas, C. C. (1927). New Forest Shooting, Past and Present. King, Lymington.

Dearing, J. (1977). Gorse, Man and Landscape Change on Dartmoor: A preliminary investigation. *Rep. Trans. Devon Ass. Advmt. Sci.* 109:135–52.

Devenish, D. C. (1964). Amberwood: Excavation of a small enclosure. *Hants. Field Club Archaeol. Soc. Report.* 13:5–7.

Dimbleby, G. W. (1955). Pollen analysis as an aid to the dating of prehistoric monuments. *Proc. Prehist. Soc.* 20:231–6.

Dimbleby, G. W. (1962). The Development of British Heathlands and their Soils. *Oxford Forestry Memoir No. 23.* Clarendon Press, Oxford.

Dimbleby, G. W. (1965). Post-glacial changes in soil profiles. *Proc. Roy. Soc. B.* 161:355–62.

Dimbleby, G. W. (1967). Plants and Archaeology. John Baker, London.

Dimbleby, G. W. & Gill, J. M. (1955). The occurrence of podsols under deciduous woodland in the New Forest. *Forestry.* 28:95–106.

Donkin, R. A. (1960). The Cistercian settlement and the English royal forests. *Citeaux.* 11:1–33.

Drapier, M. E. (1966). Variations in heathland vegetation on planation surfaces in the New Forest. *BSc Dissertation.* University of Southampton.

Duncan, J. (1840). Notices of the New Forest, Hampshire. *Quarterly Journal of Agriculture.* 10:462–80.

Edwards, P. J. In press. Effects of grazing on the development of streamside lawns in the New Forest. *Proc. Hants. Field Club Archaeol. Soc.*

Edwards, P. J. & Hollis, S. (1982). The distribution of excreta on New Forest grassland used by cattle, ponies and deer. *J. Ecol.* 19:953–64.

Eide, K. S. (1982). Some Aspects of Pedogenesis and Vegetation History in Relation to Archaeological Sites in the New Forest. *PhD Thesis.* Institute of Archaeology, University of London.

Elly, S. (1846). On the cultivation and preparation of gorse as food for cattle. *J. Royal Agric. Soc. England.* 1st Ser. 6:523–8.

Everard, C. E. (1954a). The Solent River: A geomorphological study. *Inst. Br. Geogr. Trans.* 20:41–58.

Everard, C. E. (1954b). Submerged gravel and peat in Southampton Water. *Proc. Hants. Field Club Archaeol. Soc.* 18:263–85.

Everard, C. E. (1957). The streams of the New Forest: A study in drainage evolution. *Proc. Hants. Field Club Archaeol. Soc.* 19:240–52.

Eversley, Lord (1910). Commons, Forests and Footpaths. Cassell, London.

Eyre, G. E. B. (1871). The New Forest: A Sketch. *Fortnightly Review.* 1.

Eyre, G. E. B. (1883). The New Forest, its Common Rights and Cottage Stock Keepers. J. C. Short, Lyndhurst.

Finn, R. W. (1962). Hampshire. *in:* Darby, H. C. & Campbell, E. M. J. (eds). The Domesday Geography of South-East England. CUP, Cambridge.

Fisher, G. C. (1971). Brickearth and its influence on the character of soils in the south-east New Forest. *Proc. Hants. Field Club Archaeol. Soc.* 28:99–109.

Fisher, G. C. (1975a). Some aspects of the phytosociology of heathland and related communities in the New Forest, Hampshire, England. *Journal of Biogeography.* 2:103–16.

Fisher, G. C. (1975b). Terraces, soils and vegetation in the New Forest, Hampshire. *Area.* 7:255–61.

Flower, N. (1977). An Historical and Ecological Study of Enclosed and Unenclosed Woods in the New Forest, Hampshire. *PhD Thesis.* University of London.

Flower, N. (1980a). The management history and structure of unenclosed woods in the New Forest, Hampshire. *Journal of Biogeography.* 7:311–28.

Flower, N. (1980b). Early coppice sites in the New Forest. *Forestry.* 53:187–94.

Flower, N. (1983). The ancient and ornamental woods of the New Forest. *Hampshire.* 23:55–7.

Flower, N. & Tubbs, C. R. (1982). The New Forest, Hampshire: Management Proposals for the Unenclosed Woodlands and Woodlands of Special Importance in the Statutory Inclosures. Nature Conservancy Council, Lyndhurst & Peterborough.

Forestry Commission (1947). Report of the New Forest Committee 1947. Cmnd. 7245. HMSO, London.

Forestry Commission (1976). New Forest: Progress Report on the Implementation of Conservation Measures, 1972–6, and Proposals for Future Strategy. Forestry Commission, Lyndhurst.

Forestry Commission (1984). New Forest Forestry Commission Badger Protection Group Report, 12, 1984. Forestry Commission, Lyndhurst.

Frazer, J. F. D. (1978). Newts in the New Forest. *Br. J. Herpetol.* 5:695–9.

French, H. M. (1976). The Periglacial Environment. London.

Fulford, M. G. (1973). Excavations of three Romano-British pottery kilns in Amberwood Inclosure, near Fritham, New Forest. *Proc. Hants. Field Club Archaeol. Soc.* 28:5–28.

Gehu-Franck, J. (1961). Donnees nouvelles sur l'ecologie d'*Ulex europaeus* L.: relations avec le substratum dans une lande semi-naturelle. *Bulletin de la Societe de Botanique du Nord de la France.* 14: 23–33.

Gehu-Franck, J. (1974). Contribution a l'etude Auto- et Syn ecologique de L'Ajono d'Europe (*Ulex europaeus* L.). *Doctoral Thesis.* University of Lille.

Gessaman, J. A. & MacMahon, J. A. (1984). Mammals in ecosystems: their effects on the composition and production of vegetation. *Acta Zool. Fennica.* 172: 11–18.

Gilpin, W. (1791). Remarks on Forest Scenery. II. London.

Gimingham, C. H. (1972). Ecology of Heathlands. Chapman and Hall, London.

Godwin, H. (1975). History of the British Flora. 2nd Edn. CUP, Cambridge.

Green, F. J. (1983). The plant remains from the 1979 and 1980 excavations at Church Green. *Hants. Field Club Archaeol. Soc. New Forest Section Report.* 21:17–18.

Grinsell, L. F. (1938–40). Hampshire barrows. *Proc. Hants. Field Club Archaeol. Soc.* 14:9–40, 195–229, 346–65.

Grinsell, L. F. (1958). The Archaeology of Wessex. Methuen, London.

Hammersley, G. (1957). The crown woods and their exploitation in the sixteenth and seventeenth centuries. *Bull. Inst. Hist. Res.* 30: 136–61.

Hammersley, G. (1960). The revival of the Forest Laws under Charles I. *History.* 45:85–102.

Harper, G. W. (1963). Summer 1962 in the New Forest. *Entomologist's Record.* 75:110–14.

Hirons, G. (1984). The diet of tawny owls (*Strix aluco*) and kestrels (*Falco tinnunculus*) in the New Forest, Hampshire. *Proc. Hants. Field Club Archaeol. Soc.* 41:21–6.

Hockey, F. (1976). King John's Abbey. Pioneer Publications, Beaulieu.

Hopkins, P. J. & Webb, N. R. (1984). The composition of the beetle and spider faunas on fragmented heathlands. *J. Appl. Ecol.* 21: 935–46.

Hudson, W. H. (1903). Hampshire Days. Longmans, Green and Co., London.

Hudson, M. J. H. (1957). An investigation of the vegetation of Fort Bog and its relations to stratigraphy. *BSc Dissertation.* University of Southampton.

Insley, H. (1977). An estimate of the population of the Red Fox (*Vulpes vulpes*) in the New Forest, Hampshire. *J. Zool.* 183:549–53.

Insley, H. & Clarke, M. P. G. (1975). A short history of the New Forest deer. *Deer* (J. Brit. Deer Soc.). 7:376–81.

Irvine, J. (1977). Breeding birds in the New Forest broad-leaved woodlands. *Bird Study.* 24:105–11.

Jackson, J. (1977a). The annual diet of the Fallow Deer (*Dama dama*) in the New Forest, Hampshire, as determined by rumen content analysis. *J. Zool. Lond.* 181:465–73.

Jackson, J. (1977b). When do Fallow Deer feed? *Deer.* 4:215–18.

Jackson, J. (1980). The annual diet of the Roe Deer (*Capreolus capreolus*) in the New Forest, Hamp-shire, as determined by rumen content analysis. *J. Zool. Lond.* 192:71–83.

Jackson, R. & Jackson, J. (1975). A study of breeding Lapwings in the New Forest, Hampshire, 1971–4. *Ringing & Migration.* 1:18–27.

Jebb, L. (1907). Smallholdings, London.

Johnstone, D. E. (1983). Excavations at Stoney Cross and Fritham. *Hants. Field Club Archaeol. Soc. New Forest Section Report.* 21: 19–23.

Jones, E. L. & Tubbs, C. R. (1963). Vegetation of sites of previous cultivation. *Nature.* 198:977–8.

Keef, D. A. M., Wymer, J. J. & Dimbleby, G. W. (1965). A Mesolithic site at Iping Common, Sussex, England. *Proc. Prehist. Soc.* 31:85–92.

Keen, D. H. (1980). The environment of deposition of the South Hampshire plateau gravels. *Proc. Hants. Field Club Archaeol. Soc.* 36: 15–24.

Kelsall, J. E. & Munn, P. W. (1905). The Birds of Hampshire and the Isle of Wight. Witherby, London.

Kenchington, F. E. (1944). The Commoners' New Forest. Hutchinson, London.

Kiff, J. (1972). The Use of Land by the Commoners of the New Forest. *Discussion Papers in Conservation.* No. 2. University College London.

Killip, I. M. (1963). The use of gorse in the Isle of Man. *Journal Manx Museum.* 6:162–167.

Lascelles, G. W. (1915). Thirty-Five Years in the New Forest. Arnold, London.

Lucas, A. T. (1960). Furze: a Survey and History of its uses in Ireland. National Museum of Ireland, Dublin.

Manwood, J. (1598 *et seq*). Treatise and Discourse on the Laws of the Forest. London.

Marsh, R. & Campling, R. C. (1970). Fouling of pastures by dung. *Herbage Abstracts.* 40:123–30.

McCracken, E. (1971). The Irish Woods Since Tudor Times: their Distribution and Exploitation. David & Charles, Newton Abbot.

McGregor, R. (1962). A late Bronze Age barrow at Berry Wood, near Burley, New Forest, Hampshire. *Proc. Hants. Field Club Archaeol. Soc.* 22:45–50.

McNaughton, S. J. (1979). Grazing as an optimization process: grass-ungulate relationships in the Seren-geti. *Am. Nat.* 113:691–703.

Moens, W. J. C. (1903). The New Forest: its afforesta-tion, ancient area, and law in the times of the Con-queror and his successors. *Archaeological Journal.* 60:30–50.

Moore, N. W. (1962). The heaths of Dorset and their Conservation. *J. Ecol.* 50:369–91.

Morgan-Hews, D. I. & Haynes, F. N. (1973). Distribution of epiphytic lichens around an oil refinery at Fawley, Hampshire. *in:* Ferry, B. W., Baddeley, M. S. & Hawksworth, D. L. (eds). Air Pollution and Lichens. Athlone Press, London. 89–109.

Morley, C. (1941). The history of *Cicadetta montana* Scop. in Britain, 1812–1940. *Entomologist's Mon. Mag.* 77:41–56.

Mussett, N. J. (1964). A Survey and classification of New Forest valley bogs. *BSc Dissertation*. University of Southampton.

Nature Conservancy Council (1983). The Ecology and Conservation of Amphibian and Reptile Species Endangered in Britain, NCC, London.

Nature Conservancy Council (1983). The Food and Feeding Behaviour of Cattle and Ponies in the New Forest. NCC, Lyndhurst.

Nature Conservancy Council (1984). Nature Conservation in Great Britain. NCC, London.

Neal, E. G. (1977). Badgers. Blandford Press, Poole.

New Forest Joint Steering Committee (1970). Conservation of the New Forest: A Report for Consultation. Hampshire County Council, Winchester.

New Forest Joint Steering Committee (1971). Conservation of the New Forest: Final Recommendations. Hampshire County Council, Winchester.

Newbould, P. J. & Gorham, E. (1956). Acidity and specific conductivity measurements in some plant communities of the New Forest valley bogs. *J. Ecol.* 44:118–28.

Noirfalise, A. & Vanesse, R. (1976). Heathlands of Western Europe. Council of Europe, Nature and Environment Series, No. 12. Strasbourg.

Office of Woods (1854). Abstract of Claims Preferred at a Justice Seat Held for the New Forest AD 1670. Eyre & Spottiswoode, London.

Office of Woods (1858). New Forest Register of Decisions on Claims to Forest Rights (Commissioners acting under Act 17 and 18 Vict. ch. 9). HMSO, London.

Packham, C. G. (1983). The influence of food supply on the ecology of the badger. *Unpublished Hons. BSc. Thesis*. University of Southampton.

Page, T. (1788). On the culture of furze. *Annals of Agriculture*. 11.215–17.

Palmer, S. & Dimbleby, G. W. (1979). A Mesolithic habitation site on Winfrith Heath, Dorset. *Proc. Dorset Nat. Hist. Arch. Soc.* 101:27–50.

Parr, S. J. (1985). The breeding ecology and diet of the hobby *Falco subbuteo* in southern England. *Ibis.* 127:60–73.

Pasmore, A. H. (1964). Excavation of an unusual pound earthwork in Sloden Wood. *Hants. Field Club Archaeol. Soc. Report.* 13:3–5.

Pasmore, A. H. (1967). New Forest Pottery Kilns and Earthworks. Privately Published, Cadnam.

Pasmore, A. H. (1970). The Church Place earthworks. *Hampshire Archaeology and Local History Newsletter.* 1:150–3.

Pasmore, A. H. (1977). Verderers of the New Forest: A History of the New Forest 1877–1977. Pioneer Publications, Beaulieu.

Pasmore, A. H. (1978). The Crockford excavations 1964–1966. *Hants. Field Club Archaeol. Soc. New Forest Section Report.* 16:32–7.

Pasmore, A. H. & Fortescue, K. (1977–83). Annual reports on excavations at Church Green, Eyeworth. *Hants. Field Club Archaeol. Soc. New Forest Section Reports.* 14–21.

Pasmore, A. H. & Pallister, J. (1967). Boiling Mounds in the New Forest. *Proc. Hants. Field Club Archaeol. Soc.* 24:14–19.

Pasmore, H. C. (1974). New Forest Act 1964. *Hants. Field Club Archaeol. Soc. New Forest Section Report.* 13:47–54.

Pennington, W. (1969). The History of British Vegetation. English Universities Press, London.

Peterken, G. F. (1974). A method for assessing woodland flora for conservation using indicator species. *Biol. Conserv.* 6:239–45.

Peterken, G. F. & Tubbs, C. R. (1965). Woodland regeneration in the New Forest, Hampshire, since 1650. *J. Appl. Ecol.* 2:159–70.

Pickering, D. W. (1968). Heathland reclamation in the New Forest: the ecological consequences. *MSc Thesis*. University of London.

Piggot, C. M. (1943). Excavation of fifteen barrows in the New Forest, 1941–2. *Proc. Prehist. Soc.* 9:1–27.

Piggott, Sir Berkeley (1960). The New Forest Commoners and The New Forest Pony. *In:* The New Forest. Phoenix, London.

Pollock, J. I. (1980). Behavioural Ecology and Body Condition Changes in New Forest Ponies. RSPCA Scientific Publications No. 6.

Preston, J. P. & Hawkes, C. (1933). Three late Bronze Age barrows on the Cloven Way. *Antiquaries Journal.* 13:414–54.

Prestt, I., Cooke, A. S. & Corbett, K. F. (1974). British amphibians and reptiles. *In:* Hawkesworth, D. L. (ed.). The Changing Flora and Fauna of Britain. 229–54, London.

Radley, J. (1961). Holly as a winter feed. *Agric. Hist. Rev.* 9:89–92.

Ragge, D. R. (1965). Grasshoppers, Crickets and Cockroaches of the British Isles. Warne, London.

Rankin, W. M. (1911). The valley moors of the New Forest. *In:* Tansley, A. G. (ed.). Types of British Vegetation. CUP, Cambridge.

Rankine, W. F., Rankine, W. M. & Dimbleby, G. W.

(1960). Further excavations at a Mesolithic site at Oakhanger, Selborne. *Proc. Prehist. Soc.* 26:246–52.

Robbins, M. & Bibby, C. J. (1985). Dartford warblers in 1984 Britain. *Brit. Birds.* 78:269–80.

Rose, F. (1953). A survey of the ecology of the British lowland bogs. *Proc. Linn. Soc. Lond.* 164:186–211.

Rose, F. & James, P. W. (1974). Regional Studies on the British Lichen Flora. 1. The corticolous and lignicolous species of the New Forest, Hampshire. *Lichenologist.* 6:1–72.

Russell, S. G. Castle (1952). The New Forest in the 'Nineties and After. *Entomologist's Record.* 64:138–44.

Russell, V. (1976). New Forest Ponies. David & Charles, Newton Abbot.

Savage, R. M. (1971). The natural stimulus for spawning of *Xenopus laevis* (Amphibia). *J. Zool. Lond.* 165:245–60.

Scaife, R. G. (1983). Palynological investigations of barrows V, VIII and IX, West Heath Bronze Age Barrow cemetery, West Sussex. *Ancient Monuments Laboratory Series 4002.*

Scaife, R. G. & MacPhail, R. I. (1983). The Post-Devensian development of heathland soils and vegetation. *Seesoil.* 1:70–99.

Seagrief, S. C. (1960). Pollen diagrams from southern England: Cranes Moor, Hampshire. *New Phytol.* 59:73–83.

Simmons, I. G. (1964). Pollen diagrams from Dartmoor. *New Phytol.* 63:158–80.

Simmons, I. G. (1969). Evidence of vegetation changes associated with mesolithic man in Britain. *In:* Ucko, P. J. & Dimbleby, G. W. (eds). The Domestication and Exploitation of Plants and Animals. Duckworth, London.

Sjors, H. (1976). Successional trends in boreal peatlands. *Proc. Vth International Peat Congress, Poland.* II:22–8.

Small, D. (1972). New Forest Forestry Commission Management Plan, 1972–81. Forestry Commission, Lyndhurst.

Small, D. (1973). New Forest Forestry Commission Management Plan, 1972–1981 (Revised edn.). Forestry Commission, Lyndhurst.

Small, D. (1982). New Forest Forestry Commission Management Plan, 1982–91. Forestry Commission, Lyndhurst.

Small, D. & Haggett, G. M. (1972). A study of broad-leaved woodland changes and natural regeneration in the ancient and ornamental woodlands from 1867 to 1963. *In:* New Forest Forestry Commission Management Plan 1972–1981. Forestry Commission, Lyndhurst.

Southern, H. N. (1969). Prey taken by tawny owls during the breeding season. *Ibis.* 111:293–9.

Southern, H. N. (1970). The natural control of a population of tawny owls (*Strix aluco*). *J. Zool. Lond.* 162:197–285.

Southern, H. N. & Lowe, V. P. W. (1982). Predation by tawny owls on bank voles and wood-mice. *J. Zool. Lond.* 198:83–102.

Spellerberg, I. (1975). Conservation and management of Britain's reptiles based on their ecological and behavioural requirements: a progress report. *Biol. Conserv.* 7:289–300.

Spellerberg, I. & Phelps, T. E. (1977). Biology, general ecology and behaviour of the snake *Coronella austriaca* Laurenti. *Biol. J. Linn. Soc.* 9:133–64.

Spooner, W. C. (1871). On the agricultural capabilities of the New Forest. *J. Royal Agric. Soc. England.* 2nd Ser. 7:252–61.

Spray, M. & Smith, D. J. (1977). The rise and fall of holly in the Sheffield region. *Trans. Hunter Archaeol. Soc.* 10:239–51.

Stagg, D. J. (1974a). A perambulation of the New Forest. *Hants. Field Club Archaeol. Soc. New Forest Section Report.* 13:26–7.

Stagg, D. J. (1974b). The New Forest in Domesday Book. *Hants. Field Club Archaeol. Soc. New Forest Section Report.* 13: 20–4.

Stagg, D. J. (1974c). The Orders and Rules of the New Forest. *Hants. Field Club Archaeol. Soc. New Forest Section Report.* 13:33–8.

Stagg, D. J. (1979). A Calendar of New Forest Documents 1244–1334. *Hampshire Record Series.* 3. Hampshire County Council, Winchester.

Stagg, D. J. (1983a). A Calendar of New Forest Documents: The Fifteenth to the Seventeenth Centuries. *Hampshire Record Series.* 5. Hampshire County Council.

Stagg, D. J. (1983b). New Forest Commoners AD 1792. New Forest Association.

Steven, H. M. & Carlisle, A. (1959). The Native Pinewoods of Scotland. Oliver & Boyd, London.

Sumner, Heywood (1917). Ancient Earthworks of the New Forest. Chiswick Press, London.

Sumner, H. (1919). A Descriptive Account of the Roman Pottery made at Ashley Rails, Chiswick Press, London.

Sumner, H. (1921). A Descriptive Account of Roman Pottery Sites at Sloden and Black Heath Meadow, Linwood, New Forest, Chiswick Press, London.

Sumner, H. (1921–2). Barrows on Ibsley Common. *Bournemouth Natural Science Soc.* 14: 68–78.

Sumner, Heywood (1923). The New Forest Guide. Chiswick Press, London.

Sumner, H. (1927). Excavations in New Forest Roman Pottery Sites. London.

Sumner, Heywood (1931). Local Papers. Chiswick Press, London.

Swanson, E. H. (1970). Pleistocene geochronology in the New Forest, Hampshire. *Bull. Inst. Archaeol. University of London.* 8:55–100.

Symes, H. (1963). The New Forest on the air. Entomologist's Record. 75:270–1.

Taylor, R. H. R. (1948). The distribution of reptiles
and amphibia in the British Isles with notes on
species recently introduced. Br. J. Herpetol. 1:1–38.
Tremewan, W. G. (1966). The history of Zygaena
viciae anglica Reiss (Lep. Zygaenidae) in the New
Foresti Entomologist's Gazette. 17:187–210.
Tremlett, W. E. (1965). The evolution of the Beaulieu
drainage system in the southeastern New Forest
(Hampshire). Proc. Hants. Field Club Archaeol.
Soc. 23:48–59.
Tricart, J. (1970). The Geomorphology of Cold En-
vironments. London.
Trimmer, J. (1856). On the agricultural relations of
The western Tertiary district of Hampshire and the
agricultural importance of the marls of the New
Forest. J. Royal Agric. Soc. England. 1st Ser. 16:
500–16.
Tubbs, C. R. (1963). The significance of the New
Forest to the status of the Dartford warbler in
England. Brit. Birds. 56:41–8.
Tubbs, C. R. (1964). Early encoppicements in the
New Forest. Forestry. 37:95–105.
Tubbs, C. R. (1967). Number of Dartford warblers
in England during 1962–66. Brit. Birds. 60:87–9.
Tubbs, C. R. (1968). The New Forest: An Ecological
History. David & Charles, Newton Abbot.
Tubbs, C. R. (1972). Analysis of nest record cards for
the buzzard. Bird Study. 19:86–104.
Tubbs, C. R. (1974). The Buzzard. David & Charles,
Newton Abbot.
Tubbs, C. R. (1974). Heathland Management in the
New Forest, Hampshire, England. Biol. Conserv.
6:303–6.
Tubbs, C. R. (1976). Heathland Vertebrates. In:
Sankey, J. H. P. & Mackworth-Praed, H. W. (eds).
The Southern Heathlands. Surrey Naturalists'
Trust.
Tubbs, C. R. (1985). The decline and present status
of the English lowland heaths and their vertebrates.
Focus on Nature Conservation No. 11. Nature Con-
servancy Council, Peterborough.
Tubbs, C. R. & Dimbleby, G. W. (1965). Early agri-
culture in the New Forest. Advanc. Science. 22:88–
97.
Tubbs, C. R. & Jones, E. L. (1964). The distribution
of gorse (Ulex europaeus L.) in the New Forest in
relation to former land use. Proc. Hants. Field Club
Archaeol. Soc. 23: 1–10.
Tubbs, C. R. & Tubbs, J. M. (1985). Buzzards (Buteo
buteo) and land use in the New Forest, Hampshire,
England. Biol. Conserv. 31:41–65.
Tuckfield, C. G. (1964). Gully erosion in the New
Forest, Hampshire. American Journal of Science.
262:795–807.

Tuckfield, C. G. (1968). Relict landslips in the New
Forest. Proc. Hants. Field Club Archaeol. Soc. 25:
5–18.
Tuckfield, C. G. (1973a). A Contribution to the Study
of Erosion Processes in the New Forest (Hamp-
shire). PhD Thesis. University of London.
Tuckfield, C. G. (1973b). Seepage steps in the New
Forest, Hampshire, England. Water Resources Re-
search. 9:367–77.
Tuckfield, C. G. (1976). A Geomorphological Ap-
praisal of some Recent Drainage Work carried out
in the New Forest by the Forestry Commission.
Nature Conservancy Council, Lyndhurst.
Tuckfield, C. G. (1979). Rejuvenation features in the
Cadnam River Basin in the New Forest. Proc. Hants.
Field Club Archaeol. Soc. 36:5–13.
Tuckfield, C. G. (1980). Stream channel stability and
forest drainage in the New Forest, Hampshire.
Earth Surface Processes. 5:317–29.
Turner, G. J. (1901). Select Pleas of the Forest. Selden
Society, London.
Tyler, S. J. (1972). The Behaviour and Social Organi-
sation of the New Forest Ponies. Animal Behaviour
Monographs. 5:87–196.

Webb, N. R., Clarke, R. T. & Nicholas, J. T. (1984).
Invertebrate diversity on fragmented Calluna-
heathland: effects of surrounding vegetation. J.
Biog. 11:41–6.
Webb, N. R. & Haskins, L. E. (1980). An ecological
survey of heathlands in the Poole Basin, Dorset,
England. Biol. Conserv. 17:281–96.
Webb, N. R. & Hopkins, P. J. (1984). Invertebrate
diversity on fragmented Calluna heathland. J. Appl.
Ecol. 21:921–33.
Wells, B. L. & von Goldschmidt-Rothschild, B.
(1979). Social behaviour and relationships in a herd
of Camargue horses. Z. Tierpsychol. 49: 363–80.
Welstead, N. & Welstead, T. (1984). The Dragonflies
of the New Forest. New Forest Odonata Study
Group for the Hampshire and Isle of Wight
Naturalists' Trust.
Werger, M. J. A., Prentice, I. C. & Helspar, H. P. H.
(1985). The effects of sod-cutting at different depths
on Calluna heathland regeneration. J. Environmental Management. 20:181–8.
Wheeler, B. D. (1980). Plant communities of rich-fen
systems in England and Wales. II. Communities of
calcareous mires. J. Ecol. 68:405–20.
Whitehead, G. K. (1964). The Deer of Great Britain
and Ireland. Routledge & Kegan Paul, London.
Willard, E. E. & McKell, C. M. (1978). Response of
shrubs to simulated browsing. J. Wildl. Mgmt. 42:
514–19.
Williams, O. & Lambert, J. M. (1961). Multivariate
methods in plant ecology. III. Inverse association
analysis. J. Ecol. 49:717–29.

Williamson, J. (1861). The Farming of Hampshire. *J. Royal Agric. Soc. England.* 1st Ser. 22:239–359.

Willis, J. (1808). On Waste Land. *Communications to the Board of Agriculture.* 6:16–30.

Wise, J. (1863). The New Forest, its History and Scenery. Henry Southeran, London.

Witherby, H. F., Jourdain, F. C. R., Ticehurst, N. F. & Tucker, B. W. (1943). The Handbook of British Birds. Witherby, London.

Yalden, D. W. (1976). The food of the hedgehog in England. *Acta theriol.* 21:401–24.

Yalden, D. W. & Warburton, A. (1979). The diet of the kestrel in the Lake District. *Bird Study.* 26: 163–70.

Index

The index is selective. Except for a few species without vernacular names, scientific names are not indexed. Only the more important local place names are indexed; personal names are omitted. Species of plants and animals are indexed individually where they receive an extended reference in the text, and can otherwise be located via general references in the index, e.g. plant communities, bird communities, ferns, lichens, epiphytes, etc.